Ordnance Survey Small-Scale Maps

Indexes : 1801-1998

ORDNANCE SURVEY

SMALL-SCALE MAPS

INDEXES : 1801-1998

Roger Hellyer

with a foreword by

Brian Adams

Kerry
David Archer
1999

Published in 1999 by David Archer, The Pentre, Kerry, Newtown, Montgomeryshire SY16 4PD
Telephone 01 686 670 382 Facsimile 01 686 670 551

The publisher and author are grateful to the following friends and organisations for supplying index diagrams and for allowing index diagrams to be based upon material for which they hold the copyright:

Ordnance Survey
Diagrams 20, 21, 38, 62, 63 (Sheets 1-17), 64, 65, 90, 106 are reproduced from, or based upon Ordnance Survey material with the permission of The Controller of Her Majesty's Stationery Office © Crown copyright.

Ordnance Survey of Ireland
Diagrams 33, 34, 72 are based upon the Ordnance Survey by permission of the government (Permit No.6134) © Government of Ireland.

Ordnance Survey of Northern Ireland
Diagrams 32, 40, 43, 61 (Sheet 8), 63 (Sheet 18), 77 are reproduced from, or based upon Ordnance Survey of Northern Ireland material with permission of The Director and Chief Executive © Crown copyright.

Her Majesty's Stationery Office
Diagram 27 is reproduced with permission of Her Majesty's Stationery Office.
© Crown copyright.

Richard Dean
Diagram 12.2 © Richard Dean, 1982.

Harry Margary
Diagram 1 © Harry Margary, 1975.

Macauley Research & Consultancy Services Ltd
Diagram 66.A © Macauley Research & Consultancy Services Ltd.

Soil Survey and Land Research Centre
Diagram 66.B © Soil Survey and Land Research Centre.

National Groundwater & Contaminated Land Centre of the Environment Agency
Diagram 42 © National Groundwater & Contaminated Land Centre.

British Geological Survey
Diagram 48 is reproduced by permission of the Director, British Geological Survey.
© NERC. All rights reserved.

David Archer
All other diagrams © David Archer, 1999.

ISBN 0 9517579 54

Printed by Redwood Books Limited, Kennet Way, Trowbridge, Wiltshire BA14 8RN

Contents

Foreword

Brian Adams

Maps come in an extraordinarily wide variety, ranging from a how-to-get-there-from-here sketch to the fully competent professional product, and may be manuscript, rapid copied, printed, or computer-generated; they may be individual, scattered through a book or magazine, in bulk in a traditional atlas by the hundred, or the hundred-thousand in a computer memory; and they come in wide varieties of size, of scale, and of content, not forgetting pure fiction such as Treasure Island. But in any consideration of total cartography the expression **Maps and Charts** must always be used, for depictions of Water and Air have to take their places along with those of Earth and occasionally, regrettably, Fire.

However, the maps included in the present work are distinguished by being the products of a particular group of national mapping agencies, originally one but now metamorphosed into three, the Ordnance Surveys of the British Isles, and comprise all the smaller scale maps produced by those agencies. The Ordnance Survey of Great Britain and Ireland dated its foundation from 1791, although that name only came along later, and its first operations were based on Major-General William Roy's triangulation of south-east England, carried out in 1784-88 as part of an Anglo-French operation to connect the observatories of Paris and Greenwich. Much of this was re-observed, and it was then massively extended to complete the first Principal Triangulation of the British Isles. This framework formed the basis for topographical surveys which the Survey used to construct a national map series, initially of England and Wales, on the virtually self-selecting and highly convenient scale of one inch to one statute mile, the one-inch map that became familiar as *the* Ordnance Map to much of the general public.

Before one-inch cover had been completed, the Ordnance Survey ventured into both smaller and larger scale maps. The latter were mainly used by particular professions, and totalled over 100,000 sheets by the turn of the century; they have been thoroughly described and indexed in several publications of David Archer and of the Charles Close Society which are listed in the Bibliography. Meanwhile it is the purpose of the present volume to provide indexes and identify all the smaller scale Ordnance Survey maps comprehensively for the first time, the range of scales being from 1:50,000, metric successor to the one-inch, down to 1:4,000,000, with descriptions of a few larger scale maps which are relevant to the smaller scale story. Roger Hellyer goes into this in much more detail in his Introduction, whilst the remainder of this Foreword is devoted to an outline of the construction methods of Ordnance Survey maps and map series, and associated matters. These are things that the average map user takes entirely for granted, but a pause for thought will tell that they are vital to the production of maps, and without them there would be no maps to look at.

Construction of Ordnance Survey maps

The reader will undoubtedly be aware that the representation of the curved surface of the Earth by a flat map requires the use of a **Map Projection**, and has probably seen some rather frightening diagrams of various projections at the front of an atlas. But whilst those projections are mainly used for very small-scale maps and need not concern the users of Ordnance Survey maps, a projection is still required for the construction of these maps as well as for laying down the actual topographical surveys to provide the map detail.

Most recent Ordnance Survey map series, but only a few of the earlier ones, have a statement in the marginal material of the map projection used. However, a prominent feature of the modern maps is the system of squares, the National Grid, printed across the face of the map and numbered in sequence. This is presented to the ordinary map user simply as a reference system, but strictly speaking this usage is only a by-product of the grid's fundamental purpose. What are known as the full National Grid co-ordinates, the Eastings and Northings *including* the small figures which the user is instructed to ignore, are in fact the *x,y* rectangular co-ordinates needed for constructing the map on the relevant (Transverse Mercator) projection, and derive from formulae expressing the co-ordinates in terms of latitude and longitude. These formulae are quite complex due to the need to allow for the ellipsoidal shape of the Earth in constructing the large-scale maps which the Ordnance Survey produces, as well as in rendering its accurate surveys into plane, paper-flat, terms.

The user whose interest has been aroused by the stated use of the Transverse Mercator Projection for the later series of Ordnance Survey maps may then feel frustrated by the total absence of any similar attribution on most earlier series. But wait, are not the latter's sheet line systems also rectangular?, and do not some have reference squares printed across them? Yes indeed, and all these lines are *x,y* or Easting and Northing co-ordinate lines on the particular projections involved, although not numbered with their co-ordinate values. Strictly speaking, the origins of the Survey's two main projections lie on the Equator, but for convenience algebraic origins (co-ordinate zeros) are chosen within the area of mapping, wherefrom the co-ordinates may be negative or positive, or in other words may be west or south as well as east or north.

Thus, for example, the sheet lines of one-inch *Popular Edition* Sheet 75 *Ely* are, in cyclic order from the northern neat line, 236,180 feet south, 709,110 feet east, 331,220 feet south, 566,550 feet east, from the projection origin of Delamere (of which more below). The map is crossed by a net of two-mile squares with an alpha-numeric reference system, but the lines forming these squares are co-ordinate lines at 10,560 feet intervals. The reason that National Grid co-ordinates are all east and north is explained below.

A detailed study of all the projections used for the construction of the Ordnance Surveys' "ten-mile" maps (scales 1:633,600 and 1:625,000) has been made by myself, and is to be found at Appendix 1 in Hellyer (1992). Incorporated in that study are all the projections which have been used for the Survey's regular map series on scales larger than 1:625,000 that are included in the present work. No similar review is available covering the projections used for Ordnance Survey maps at scales smaller than 1:633,600, but where known, details are included in the individual map or series sections; in the absence of any other information, the relevant items are taken from the title or other material on the face of the map, unless my own professional experience suggests any reservations thereon, as such annotations are not always totally to be trusted.

In a number of the particularly small-scale series the sheet lines are not rectangular, but are formed by portions of the **Graticule** comprising parallels of latitude and meridians of longitude as depicted on the relevant projection. On some projections, usually described as *Modified,* the meridians are drawn straight instead of very slightly curved as they would be on the true projection.

In the body of this volume many of the projection references are given in standardised form, and to avoid confusion the various projections are referred to by their accepted names as given in the Royal Society *Glossary of Technical Terms in Cartography.* Meanwhile, the reader who wishes for extended technical details of map projections is referred to Maling (1991). The simple reference "National Grid series" or occasionally "National Grid map" signifies in total that the maps are constructed on the Transverse Mercator Projection, specifically the 1936 national projection with its origin at 49°N,2°W, that the sheet lines are formed by co-ordinate lines of the national projection (i.e. National Grid lines), and that the National Grid is printed across the face of the maps.

The national projection originated in 1929 in the days of Imperial units, and pre-war maps constructed on it carried the National Yard Grid; whilst this grid and the National Grid in its early days were subject to some variation in nomenclature, they are given the standard names herein for the avoidance of doubt. Maps originally published with the National Yard Grid and later converted to the National Grid will be found to have the latter's sheet line co-ordinates in very non-round figures.

"Irish National Grid series" or "Irish National Grid map" signify that the projection is the Transverse Mercator Projection of Ireland with its origin in 53°30'N,8°W, that the maps have Irish National Grid sheet lines, and have that grid across the face of the maps.

For over eighty years prior to the adoption of the 1929 projection the regular series of Ordnance Survey maps of England and Wales, and latterly of Great Britain, were constructed on Cassini's Projection on the origin of Delamere. This was an early primary triangulation station, known originally as Delamere Forest, situated in Cheshire in position 53°13'17".274N, 2°41'03".562W.

The large-scale plans in both Ireland and Scotland had been constructed on Cassini's Projection, on a county-by-county basis, but when the Ordnance Survey came to prepare the one-inch series of these countries they adopted Bonne's Projection. No firm reason is known for that decision, although Bonne's had some vogue at the time, but it involved an extra stage in the reduction of the large-scale material to provide the detail for the one-inch mapping. This was partly due to the curvature of the parallels on Bonne's Projection being generally noticeably different to that on Cassini's. For the first time these two series used origins which were precise intersections of latitude and longitude, the Irish being in 53°30'N,8°W, and the Scottish in 57°30'N,4°W.

In due course the Scottish one-inch and smaller scale mapping were republished on Cassini's Projection on the origin of Delamere, the better to join up with English mapping. Prior to this, some of the smaller scale Great Britain series had combined maps on the two projections with varying degrees of success, and I have dubbed these (with hopeful decorousness) as mixed parentage mapping.

The *International Map of the World on the Millionth Scale,* to give it its proper title in the English-speaking world, has its sheets constructed on their own projection, devised by the map's originating committee and a form of Modified Polyconic Projection. This is referred to in the body of this work as the *IMW Projection.*

True conical projections are calculated with reference to a central parallel of latitude, and have no central meridian as such. However, they may well have an initial meridian which is used for the calculations to lay out the projection, and possibly for the zero true easting line of a military grid. *Minimum Error Conical Projection* does not refer to a specific projection, but to a type of projection in which specified classes of error are reduced to a minimum when meaned across the map. The process may be carried out conventionally or mathematically, and some projections are more "minimum error" than others. It is, however, probable that those Ordnance Survey maps quoted as Minimum Error Conical Projection are all on the same basic projection, with difference due to latitude.

As I mentioned earlier, National Grid co-ordinates are fundamentally the dimensional construction co-ordinates of the 1936 national projection, but are also utilised as a reference system. However, it is from the latter usage that the term **Grid** derives, since in cartography the word originally denoted an arbitrary system of squares printed on the face of a map and used for military referencing. Arbitrary systems were soon largely replaced by survey-related systems, where the grids appeared as true squares on the maps they were initially applied to. But the grids had to be printed on other maps to provide unique referencing, and in such cases might not be precisely true squares (although not necessarily visibly out of true), and would very often lie at an angle to the new sheet lines.

When a grid is stated to be on a certain projection, this is its original map projection upon which it forms absolutely true squares and for which it also provides the construction co-ordinates. However, to eliminate a potent source of error in referencing, grid co-ordinates are usually measured from a **False Origin** lying to the south-west of the mapped area, rendering all co-ordinates positive, that is east and north only. Thus the False Origin of the National Grid lies west by south from the Isles of Scilly and south-west of the whole of Great Britain, whereas the **True Origin** of the national projection lies to the south of Dorset.

Derived series

Many Ordnance Survey map series are derived directly or indirectly from series on other scales, generally involving a reduction of scale, but occasionally an increase for some particular purpose; the reader should appreciate that in the latter instance there is no gain of accuracy. Sometimes a change of projection may be deliberately introduced along with the change of scale, but otherwise two different effects are possible. Where maps have been constructed on one of the transverse cylindrical projections, Cassini's or Transverse Mercator, or on Bonne's Projection, then any amount of amalgamation or sub-division of sheets results in a map on the same original projection. But in other cases, with the International Map of the World being especially involved, the result from manipulation of sheets is a map which as an entity is on no projection at all. Such a map can then only truly be described by its method of derivation from the original.

Parsons Green
London SW

Introduction

Projections and sheet lines

I asked Brian Adams, who has kindly contributed the Foreword, also to oversee the accuracy of the technical data in this book, my contention being that introductory notes to each section giving details of the sheet lines of each map and the relationship between them and the map's projection might prove useful. He readily agreed, commenting that "it is surely obvious, once the user's attention has been drawn to it, that [rectangular] sheet lines are parallel and perpendicular to something, and at least some of them would be interested to know what."

The something to which Brian refers is, of course, the central meridian of a projection, the north-south line drawn through the point of origin, and in fact the only line in a rectangular sheet line structure entirely coincident with a meridian of longitude. Of course, not all sheet line systems are rectangular, the most commonly found exception being the graticule sheet lines (i.e. those wherein the north-south sheet lines are not parallel because they follow meridians of longitude, and the horizontal sheet lines are curved because they follow parallels of latitude) usually found on maps which over all cover areas much larger than the British Isles. The other exceptional case central to this book is the system of sheet lines which evolved on the one-inch *Old Series* map of England and Wales - the reader may examine a diagram showing this in section 2 (such cross references will hereon appear as "**✣2**"). This is important because from it grew the system that was to govern the sheet lines of most Ordnance Survey small-scale maps in England and Wales, the final remnant of which was not to disappear until the 1960s with the full implementation of National Grid series.

We will thus jump straight in at the deep end. The publication of the *Old Series* began in 1805 with the Essex sheets (1, 2, 47, 48), constructed on the meridian of Greenwich. Next to be published were the Devon sheets (20 to 27) in 1809. At the time of their making it would have been scarcely possible for them to have shared the central meridian of the Essex set, and Brian Adams has demonstrated that one through 3°W was chosen. This was of course at an angle to the Greenwich meridian which came to be used not just for the Essex set but, as Brian has further demonstrated, all East Anglian sheets including the set of eight full sheets, 64, 65, 69, 70, 83 to 86, that cover Lincolnshire. This is not the place for a rigorous examination of how the sheet line system of the *Old Series* evolved, but self-evidently the western block of sheets was converging, as progress northwards was made, towards the Lincolnshire set which had been in place since 1824. The area between the two blocks was inevitably becoming ever narrower. How to proceed north became a compelling problem the Ordnance Survey had to solve.

The solution adopted required the scrapping of the variety of origins that had supported *Old Series* mapping so far and the continuation through northern England on a single projection. This was to be Cassini's, from an origin at Delamere Forest. Equally vital a choice was the location of a base line for the new block of maps. This could hardly run through the point of origin since Delamere Forest (later known just as Delamere) itself lay within an area of mapping long since published. A false base line further north was therefore a necessity. By running this through the north-west corner of sheet 86 (inevitably at an angle to it since the Lincolnshire sheets had been created on another origin), the overlap with published mapping (sheets 85 and 86) was the minimum necessary to avoid a gap in coverage. This line, commonly known as the Preston to Hull line, has been confirmed by Brian Adams as an exact northing line of Cassini on Delamere. The earliest known appearance of both constructional lines, the Delamere meridian and the Preston to Hull line, is on a ten-mile Index, dating from about 1839 (Hellyer (1992, page 36) state M-P3) [**✣84**].

From this generally accepted piece of *Old Series* history Brian Adams deduced several important conclusions that affect the sheet lines of Ordnance Survey small-scale maps. "The entire sheet line systems of the *New Series, Third* and *Popular Editions* of England and Wales and the *Popular* of Scotland, not to mention other scales, depend on the north-west corner of *Old Series* sheet 86, and the co-ordinate systems depend on the figures given to that corner on Delamere, having itself been laid down from Greenwich." Brian made this rather startling claim and supported it with completely irrefutable logic in a letter to me three years ago. First, the decision to construct *Old Series* sheets 91 to 110 on Delamere north from the Preston to Hull base line must have occurred earlier than the production of sheets 87 to 90 to the south of it, since the northern sheet lines of these four sheets lie precisely on the Preston to Hull line, yet have no particular relationship with their southern sheet lines. Secondly Brian established that the northern borders of sheets 87 to 90 are each precisely 27 miles wide, these distances being calculated westwards from the north-west corner of sheet 86, and some manipulation of their eastern and western sheet lines was required in order to achieve this. Thirdly, precisely where to plot the sheet lines of the new block of quarter sheets (which were to be rectangular and eighteen miles wide) northwards of the Preston to Hull line was a direct consequence of this, since the next row up was laid out ensuring that sheets 92 and 93 met at the same point as sheets 88 and 87, and, 54 miles further west, sheets 91SW and 91SE met at the same point as sheets 90 and 89.

Thus a system of sheet lines was set up only distantly related to the actual origin of the projection, at Delamere Forest. Usually the north-south line, or central meridian, through the origin would be literally the origin of all construction measurements. But in this case sheet lines bear a more natural relationship to what was *de facto* their point of origin at the north-west corner of sheet 86, and co-ordinate systems had first to take into reckoning the distance of that point east (376,470 feet) and north (207,340 feet) of Delamere Forest. Small wonder perhaps that such figures were never published, but were used by the Ordnance Survey for constructional purposes only. Such maps of this generation as bore grids at all in fact carried simple alpha-numeric squaring systems, which, as Brian Adams points out in his Foreword, are actual though unnumbered co-ordinate lines of a national Cassini projection.

The relationship of sheet lines of related series can now be quickly described. The *Old Series* [**✢2**] quarter sheets in the range 91 to 110 were all rectangular at eighteen miles by twelve miles. There was no reason to alter more than their system of numbering when *New Series* [**✢3**] superseded *Old Series.* They thus became Sheets 1 to 73 of the *New Series,* and a continuation of the same system of abutting non-overlapping sheet lines measuring eighteen by twelve miles replaced *Old Series* sheets south of the Preston to Hull line, reaching Sheet 360 at the Isles of Scilly. In the early twentieth century larger sheet sizes covering 27 miles by 18 were approved for the *Third Edition (Large Sheet Series)* [**✢8**], and four of the larger sheets covered the area of nine of the smaller. The system did not have the remorselessness of the small sheets, as overlapping of sheet lines and non-standard sheet sizes caused many exceptions to the basic pattern of sheets. Similarly four sheets in the *Popular Edition* [**✢10**] covered nine of the smaller, but with better organisation that related them also to the large-sheet half-inch map [**✢36**] covered the country in six fewer sheets.

The sheet lines of maps at other scales were indeed interrelated. Such maps were in England and Wales reduced from the one-inch *New Series,* and publication at each scale began using similar systems of equal-sized sheets that abutted each other without overlaps. Later, larger sheet systems were employed that permitted both overlaps and non-standard sheet sizes that avoided the liberal display of marine areas that was often a feature of the early systems. The earliest half-inch of 1903 [**✢35**] was a small-sheet map, each sheet of the same dimensions as a one-inch *New Series* sheet, organised in a system without overlaps (that is until some coastal sheets came to be combined). Each sheet thus covered the area of four small one-inch sheets. The subsequent larger sheets [**✢36**], again more flexibly disposed in a system allowing overlaps, covered the same area as nine small one-inch sheets, or, in their turn, four of the *Popular Edition* one-inch sheets [**✢10**]. The earliest quarter-inch map [**✢50**] was a derivative of the one-inch *Old Series,* with sheet lines irrelevant in this context. The small-sheet quarter-inch maps [**✢51, 52**] covered the area of 25 of the small one-inch sheets. The large-sheet map [**✢53**] had no standard sheet size, but its successor, the *Third Edition* [**✢54**], had sheet lines again related to those of its contemporary at the one-inch scale, by now the *Popular Edition,* sixteen sheets of which fitted neatly within the sheet lines of a standard quarter-inch sheet.

Construction of one-inch mapping in Scotland and Ireland was more systematically organised from the start. Bonne's Projection was used, in Scotland on the central meridian of 4°W and in Ireland 8°W. Sheet lines were to be parallel and perpendicular to these meridians. In Ireland the one-inch map [**✚22**] was conceived in 59 full sheets each covering 36 by 24 miles, but the decision to divide these sheets into quarters covering eighteen by twelve miles led to quicker publication. The smaller scale sheets were again interrelated. Half-inch sheets [**✚39**] adopted the large sheet size introduced into England and Wales in 1906, covering the area of nine one-inch maps. The quarter-inch sheet [**✚69**] was smaller than that in England, and being identical in size with the one-inch sheet covered the area of sixteen of them. In Scotland a different basic unit was adopted at the outset for the one-inch sheet [**✚13**] when the area of half the standard English full sheet was chosen, thus covering an area of 24 miles by 18. The half-inch sheet [**✚37**] had the same dimensions, and so covered the area of four one-inch sheets. The earliest quarter-inch map [**✚57**] had large sheets that covered 25 one-inch sheets; the successor small-sheet map [**✚58**] had sheets that covered only nine.

Most of these series and their related sheet lines have now been superseded by National Grid series in both Great Britain and Ireland. This process began in Great Britain in 1931 with the introduction of a new generation of maps constructed on the Transverse Mercator Projection with its origin at 49°N,2°W. Alpha-numeric squaring systems unique to single sheets were abandoned and replaced by a system of lines parallel and perpendicular to the central meridian of the projection that offered precise measurement of distance from its origin. In fact they were calculated from a "false" origin placed south and west of the land mass in order to allow all values to be positive. A combination of the distance east (easting) and north (northing) provided a unique co-ordinate value for any location. Sheet lines of all new maps corresponded with natural grid values. The first system chosen, with values in yards, proved a false dawn, and of the maps published during the 1930s that used National Yard Grid sheet lines, only the one-inch *Fifth Edition* [**✚11**, **12**] and the half-inch map of *Greater London* [**✚36**.C.3] were to be constructed on the Transverse Mercator Projection. All the others used mapping constructed on Cassini's Projection for earlier publication, which was transferred, presumably by some manipulation of photography, to the Transverse Mercator Projection. Such maps are the quarter-inch *Fourth Edition* Maps of England and Wales, and Scotland [**✚56**, **60**], the *Ten Mile Map of Great Britain* [**✚89**] and some Scottish one-inch and English half-inch district maps [see **✚18**.B.1, **36**.C.1, **36**.C.2]. A characteristic common to all is the angle apparent between the map lettering and the National Yard Grid across the map.

Even before the Second World War the decision had been taken to abandon the yard grid and replace it with a metric system that could control all scales of maps from the smallest to the largest, though this could not be generally implemented until hostilities were at an end. The projection remained the same, but a different false origin was chosen for the grid, though still south and west of the land mass in order to give positive grid values. Again the one-inch map was the first, its sheet lines designed to fall on National [metric] Grid co-ordinates, and the English and Welsh sheets in the *New Popular Edition* [**✚19**] were published within two years of the end of the war. Meanwhile the one-inch in Scotland, the quarter-inch and ten-mile scales all had to survive as an unhappy marriage of mapping originally drawn on Cassini's Projection with either Cassini or National Yard Grid sheet lines, superimposed with National Grid values until they in their turns could be replaced by new maps [**✚20**, **62**, **90**], a process not complete until 1963. A new British half-inch map [**✚38**] was also started, but abandoned after the issue of five sheets.

Proceedings were similar in Ireland. The Ordnance Surveys in Dublin and Belfast agreed upon the use of the Transverse Mercator Projection, employing at 53°30'N,8°W the same origin as Bonne's, and their own metric National Grid. As in Britain the grid was first imposed upon extant mapping (the one-inch in Northern Ireland [**✚31**], and the half-inch throughout the island [**✚39**]). Belfast then produced National Grid series at the one-inch, half-inch, quarter-inch and 1:500,000 scales [**✚32**, **40**, **76**, **100**]. Dublin meanwhile produced a 1:250,000 series [**✚72**] and island maps at 1:575,000, 1:625,000 and 1:750,000 [**✚97**, **98**, **99**]. However nothing further was achieved until the decision by Dublin and Belfast to produce joint maps which would adhere to agreed sheet line systems throughout the island. The 1:250,000 [**✚77**] was ready by 1980, the 1:50,000 map [**✚34**] by 1999. The 1:100,000 map [**✚43**] remains (1999) in abeyance.

Organisation of the book

This volume of indexes is ordered according to scale, starting, as did the Ordnance Survey, with the one-inch map. The natural progression through ever reducing scales follows, wherever appropriate pairing an imperial scale with its metric equivalent. A short section of Salisbury Plain, London and island maps at larger scales up to four inches to the mile concludes the volume. All maps at scales 1:25,000 and 1:25,344 and most at 1:20,000 are omitted: such is the extent and importance of mapping of this type that it is deserving of far more than the incidental treatment it could receive here.

Within each scale the sequence of treatment is first from the larger to the smaller geographical area, then chronological, the most important exception to this principle being that British series are placed after those of England and Wales, and Scotland, where they follow them chronologically. Ireland's and Northern Ireland's series follow British series. The 1:1,000,000 series are primarily distinguished according to projection and numbering system; world and European maps precede British maps within each category. A full list appears on page 250.

Each section comprises the various map series that share a common system of sheet lines. In most cases an index diagram is included, *showing sheets as they were first issued.* Later developments are described in the text. For maps consisting of one or perhaps two sheets diagrams seemed a pointless luxury. In these cases sheet co-ordinates, if readily identifiable, suffice instead. The few editions such as the England and Wales one-inch *War Revision* that draw sheets from more than one civilian edition receive divided treatment with appropriate cross references. Each section is given a sequential reference number in bold figures. A cross reference to a map series supported by a diagram in another section will always include this figure, in bold, accompanied by the symbol **✣**, thus **✣23**.2.3. Reference to a series sharing the same diagram excludes this bold figure and is accompanied by the ✣ symbol, thus ✣2.2. Otherwise reference numbers are given in full. Most cross reference numbers, as well as additional editorial matter, are in [ ]. Occasional notes may be found marked by a • that direct the reader elsewhere for details of a map that could have been listed in more than one place. Matter in *italics* is usually directly quoted from maps.

Information universally relating to the map series in each section is offered in introductory paragraphs or section headings, and, rather than indulge in unnecessary repetition, such information may be guarded by such words as "unless otherwise noted" when it is almost always true. Information provided here concerns the projection used, the number of sheets, sheet lines and standard sheet size or coverage, origin of mapping, grid or graticule information, map heading details, and in some cases lists of sheets with insets, extrusions and blank areas. Similarly the information in subsection headings should be assumed to be generally relevant to the maps listed below them. Exceptions are noted where they are recorded, but it was not felt necessary to get too pedantic about this. For instance it is self-evident that "water and contour" issues have no black plate and therefore no grid.

A rigid overall consistency in the organisation of the sections was not attempted, and indeed such an approach would often have wasted space. But its logic should be obvious and readily accessible to readers, with complete standard editions, or those planned to be complete, preceding those which include few sheets or are not part of the mainstream published output of the Ordnance Surveys. Special maps may be ordered either chronologically or, in respect of district maps, alphabetically. Some sections, with headings shaded and boxed, are divided by letter before any numerical system. These separate distinctive series which happen to share the same index diagram, for instance a pre-war map with alpha-numeric squaring system from the post-war version with the National Grid. One might argue that kindred series such as the various editions of the England and Wales one-inch *New Series* be distinguished by such letter separators all within a single section, but their complexity is such that in these cases we felt it desirable to keep each edition wholly separate. Military maps are listed separately under "M" headings where subdivision was felt to be necessary, perhaps because of the use of a military grid. Cross references to such military maps will include the letter "M"; similarly, cross references to one-inch geological maps include a "G". Subsidiary headings that are shaded but not boxed usually provide supplementary information on grids. Unshaded headings usually refer to no more than a change in publisher.

Within each section map editions are listed either using a note which is descriptive in character, or one which may quote directly from the map's heading. In many cases entries are subdivided. It should be stressed that this may be as much to describe variants in cartographic specification as to tabulate a revision of the map content. The interested user may investigate further by inspection. Sheet titles are also quoted occasionally for series sheets, and generally for district maps, though prefatory phrases such as *Ordnance Survey Map of.....showing* are generally ignored. Military maps in particular often have complex series titles, elements of which may be situated in different areas around the map. The initial point of reference for any military map is its GSGS number or equivalent, if there is one.

By default all sheets in a map edition were published. Considerable effort has been taken to discover precisely how complete editions actually were, but it has proved impossible to verify every one. Some published maps are lacking in the Publication Reports, some listed there are in fact apparently unpublished; a few which reason dictates must exist have resolutely failed to turn up. There is little such documentary support in the case of military issues: all one can do is seek in the hope that one shall find. However, in the cases where "All sheets" is noted, the compiler has indeed either recorded all the sheets of that edition, or confirmed their existence from reliable documentary sources. Otherwise he has employed less positive devices, such as "?All sheets", or listing the sheet numbers recorded (or unrecorded). The sheet numbers present (or absent) are also quoted when an issue is known to be incomplete. Caution has been our watchword in this regard since during research for this book so many sheets have emerged of which we had no previous suspicion.

In many cases specification changes were made before the publication of all sheets of a map edition had been completed. It was left to the compiler to decide which to ignore (for instance the change from hand-written lettering to photo-typeset letterpress in the one-inch *Seventh Series* [**✚20**]) and which to include (the reduction in the number of colour plates in the same map). But the point needs to be made that while in most cases one can be certain about the number of sheets issued before the change, afterwards the situation is rarely so positive. The issue of the previously unpublished sheets is usually certain enough, but what of reissues of sheets already published before the change? If they were merely reprints and not new editions, they would rarely appear in the publication reports and thus equally rarely in legal deposit collections. Locating them is thus a matter of chance. The Outline Edition of the England and Wales one-inch *Popular Edition* [**✚10**.2] and the first half-inch map [**✚35**] are good examples where much work remains to be done before we will know the total number of sheets issued in the revised specification. Occasionally it is unclear how many were done in the initial specification. The subsequent half-inch with layers [**✚36**.A.2] is a case in point, where apparently sheets with revised specification were supplied to legal deposit libraries.

District maps (the term used here to cover the whole range of special area maps often summarised as "Tourist and District Maps") are placed with the series maps to which they are related, and are included in the same numerical sequence as the parent map. District map headings are those which appear on the map, where they are present at all, though the lists of component sheet numbers that sometimes appear as headings are usually omitted. If there is no heading, the generic term "district map" is used. Section headings may be qualified with a note referring to some universally relevant characteristic. Readers are reminded that the top margins of many maps issued in covers are trimmed, often resulting in the loss of any heading a map may have had. Some district maps are listed with their sheet titles as headings, usually those that exist in more than one version with characteristics independent of other district maps. District maps with identical sheet lines may exist in more than one version, sometimes with title alterations. Many of them appear in more than one section of the book. Such kindred maps are chained together by cross references in ( ). Even when apparently identical, minor shifts in the mapping may be detected. If maps with the same or similar names are not so marked, it may be assumed that the sheet lines are different. Reprints of pre-war district maps following each of the two World Wars are noted, usually by date. Special sheets that are created by enlarging or reducing a map at a different scale will generally be found listed under the maps from which they are derived, or else cross references should assist in tracing them.

Section Headings

On first consideration it may seem a little peculiar how infrequently the section headings adopted here are directly quoted from the maps which they support. Considerable thought was given to this subject, and what emerged was that some overall consistency would be of more assistance to the user than direct quotations of map headings. An original ambition was to provide uniquely worded headings for each section, but this ultimately proved impractical if the phrases adopted were to remain pithy. Consequently headings with identical wording are present, but are distinguished by serial numbers. A more detailed description of headings as they appear on the map usually forms part of the prefatory notes provided for each section. Until he investigated the matter for this book, it had not occurred to the compiler just how inconsistent, over the years, the Ordnance Surveys' use of headings has been. As a simple example the reader is invited to set side by side examples of all the series of England and Wales one-inch maps and he will discover headings which range from nothing at all to the inclusion of descriptive words like "Relief" or "Black" as an integral part of *Fifth Edition* headings. The positioning of elements of the heading along the top margin is also variable. Some elements, such as the expression *Large Sheet Series* occur only intermittently, but its very existence permits the logical use of the comparative "Small Sheet Series" as a description of the series which usually preceded them. Such expressions only came to be used retrospectively, in similar fashion to the acceptance of *Old Series* once *New Series* terminology was adopted for the England and Wales one-inch map. In its literature and especially its catalogues the Ordnance Survey employed such expressions even though in many cases they never appeared on a map. Otherwise these sources rarely offer additional guidance, and terminology derived from Ordnance Survey documents can often be actually misleading. The use of the term *Fourth Edition* when referring in fact to the one-inch *Popular Edition* map in England and Wales is commonplace, and a shorthand expression like 1/M, while beautifully succinct, is hardly a suitable alternative here for the 1:1,000,000 scale.

Sheet lines and numbers

The first ninety sheets of the one-inch *Old Series* excepted [**✣2**], early Ordnance Survey editions were laid out on regular systems of abutting sheet lines, generally without overlaps. Such a system led to a disproportionate amount of blank paper in coastal sheets which the Ordnance Survey took steps later to avoid. For instance, small coastal areas came to be included as extrusions or insets on neighbouring sheets. Some of these were outside the plotted sheet layout, others within it, but their use obviated the need to publish extra sheets. In some cases coastal areas may appear a second time as extrusions on neighbouring sheets even when published in their proper sheets. Such areas are treated in this book as extrusions or insets when their sheet numbers are not recognised. When their sheets numbers are included in the sheet heading they become classified as combined sheets. A change in this status could occur within the lifetime of an edition: for instance Sheet 261 in the England and Wales one-inch *New Series* [**✣3**.3.4] was first an unnumbered extrusion on Sheet 262; when reissued a combined sheet number was used. Once the concept of overlapping sheets, and in some cases variety in sheet dimensions, became standard practice, usually with the introduction of coloured editions, only insets of land areas located outside the sheet line system are noted and extrusions generally ignored. They are also usually ignored on the diagrams.

The complex sheet numbering of combined sheets has been reduced to a standard pattern, partly because in this matter the Ordnance Survey was over the years far from consistent and a standard practice here seemed desirable. The component sheet numbers are thus listed here *in the sequence quoted on the first issue of the sheet* (there are numerous instances of change, and addition of further sheet numbers, later), even when these are apparently numerically illogical, with the sheet numbers divided by "/" and all the various forms of "Part of" reduced to "pt" after the sheet number, thus 40/39pt/41pt. The Ordnance Survey usually did not consider a sheet to be only partially complete if the area removed from the original was offshore. Conversely there are several cases of inland combined sheets containing partially complete sheets which are not identified as such. Another irregularity in sheet numbering occurs with those beginning with a reference to their position north or south of the equator. Some give "North", variants include "N", "N.", "N ", "N-" preceding the remainder of the sheet number. Here we have adopted the standard "N", though in brackets in those cases where it is missing altogether and it was felt desirable to supply it.

Dates of publication

For most map series the full date range printed on its component sheets on publication is offered, followed by what was actually the case, using for reference the Ordnance Survey Publication Reports. Sheets with maverick dates may be noted separately. Ordnance Survey methods here are often inconsistent, for instance the survival of dates of earlier editions, or "printed" rather than "published" dates. Reprints often carry erroneous publication dates, some even earlier than the original, probably because the original printing plate on which any late alteration of date may have been adjusted was unusable, meaning recourse to the unaltered master. Reference cannot be made to all eventualities here.

Many map series were of course not published, in the strict sense of the term, of being available to the public, in that they were issued for official or military use. Nevertheless such maps often carry "publication" dates. Several military series, however, are unfortunately not dated, especially during a period in the late 1930s when the War Office went through a phase of not supplying publication dates to maps. We have had to rely on a print code or other such indication from which to derive a date of issue, though these too need to be handled with caution. Civilian publication dates that survive on military issues have been ignored. Many civilian publication dates on aeronautical maps may as well be ignored, since it is usually possible to date them more accurately from their air information date than the publication date. Publication dates as given here may, after the first issue, have been taken from the print code or other dating devices, without further comment.

Other terms that appear here include:

Printed: sometimes used by the Ordnance Survey as the issue date of coloured maps, when the "publication" date on the sheet refers to the earlier date of issue of the parent outline edition. In that they are *de facto* the publication dates of coloured sheets, these instances are treated as such here, and those noted are direct quotations from the maps.

Published in a new edition: such new issues are usually listed until the Second World War, and generally in respect of district maps, the implication of the expression being that the map has been revised and carries a new publication date.

Republished: the term is used when directly quoted from a map.

Reprinted: most reprints are ignored in these lists, but the term is intended to imply a new printing made available for sale to the public with little or no revision to the map. The original date of publication remains unless noted as updated.

Dated: many dates survive on maps that are known to be those of an earlier issue. In some instances there are no further clues as to a map's actual date of issue. Thus such dates may be quoted if for no other reason that they provide a *terminus post quem.*

Reissued: is a term used here in relation to engraved maps which cannot literally be said ever to be "reprinted". More generally the term has been adopted for military editions after the first, or when the compiler lacks concrete evidence as to whether a new issue is a revised new edition or merely a reprint. It was also found to be a useful term to describe the specific reasons for a new issue, such as the application of a new grid, the filling of a previously incomplete map, the use of combined sheet lines, the use of a different base map where the overprint is pre-eminent, as in administrative issues.

Distributed: appears only twice, to suggest the private dissemination of a map.

Since 1970 Crown Copyright dates have been preferred to publication dates. "Copyright Reserved" was introduced in Ireland in 1922, and now copyright is held by the Government of Ireland. Copyright dates used to alter only when a map appeared in a revised edition, but in both countries they are changing on modern maps with increasing frequency, such that a new printing with even minor revision is now given a new copyright date. With few exceptions, our policy of offering the dates of newly revised editions terminates at the Second World War. Also excluded are reissues of the one-inch *New Series* of England and Wales and the comparable editions in Scotland, where a minefield of publication dates awaits the unwary. Until a catalogue raisonné has been published of these series, it was felt wiser to adopt the dates appearing on the copyright sets in the British Library. Also passed by for want of carto-bibliographical support are reissues of the one-inch geological map in England and Wales.

Graticules and grids

The various graticules, grids and squaring systems carried by maps are described. Indeed, in this book differences between these constitute the primary means of classifying maps within each section. Care has been taken to distinguish between grid lines across the map face and those restricted to the map border only. The names of grids, which were not always noted on the map anyway, altered over time, and the terms offered in the Royal Society *Glossary of Technical Terms in Cartography* have been adopted as far as possible. Three particular cases have required especial care. The term *National Grid* when used before the Second World War referred to the new yard grid introduced in 1931. This has in all cases been noted here as *National Yard Grid,* leaving *National Grid* available for the metric grid in use today. Where there is the possibility of confusion between pre-war and post-war National Grids, the term *National [metric] Grid* is adopted for the latter. The few occasions during the war where the National Grid is named *Ordnance Survey Grid* on maps are listed. The *National Grid (Military System)* is noted for as long as it was at variance on map faces to the civilian system.

Secondly, the *War Office Cassini Grid* was modified in about 1931 when a revised system of referencing was introduced which reduced the repetition of its values from once every 50 km to once every 500 km, or even more, depending on the number of prefix letters used. This book follows conventional practice in naming the earlier form *War Office Cassini Grid (British System)* and the latter *War Office Cassini Grid,* with the addition, when confusion may be possible, of the words *(Modified British System).* Thirdly, the *War Office Irish Grid,* introduced in the 1920s, was similarly modified by 1931. It was superseded in the 1950s by the superficially similar *Irish National Grid,* usually referred to by Military Survey as the *Irish Transverse Mercator Grid* or *Irish TM Grid.* The grid implemented in 1940 by the Department of Defence in Dublin is referred to here as the *Irish 5000 yard grid.* It always appears in red.

Since the Second World War, map series in Ireland and Northern Ireland as well as Great Britain have almost universally been designed to conform with the National Grids now in operation throughout the British Isles. That is to say they are constructed on the Transverse Mercator Projection through the origin of 49°N,2°W for Great Britain and of 53°30'N,8°W for Ireland, and their sheet lines fall on the metric co-ordinate values of the National Grids that are in each case parallel and perpendicular to the central meridian of the projection. Such maps are referred to here simply as National Grid series, or Irish National Grid series. For further information on this refer to Brian Adams's Foreword on page ix.

Grids are by default drawn at 1 km intervals on 1:50,000, one-inch, 1:100,000 and half-inch maps, and at 10 km intervals on quarter-inch, 1:500,000 and ten-mile maps. Exceptions to these are described, as are graticule intervals. Alpha-numeric squaring systems are in two-inch divisions. These often appear only in the sheet border. Grids and graticules are usually cleared on maps which have been overprinted with another. Those which survive are generally ignored, as was no doubt the intention.

Map borders

A decorative border with the appearance of a piano keyboard was a feature of many of the earliest Ordnance Survey maps [✣**1**, **2**, **84**.2], and the pattern was still obvious in the *New Series* border design [✣**3**]. The graduation of degrees of latitude and longitude, until recently usually represented by a narrow band diced black and white, has been an element typical of the majority of Ordnance Survey map borders since it became a regular feature of *Old Series* maps in the 1850s. Quarter-inch and half-inch series maps included it from their inception. Exceptional were the new one-inch coloured editions from 1896 [✣**5**, **7**, **8**, **16**, **24**], wherein plain borders without graduation were divided into two-inch sections numbered west to east and lettered north to south (see page xxiii). Alpha-numeric systems were first incorporated into graduated borders with the England and Wales half-inch map in 1909. One can plot the steps, starting with the half-inch map of 1903 [✣**35**], via the Scotland and Ireland half-inch maps [✣**37**, **39**], thence to the one-inch in 1913 with the *Killarney District* map [see ✣**8**.10, **16**.3, **26**], by which the design used on the *Popular Editions* was developed. It was applied to quarter-inch and ten-mile maps after the First World War. Simple borders, usually just a frame around the neat line, were commonly applied to special maps when it was presumably not felt necessary to design a graduated border. These are only noted here when distinctive.

Map issues before the First World War

Where there is no mention to the contrary the reader may assume that before the First World War maps were uncoloured, and furthermore that one-inch maps were engraved. Confirmation of these characteristics is only given where there is the possibility of confusion. The production method of one-inch maps which were not engraved is described as accurately as possible, so too that of outline maps at other scales; the information is almost entirely taken from the maps' marginal material (see page xxiii). Engraved maps with hachures are listed as *Hachured edition* rather than (perhaps more precisely) *Outline edition with hachures*. Distinction is made between those engraved in a single plate (until 1895) and those (newly made or separated after 1892) which utilise a separate plate for the hachures, which may therefore be in a different colour. Other editions showing hills are listed by description of the process used, by direct quotation if possible. The absence or presence of contours, an integral feature of the engraved plate, is noted. The outline editions of these small-sheet maps did not disappear with the 1914-18 hostilities, and there remained a continuing demand for reissues, usually by lithography, presumably until the means of supplying them was abruptly terminated by the bombing of Southampton early in the Second World War.

Coloured maps

Ordnance Survey colour printed editions were virtually unknown before 1896, and it took a decade or more before they were to achieve a dominant position in the Survey's small-scale output. This development went hand in hand with the move towards the publication of large-sheet series. The change in emphasis is reflected in the ordering of map editions in this book. Coloured editions are usually so described without reference to the number of colours included. This was felt to be relevant information only when a change in the number of colours was a significant alteration of specification. It should be noted that the full number of colour plates may not apply to all sheets in a map series; a green plate may often be missing, for instance, from sheets covering Scottish islands where there are few or no woods. The method of depicting relief is noted, be it by hachures, layering or hill shading, or a combination of these methods. With maps produced since the introduction of four-colour process printing, what the eye perceives is described though this may be more apparent than real.

Outline editions of coloured maps

Since the First World War outline maps have increasingly become a byproduct of a coloured map, often employing a limited number of colour plates in addition to the black outline plate. Features such as water, woods or contours that are present in subsidiary colours are specifically mentioned. Contours are usually orange, red or brown: survivals on the black plate are usually ignored. Water refers to the solid blue plate used for rivers, canals, etc - again, water detail transferred to the black plate is usually ignored. The presence or absence of the water tint used for the sea is not noted, unless the solid blue plate is not itself present. Curiously in some map editions, such as wartime outline and water issues, water tint was itself inconsistently applied, but it was not considered a high enough priority to use space listing exceptions. Outline editions listed here are in black or grey unless noted otherwise.

Contours

The presence or absence of contours is generally noted on one-inch maps published before the First World War. Unless specified they are on the black plate on outline maps and coloured on coloured maps. Up to that point it may be assumed that half-inch maps do carry contours, smaller scales do not. Thereafter coloured maps usually carry contours unless noted otherwise. "With contour" editions *de facto* do not have them if the land is not high enough to warrant them as in one-inch *New Series* Sheets 73, 91, 144, 226, 259, 321, 354.

Exclusions

Certain map types have been excluded from this book. Exceptions occur to our guiding principles wherever maps are perceived to be uncommonly interesting, if they are on the sheet lines either of standard series sheets or of district maps. Maps which have been omitted include:

Administrative maps and diagrams, unless on series or standard district map sheet lines.

Maps which were produced as indexes to other maps, often in fact the same as the previous.

Small-scale outline diagrams with little or no topography.

Maps and diagrams used for Ordnance Survey and War Office *technical processes* such as triangulation, contouring, levelling, revision or the development of the sheet lines of new series. The ten-mile maps **✢89**, **90** were especially favoured base maps for such work, and use was also made of the 1:1,250,000 scale map [**✢114**].

Ordnance Survey *experimental and proof sheets* generally. Many maps may be encountered wherein the colour or number of plates used for printing is different from that used on published editions. Many of these were for internal experimental purposes of the Ordnance Survey, or merely as printing testers. Within the Ordnance Survey and their files in the Public Record Office and elsewhere, even the survivors run into hundreds. These have generally been passed over without comment unless of exceptional interest, or because there may be some possibility of their issue, if not actual publication. Proof copies are usually noted only in the case of maps which in the event were unpublished.

Repayment service maps. This catch-all expression could theoretically cover any map that the Ordnance Survey made for others, from private individuals to Government departments. Because by definition they were rarely "published", it is probable that only a small percentage of such maps have even been recorded. Many maps unknown at present will in the future emerge which perhaps should take a place in a book like this. Our policy was to exclude repayment service maps by default, but to include those we felt to be exceptional. Some are listed because they were latterly published or made widely available to the public. Thus:

Maps for educational use, in classroom or examination hall, are usually omitted, whether on regular or special sheet lines. These could be a requirement either of school or military authorities, such sheets usually being identifiable by a legend limiting the use of the map to a particular institution or occasion. The most commonly found military examination sheets were for entrance into the Staff College or for the subsequent advancement of officers. Between the wars these papers had headings such as *Training for War,* or *Strategy and Tactics,* and after the Second World War they were numbered in the GSGS Miscellaneous sequence. Furthermore quarter-inch aeronautical maps survive which were used in the examination of Royal Air Force officers. Many other maps not so marked may also have been made for educational use. Some on regular sheet lines with or without headings may be included where they are of interest in possessing a revised specification, such as some variation in the number of colour plates used. "Morphological pulls", usually employing water and contour plates only, may be included in this category. Reference is made to their existence, where known, but without the presence of the black plate it is in the nature of things difficult to identify specific sheets, and for the purposes of this book felt to be unnecessary.

Educational extracts, indeed most map extracts, are omitted.

Specially made maps in official state papers, or for the use of Government departments, are usually excluded. Those on series sheet lines may be included, where known, but no claim can be made for the inclusion of all such maps in state papers. Anyone who has ever attempted to find them will understand the enormity of the task, and their complete listing was hardly a function of this book.

Maps in printed books, where they have been specially made for the purpose, are excluded. Complete sheets are noted, with sources, where they have been located, but again such maps are rarely catalogued and only encountered by chance. Readers are advised that almost all the period maps published by the Ordnance Survey were accompanied by letterpresses, details of which may be found in Hellyer (1989). Reference to those at the ten-mile and 1:1,000,000 scales is omitted here for want of space, but it may be pointed out here that the pre-war publications were usually the work of O.G.S. Crawford, and the post-war of C.W. Phillips and A.L.F. Rivet. All the monastic maps were prepared by R.N. Hadcock. Similarly Explanatory Texts were issued for some of the ten-mile planning series maps issued after the Second World War. These are noted in Hellyer (1992), Appendix 5.

Some *maps of Ireland* are omitted. After 1922 the Ordnance Survey of Ireland printed several maps of the island for the Irish Tourist Association at unconventional scales, and in 1997 a road map at scale 1:600,000 was published. There are also in state papers some maps of Ireland at nine miles to the inch: these are all omitted here.

Soil Survey maps are included for as long as they remained nominally on series sheet lines. That perhaps requires some elucidation: the series began in both England and Wales and Scotland using the standard non-overlapping sheet lines of the one-inch *Third Editions* [✢**6**, **15**]. Larger sheet sizes quickly came to be adopted using combined sheet numbers tied to the *Third Editions.* Some sheets were even published using the post-war metric sheet lines of the *New Popular Edition* [✢**19**] or *Seventh Series* [✢**20**], though still numbered as *Third Edition* combined sheets. Later still a few were published using one-inch *Seventh Series* and 1:50,000 *Second Series* [✢**21**.B] sheet numbers.

Geological Survey series maps are included. However the modern district maps (including the *Coastal Geology Series* maps) published by the British Geological Survey for which the only responsibility of the Ordnance Surveys may have been in the printing (and ultimately the base map) are excluded. Hydrogeological Survey maps are included only when on series sheet lines. There is a special section for the 1:250,000 *UTM Series* [✢**48**].

It has been our intention to include *military maps* when they were not specially made for a one-off purpose, such as examinations or manoeuvres. However we are not even close to finding them all, and many more, for instance series sheets overprinted with exercise areas, never mind those classified restricted or even secret, have yet to emerge. Many titles in the regular GSGS sequence of numbers, and probably even more in the associated Miscellaneous and Office Reference sequences, have not been viewed by the compiler, and in many cases variant maps were made within known GSGS numbers (especially 3907, 3908, 3957, 3958) that have yet to be recorded. Military outline states are particularly elusive, and many must exist that are as yet unrecorded. Several military training area maps are noted, though often no more than a documentary reference has so far been recorded, usually without details of sheet lines, let alone further information on specification. Perhaps a passing reference to them here will encourage others to make public more detailed information. Intentionally excluded are composite maps especially made for a particular manoeuvre, defence scheme or exercise, unless such maps went on public sale, or were taken up for civilian use afterwards. Instances of this practice are the one-inch maps of Wareham (1906) [✢**7**.3] and Dublin (1904) [✢**24**.A.4]. These guidelines have led to the occasional idiosyncracy. For instance the southern section of the 1934 *Southern Command Manoeuvre Area* [✢**10**.M.6.2] is included because the regular *Salisbury Plain* sheet was used; the north sheet, being specially made, is excluded. Also excluded are the nineteenth-century military maps mainly at the ten-mile scale which are essentially diagrammatic, with severely reduced topographical detail, so too the full panoply of specialist aeronautical navigation aids such as plotting series maps and diagrams, aeronautical plotting charts, consol plotting charts, miniature lattice charts, lattice topographical maps, radar plotting and fixing charts, Gee fixing charts and the like, unless they are on series sheet lines. Finally, Joint Operations Graphics (JOG) charts are not listed, nor special sheets at the 1:50,000 scale. The compiler's method may not always be completely logical, but he has erred, if anything, on the side of inclusion more than exclusion.

Copies of British mapping by the Generalstab des Heers and the Generalstab der Luftwaffe during the Third Reich are excluded, as are Soviet copies of maps such as the International Map of the World. While their roots are often Ordnance Survey most were redrawn and the maps as issued were usually very different products. Maps made by the **Army Map Service** of the United States Army are included, insofar as they have been recorded, though again not those that were redrawn. Ordnance Survey or War Office source materials including printing plates were made available to the Americans and the maps they produced were often little different to British originals. More subject to variation than anything else are the colours used, with layer colours often omitted. A compass rose and isogonals often formed part of the overprint of air information at a time when these details did not appear on British made maps. American publication information is also present. But the maps themselves were rarely redrawn. Other foreign issues are included when they are essential to the complete coverage of a map of the British Isles. For instance, Sheet NM31, covering south-east England in the 1:1,000,000 International Map of the World [✢**101**.3.2], was the responsibility of the French.

Dyeline copies are omitted, though some are noted as the only recorded evidence of the existence of printed maps. Many such were made during and after the Second World War for official purposes, and similarly there are several instances of Geological Survey maps issued as dyeline maps, some of them preparatory to printed editions.

Other matters

Until the Second World War *edition numbers on military series* were rarely displayed; those lacking are sometimes supplied here in editorial brackets for reasons of clarity. The method of displaying edition numbers was revised in about 1954 from "Second Edition-GSGS" to "Edition 2-GSGS". The earlier terminology is employed here on maps issued overlapping the change. Some military maps were updated in a generational way, so that all sheets appeared in a new edition at much the same time, perhaps with some specification change; in others each sheet was updated independently. It is in the nature of things that current or recently superseded military maps are unfamiliar, if not wholly unknown, to the civilian researcher. The number of editions issued of each sheet is unclear, so too whether they are superseded independently or generationally. Edition numbers are included here in the main only on standard topographical series; those military maps overprinted for special purposes are usually only listed by title; the date, if known, is that of the first issue. Later editions may be noted. Some series are at present known to the writer by no more than the record of a single sheet; for these a general comment must suffice pending more accurate information.

The names of *publishers,* especially those which are official bodies, often change during the period of currency of a map, the most obvious example being that of the official British military mapping authority which has seen five or more versions of the basic "D.Survey" format since the change from "War Office" occurred in 1956. Here the simple form "Military Survey" is preferred. Otherwise, where quoted, the issuing authority appears here as on the earliest known sheet in any series, and subsequent changes are ignored.

War Office marginalia (marked by the ↑ symbol) is the term coined here for the marginalia introduced on War Office editions of one-inch and quarter-inch maps in 1941-42. The work was presumably done by the Ordnance Survey, perhaps at the behest of the War Office. The remnant of the civilian marginalia that to that point had survived on military printings of these maps, most obviously legends and civilian publication information, was swept away, to be replaced by standard marginalia that varied only according to the function of the map. The War Office publication information in the bottom left corner is printed in black. A new standard lettering was adopted for map headings and sheet titles. Maps intended for ground troops - the one-inch maps and the quarter-inch *Military* edition in England and Wales and *Army/Air* editions in Scotland and Ireland [✚**56**.M.8, **60**.M.4, **60**.M.5, **71**] all have another obvious feature, a large black arrow printed somewhere across the face of the map for measuring the magnetic variation. This is not present on purely aeronautical editions. Isogonals appear as part of the air information apparatus, overprinted in red on quarter-inch maps. The one-inch series affected are the *Second War Revision* in England and Wales [✚**10**.M.11, **10**.M.12], some *War Revision* sheets [✚**10**.M.8.2, **11**.M.2.2, **11**.M.6], two *New Popular Edition* maps [✚**19**.M.1], and both *War Revision* and *Second War Revision* in Scotland [✚**18**.M.3.2, **18**.M.4.2]. Most of the outline and water printings made of the Scotland one-inch map in 1941-42 [✚**18**.A.3.2] were derived from military printings and were thus also affected, though these usually lack the War Office publication information.

Sales copies of *War Revision* and *Second War Revision* one-inch and quarter-inch maps were noted in Ordnance Survey Publication Reports, and those recorded are listed here. They are identifiable by a "Sales Copy" sticker or stamp, mostly in the bottom right corner of the map. So far no one-inch outline map has been recorded without such designation.

United States Army Map Service issues are usually located in the lists immediately after the British military issue from which they were derived. Sometimes an AMS edition was compiled from various British sources, but even so it usually proved possible to follow this principle, with some cross referencing, except in the case of American issues of GSGS 2758 (AMS 1301) [✚**102**] which here has been listed separately. The compiler has no doubt that this list in particular is incomplete.

Numerical adjectives, as "2nd" for "Second", are commonly to be found on military maps, Geological Survey maps and also maps published by the Ordnance Survey of Ireland. In many cases a review of all the sheets of a series will demonstrate this to have been done inconsistently. The compiler was strongly tempted to convert all such adjectives to word forms, but has on balance decided to retain them except where both forms occur on the one map, when the word takes precedence. No doubt readers will record other printings of the same map where this did not apply.

Three one-inch maps, the coloured Revised New Series [**✢5**] and *Third Edition* [**✢7**] in England and Wales, and the coloured map in Ireland [**✢24**], underwent a *design change* in 1905, when in order to achieve a reduction in paper size the width of the alpha-numeric border was reduced from a half-inch to a quarter-inch (in round figures), and marginalia was redesigned. The legend which had appeared in a single block was spread along the bottom margin in four or even five sections (though on some Irish coastal sheets there remained enough space not to necessitate this alteration), and other items were redrawn or withdrawn. On the Irish maps the six-inch sheet diagram was cleared, and publication information was adjusted - the date that the map had been *Printed at the Ordnance Survey Office, Southampton* or *Printed from transfers to stone* was replaced by the publication date of the coloured map, not that of the preceding outline issue. These changes affected all new issues from 1905, and it was evidently policy that reprints also should be amended, though in the event several slipped through the net. The width of border and legend of the small-sheet half-inch map in England and Wales [**✢35**] were similarly if less consistently affected. Curiously, the border of the one-inch coloured map in Scotland [**✢16**] remained almost half an inch wide.

There is in the prefatory notes to most maps a reference to the *standard sheet size* of the series. This is not intended to imply that all sheets in the series were of uniform dimensions, merely the majority. Exceptions may be identifiable from the index diagrams.

Layer colours are usually either brown or purple. During the 1950s and 1960s printings of those here classified brown become increasingly yellow in appearance. However this detail did not seem important enough to note the alteration as a change in specification.

The Ordnance Survey had its own, somewhat idiosyncratic, batch of terms for the processes used in *map production and reproduction,* and those terms largely remained in use until the period between the two world wars. One particular usage to be noted is the restriction of the term lithography to its original meaning of printing from stone, a restriction that lasted well after the extension of the term to cover the whole lithographic process in the outside world. Information on reproduction processes where relevant to the present work is perforce taken almost entirely from marginal material on the maps (although Brian Adams has expressed the reservation that such material, indeed on this or any other subject, is not necessarily completely trustworthy; this is an insight from a professional cartographer).

There are several references here to *superseded maps.* The implication of the term is that no later printings are known to have been made of a map once a successor has been published. It does not imply that stocks of the earlier map were withdrawn from sale. Indeed in many cases there are obvious signs, such as the updating of map covers, or catalogue references, that superseded maps remain on sale, presumably until the stock ran out.

Map locations are offered for maps that are rarely encountered; the abbreviations used (accompanied by the ▮ symbol) may be found in the list on page 241. Users should note that it is not necessarily the first printing of a map that is recorded - indeed in many cases first issues have not been located by the compiler. Furthermore an accessible public source seemed of more value to users than unrevealed private collections, even if it was a later issue. Legal deposit collections usually identified their requirements by inspection of Ordnance Survey publication reports. Locations of such standard mapping are usually only noted for those few sheets which were overlooked in the reports.

Map covers and the information they offer have been largely ignored in this study. It has been our endeavour in all cases to locate flat copies of maps because those in covers are so often trimmed with considerable loss of marginalia. In some cases cover information is at variance with that on the map, and readers are advised, if no listing is to be found under data derived from cover sources, to seek a flat copy of the map in question to find alternative information. Two instances must suffice: cover spines of the one-inch *New Popular Edition* refer to the *1" 6th Ed[n].*, an expression absent from all civilian issues of the map, and some quarter-inch *Fourth Edition* maps were issued during the Second World War in long covers coloured red referring to a *War Office Edition* when the maps themselves are headed *Military Edition.*

It seemed pointless to list the sheets issued so far of *maps which are currently being published* (1999) when even on publication of this book such a list would be out of date. The note that "publication continues" is made in regard to these series, sometimes with a list of the sheets it is intended to publish, if not obvious from the index diagram.

Acknowledgements

It is a pleasure publicly to thank colleagues and friends who have assisted in the compilation of this work, and the author apologises at the outset to those whose names perhaps ought to be included among those listed below, but who have been overlooked. Many are the people who have answered letters, phone calls, or offered advice and information in conversation, providing assistance in many different ways:

John Andrews, Mike Ashworth, Andy Barton, Christopher Board, Alison Brown, Chris Bull, David Burles, Peter Clark, John Coombes, John Cruickshank, Richard Dean, Peter Ennor, Sarah Evers, Rodney Fry, Alan Godfrey, Jim Gould, Bill Henwood, Yolande Hodson, Clare Jackson, Tony Jenkins, Nick Krebs, John Langford, Alan Leather, the late Harry Margary, Maria Mealey, Tony Meatyard, Ian Mumford, Tim Nicholson, Rod Sladen, John Taylor, David Watt, Mike Young.

It is impossible to acquire the information offered here without access to literally thousands of maps, and my debt of gratitude to librarians up and down the land, not to mention the east coast of America, is huge. They have been prepared either to allow me direct access to their collections, or to have maps brought to me by the trolley-load, and I am all too aware of the time and trouble this has caused. I thank here all those who performed this physically demanding work, and especially to the following librarians, archivists and others who in some capacity have custody of maps, who on many occasions permitted me access to maps and provided me with working space:

Brian Allaker, Peter Atherall, Linda Atkinson, Tony Campbell, John Clatworthy, Val Clinging, Antonio da Cruz, Robert Davies, Wayne Debeugny, Peter Elliot, Paul Ferguson, Alastair Fleming, Rodney Fry, Richard Haworth, Francis Herbert, Pauline Hull, Leonard Hynes, Ann Inie, Nigel James, Chris Lewis, Rob McIntosh, Doreen McShane, Frances Magee, Nick Millea, Peter Milne, Bob Parry, James Peart, Chris Perkins, Lilian Sherwood, Ann Sutherland, Anne Taylor, Garth Thomas, Margaret Wilkes, Commandant Peter Young, and others whose names, sadly, I never learned, in Belfast, New York, Washington DC and elsewhere. The names of the institutions I visited or corresponded with are listed on page 241.

Finally I would single out four people for particular mention:

Brian Adams, author of the Foreword, who was always available with expert advice, supported by a lifetime of professional experience, whenever I as author felt the need. Though not the only person to have checked this book for accuracy Brian has read and seen more of the technical sections than anyone else and in this respect was my principal support. However the responsibility for any errors that remain is mine alone.

Richard Oliver, who has been involved with the project from its inception, and whose advice, fully and freely offered whenever sought, assisted the author in overcoming many problems.

Peter Stubbs, who rescued the book from digital disintegration when the computer programme appeared unable to accommodate both text and index without seizing up.

David Archer, whose concept this work was, who produced the index diagrams, and without whose guidance and support throughout there could have been no book.

INDEXES

1. One-inch Map of the County of Kent

Surveyed 1788-99 and made by the Ordnance Survey under the direction of Captain William Mudge of the Royal Artillery. It was engraved and published in four unnumbered sheets by William Faden. With a piano key border graduated at 1' intervals applied only to the outer edges of the county set. The Essex and Middlesex areas are mapped, though not those of Surrey or Sussex. A fuller reading of the title is: *General Survey of England and Wales. An entirely new & accurate Survey of the County of Kent, With Part of the County of Essex, Done by the Surveying Draftsmen of His Majesty's Honourable Board of Ordnance, on the basis of the Trigonometrical Survey carried on by their Orders under the direction of Captn W. Mudge of the Royal Artillery: F.R.S.*

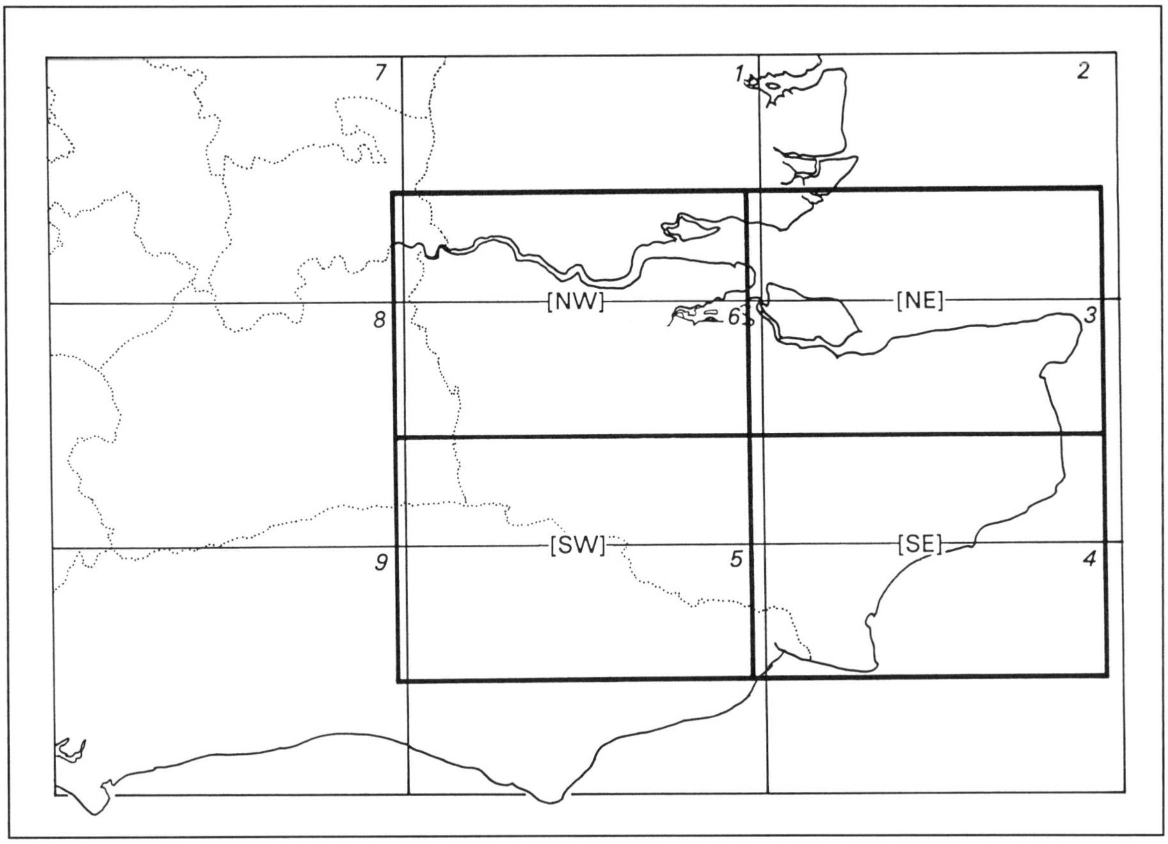

Map of the County of Kent set against the sheet lines of the one-inch Old Series

1. Hachured edition, 1801. All sheets.
   With an illuminated title on the south-west sheet.

2. Facsimile reprints. By zincography. All sheets.
   1. In black, published 1934. All sheets.
   2. In brown, published 1934. All sheets.

Symbols **:** a **bold** number prefixed with ✢ is a cross reference to another section of the book; a number prefixed with ✣ is a cross reference within the current section; a reference number in ( ) at a district map identifies the next, or previous, such map listed with the same sheet lines; the ▮ symbol accompanies a source reference for maps rarely encountered (library sigla are listed on page 241); ❍ warns that there are noted exceptions to the information given in headings; ↑ identifies what is referred to here as War Office marginalia (for a description see page xxii); ❋ refers to the exceptional use of the heading *Ordnance Survey of Great Britain.*

2. One-inch Old Series Map of England and Wales

Surveyed c.1784-1869. Laid out in 110 sheets, on initial publication in a mixture of 263 full sheets (maximum coverage 36 by 24 miles) and quarter sheets (maximum coverage 18 by 12 miles). Roman numerals were used for sheet numbers, later duplicated by Arabic. Full sheets 1 and 48 were later replaced by new editions in quarter sheets. Only sheets 91-110 fully reach the above dimensions. It is doubtful if the early sheets were constructed on a strict projection; the surveys were computed in plane terms on nine origins across the country, but the sheet lines were mainly determined independently. The sheet lines of sheets 1-9, 11, 12, 46-52, 64-70, 83-86 were constructed on the central meridian of Greenwich, and those of the western block, 20-33, 38-40, 58, demonstrably on the central meridian of 3°W. The remaining sheets numbered in the range 10 to 90 had perforce to fit between these blocks and under the "Preston to Hull line" mentioned below, and many are narrower and trapezial or trapezoidal in shape. Sheets 91-110 were constructed on Cassini's Projection on the origin of Delamere Forest, later Delamere. The southern limits of sheets 91-94 lie on a line running approximately from Preston to Hull, which forms an elongated triangular overlap over sheets 85 and 86 constructed on the meridian of Greenwich.

54 sheets, 1-41, 44, 47, 48, 58, 64, 65, 69, 70, 83-86, [100] *Isle of Man,* were published as full sheets, the last in portrait format. The *Old Series* sheet number 100 is present on Geological Survey issues, but was not current even on early Ordnance Survey issues pending in 1873-74 the imminent change to *New Series* numbering [**✚3**]. Also in portrait format was the second version of sheet 33 published in 1839. Sheets 47 and 48 were unnumbered when published. A pre-publication state of sheet 48 [▮RGS] is numbered "4", suggesting that its publication took place between numbering by county and national systems.

Full sheets were initially issued in county sets, the first three, *Essex, Devon* and *Cornwall,* forming Parts of the *General Survey of England and Wales.* After 1813, titles of county sets usually refer to the *Ordnance Survey of Great Britain.* The sheets in each part are: *Part I* - 1, 2, 47, 48; *Part II* - 20-27; *Part III* - 29-33; *Part IV* - 15-18; *Part V* - 4, 5, 9-11; *Part VI* - 8, 12; *Part VII* - 14, 19; *Part VIII* - 3, 6; *Part IX* - 28, 38-40, 58; *Part X* - 64, 65, 69, 70, 83-86. *Part I* was issued with an illuminated title on sheet 2, *Parts II* and *III* with separate illuminated title sheets. The only individual *Old Series* sheet to carry a heading is sheet 10 (1810): *Ordnance Survey of the Isle of Wight and Part of Hampshire.* This is the earliest known reference to the Ordnance Survey. The sheet lines were offset north and west in order to centre the island, so overlapping the adjoining sheets, which areas were published without hachures. Sheet 39 also overlaps 40, where there is only skeleton engraving.

Sheets 42, 43, 45, 46, 49-57, 59-63, 66-68, 71-82, 87-99, 101-110, plus new editions of 1 and 48, appeared as 217 quarter sheets mostly with numbers suffixed *NW, NE, SW, SE.* Sheet 68 was published in six quarters, the additional two being numbered "68 East Pt No.1" and "68 East Pt No.2". The two quarters published of sheet 76 were numbered "76N" and "76S". Some quarter sheets wholly covering sea or Scotland were not issued: 49NE, 49SE, 67NE, 67SE, 76NW, 76SW, 77NW, 77SW, 95NE, 99NW, 99SW, 104NW, 104NE, 107NW, 109NE. However, sheets 59NW, 59SW, 68 East Pt No.1 did appear, and a single dummy sheet 90 was published to serve both for 90NW and 90SW. For sheet 108NW see the next paragraph.

Sheets 5, 9, 33 (landscape), 39, 48NE, 76S, 86, 108SW have extrusions, that on 108SW being the English portion from the unattributed and otherwise unpublished 108NW. The area of England north of the River Tweed outside Berwick is blank on sheets 110NW and 110NE: it appears on Scotland one-inch Sheets 26 and 34 [**✚13**]. The Isles of Scilly are not covered. The Scottish portions of Sheets 106NW, 107NE, 107SW, 107SE, 108NE, 108SW, 108SE, 110NW, 110SW are blank. The words "Old Series" only appear on some Geological Survey issues.

The Essex sheets 1, 2, 47, 48 were provided with piano key borders graduated at 1' intervals, otherwise graduated borders were not generally added until the 1850s. Sheets may exist (hand) coloured in a variety of ways, for instance by county, or with turnpike roads coloured. For topographical issues with geological symbols see ✚G.1.

For the continued though renumbered use of sheets 91-110 in the *New Series* see **✚3**.2, **3**.4.

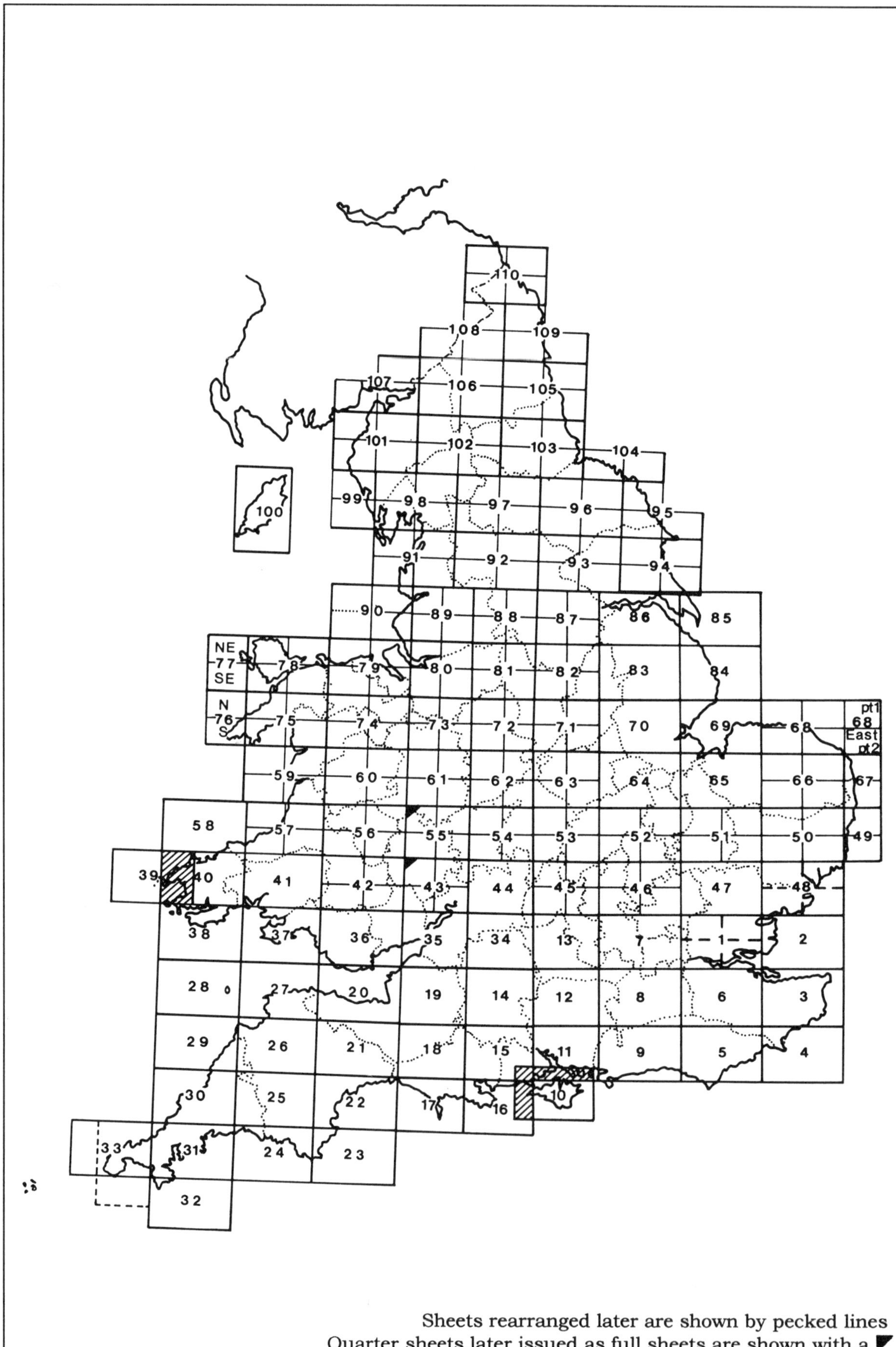
Sheets rearranged later are shown by pecked lines
Quarter sheets later issued as full sheets are shown with a ◤

2. One-inch Old Series Map of England and Wales

1. Hachured edition. All sheets.
   Incomplete copies may be encountered, notably lacking sheet numbers or hachures.
   1. Full sheets with a piano key border on the outer edges of county sets only, 1805-09. 12 sheets: 1, 2, 20-27, 47, 48.
      South Wales mapping was added to sheet 20 after first issue.
   2. Full sheets with a neat line border, 1810-22. 25 sheets: 3-9, 11, 12, 14-19, 28-33, 38-40, 58.
      Sheet 65 survives in proof [▮Cu]. Sheet 28 was reissued after 1831 with its date unaltered. Separate sheets of piano key border strips were produced.
   3. Full sheets with a complete piano key border, 1824-33. 53 sheets: 2-9, 10 (1810), 11-41, 43, 44, 55, 58, 64, 65, 69, 70, 83-86, [100] *Isle of Man* (1874).
      Sheet 2 was published in a new edition in this form in 1840, otherwise the sheets also noted in ✣1.1, 1.2 are reissues. Later sheets 33 (in portrait format, 1839), 38 (1839), 40 (1843), 58 (1834) were published in new editions. Sheets 28 and 58 were again reissued without alteration to publication date. Sheets 43 and 55, originally issued as quarter sheets [✣1.4], were united by electrotype as full sheets in about 1863. For sheet [100] see also **✣3**.4.3.
   4. Quarter sheets with a piano key border on the outer two edges only, 1831-32. 12 sheets: 43, 54, 55 as detailed in headnotes [▮PC].
   5. Quarter sheets with a complete piano key border, 1832-69. 217 sheets: 1, 42, 43, 45, 46, 48-57, 59-63, 66-68, 71-82, 87-99, 101-110 as detailed in headnotes.
      This includes reissues of the sheets listed in ✣1.4. Reference to sheets 91-110 continues in **✣3**.4.
   6. With a graticule at 5' intervals added after publication, c.1857. Sheet 91NW.

2. Outline edition. 66 sheets.
   1. Quarter sheets, with contours, 1857-68. 65 sheets: 91SE, 92-99, 101-110 as detailed in headnotes; also see above regarding sheet 108NW.
      Sheet 91SE was displayed at the Great Exhibition, 1851; its date of issue is unknown. Partially completed states of thirty sheets numbered in the range 91 to 110 are recorded. They lack contours, some having incomplete topography. Reference to sheets 91-99, 101-110 continues in **✣3**.2.1.
   2. Portrait full sheet, without contours, 1873. Sheet [100] *Isle of Man* [see **✣3**.2.2].

3. *Index to Tithe Survey,* published c.1848-c.1867. 181 sheets.
   Early states either lack the title or have one added in manuscript.
   1. Full sheets. 49 sheets: 2-27, 29-38, 40, 41, 44, 47, 58, 64, 65, 69, 70, 83-86.
   2. Quarter sheets. 132 sheets: 1, 42, 43, 45, 46, 48-57, 59NE, 59SE, 60-63, 66-68, 71-75, 76S, 78-82, 87SE, 88SW, 88SE as detailed above.

4. Hill edition, with shaded contours, 1867. 10 sheets ?only: 98NW, 98NE, 98SW, 98SE, 99NE, 99SE, 101NE, 101SW, 101SE, 102SW [▮RGS].
   Engraved sheets, with *contours shaded at intervals of 250 feet.* All but sheet 101NE were also assembled by zincography into two composite sheets to accompany the *Report of the Royal Commission on Water Supply* (BPP(HC) 1868-69 [4169-II], XXXIII). By 1870 these nine were also independently published as the *Map of the Lake District of Cumberland and Westmorland, with shaded contours;* sheet 101NE apparently was not. This was effectively the same technique as the *shaded zones of altitude* used in 1858 on Sheet 32 in the Scotland one-inch First Edition [**✣13**.3].

5. Hachured edition, 1837, printed 1838. By lithography. Sheet 59NE only [▮Ob].
   Lithographed by Standidge & Co for Ordnance Survey experimental purposes.

6. Facsimile reprints, published 1928-35. By zincography.
   1. Full sheets. 14 sheets recorded: 3-6, 8, 9, 15-19, 66 *(sic)*, 85, 86.
   2. Quarter sheets. 9 sheets recorded: 67NW, 67SW, 68 (5 sections), 74SW, 88SW.
   3. *Index to Tithe Survey.* Sheet 11. Sheet 12 is documented, but not found.

7. District maps. By engraving: part or whole plates united by electrotype.
   Aldershot, 1856. Another edition, 1862 [▮Dtc, Ob].
   London and its Environs, 1857. Another edition, 1861 (✣G.7) [▮BL].

G. Geological Survey of Great Britain, later England and Wales

Geology was added from 1834 to the topographical plates of 21 full sheets and thirteen quarter sheets. The process of duplicating plates by electrotype was introduced in 1847 and the remaining sheets (as well as any reissues of these 34) were made by this method from about 1850. These duplicate plates usually have the headings *Ordnance Survey of England and Wales* (not on sheets 19, 36, 38, 44, 47, 85) in tandem with *Geological Survey of Great Britain.* The latter heading was later altered to *England and Wales,* a change probably initiated once the publication of geological mapping in Scotland had begun in 1859.

Drift editions were introduced in 1871. In *Old Series* mapping drift geology is primarily distinguished from solid in the hand colouring. The words "Solid" or "Drift" are not printed on the sheets, though they often appear stamped or handwritten. In the legend of such sheets reference to new or revised editions was added, by no means always specifying drift. Generally the same black plate would have remained in use for the solid edition as well.

It is presumed that only sheets covering land areas were produced, thus sheets 59NW, 59SW, 68 East Pt No.1, 90[NW/SW] are lacking. Furthermore sheet 77SE was not issued, and for sheets 28 and 39 the Ordnance Survey plates sufficed without alteration. Sheets 67NW and 68 East Pt No.2 were combined and renumbered "67N (including 68 No.2)", and similarly sheets 68NE and 68SE became "68E". Sheets 1 and 48 were issued in quarter sheets. Thus 52 full, two half, and 208 quarter sheets were issued in the Geological Survey, a total of 262. Neither solid nor drift edition included issues of them all. Sheets not superseded by *New Series* mapping could have remained in print until 1940 when the stock was destroyed.

An extrusion was added on sheet 48SW to encompass the estuary of the River Blackwater.

In the sheet lists below the information offered on new editions has been compiled from sheet marginalia and Geological Survey catalogues. Neither source offers complete information. Readers should be aware that many marginal references to "New Edition" in fact relate to the first appearance of an edition showing drift geology, which sheets are listed in ✣G.4.

With geology first engraved in the topographical plates ○

1. Solid edition. 36 sheets.
   Early issues were merely hand-coloured printings from the Ordnance Survey plates; duplicate plates with Geological Survey headings and marginalia were used later.
   1. Full sheets, 1834-50. 23 sheets: 19-33, 35-41, 58.
      The Devon sheets 20-27 were first issued in 1834-35 [▮Nbgs]; revised editions of all eight appeared in 1839 [▮BL]. Geology first appeared in sheets 33 and 40 in their new editions of 1839 and 1843 (published 1845) respectively. Sheet 33 was in portrait format. The Ordnance Survey sheet 28 was issued with geological hand colouring in 1839 and sheet 39 in 1845, the engraving of geology being unnecessary in these areas. After 1850 new editions showing revisions or additional information were made from duplicate plates; sheets 19, 35, 36, 40, 41, 58 are so recorded.
   2. Quarter sheets, 1845-48. 13 sheets: 42, 43, 57, 59SE as detailed in headnotes.
      After 1850 new editions of sheets 42NW, 43NE, 43SE showing revisions or additional information were made from duplicate plates.

2. All published sheets were available uncoloured.

With geology first engraved in duplicate plates

3. Solid edition. 206 sheets.
   1. Full sheets, ?1850-98. 27 sheets: 2-18, 34, 44, 47, 64, 65, 69, 70, 83, 86, 100.
      On sheet 10 only the Isle of Wight is coloured. New editions showing revisions or additional information are recorded of sheets 3, 6, 8, 11, 17, 18, 34, 44. See ✣G.4.1 for the numbers of those sheets that may also have been reissued showing drift geology. See also the note to ✣G.1.1.

2. Quarter sheets, 1850-95. 179 sheets: 1, 45, 46, 48SW, 48SE, 51-56, 59NE, 60-63, 68NW, 71-76, 77NE, 78-82, 87-93, 94NW, 94NE, 94SW, 95-99, 101-106, 107NE, 107SE, 108-110 as detailed in headnotes.

   New editions showing revisions or additional information are recorded of sheets 45NW, 45NE, 46NE, 52NW, 52SW, 53, 54, 55NW, 55NE, 55SE, 59NE, 60NW, 60NE, 61, 62, 63SW, 71NW, 71NE, 71SE, 72NE, 72SW, 73SE, 74, 75NE, 75SE, 79NE, 79SE, 80NW, 81NE, 81SE, 82NW, 82NE, 82SW, 87SE, 91NW, 92SW, 98SE, 103, 105SW, 105SE. See ✣G.4.3 for the numbers of those sheets that may also have been reissued showing drift geology. See also the note to ✣G.1.2.

4. Drift edition. 121 sheets.
   1. Full sheets, 1871-98. 17 sheets: 2, 3, 5-9, 47, 64, 65, 69, 70, 83-86, 100.

      The "Sheet 10" listed in the 1891 Geological Survey catalogue is probably an erroneous reference to the 1888 *New Series* equivalent [**✚3**.G.2.2].
   2. Half sheets. 2 sheets: 67N (including 68 No.2) (1881), 68E (1883).
   3. Quarter sheets, 1871-98. 102 sheets: 1, 45NE, 46NE, 46SE, 48-51, 66, 67SW, 68NW, 68SW, 79NW, 79NE, 79SE, 80, 81NW, 81SW, 88SW, 89NW, 89SW, 89SE, 90, 91, 92NW, 92SW, 93NE, 93SE, 94-96, 97NW, 97NE, 97SW, 98NE, 99, 101NW, 101NE, 101SW, 102-110 as detailed in headnotes.

      In addition sheets 92NE, 97SE, 98NW, 98SW, 98SE, 101SE were from time to time listed in Geological Survey catalogues until 1893; all were removed from the 1894 catalogue, so their publication in this format must be suspect. Sheet 98NW also appears in Stanford's catalogues at least until 1893. Also, the keys on sheets 93NW, 98NW, 98SW, 98SE have boxes to accommodate information about glacial or post-glacial deposits. A copy is recorded of sheet 98SW showing drift, with the key amended by hand [▮Nbgs].

5. All published sheets were available uncoloured.

6. *Index to the Geological Survey Map, Sheet 13* (at scale 1:253,440), [1861].

   Sheet 13 was redrawn as a quarter-inch map without hill features for use as a hand coloured frontispiece in E. Hull and W. Whitaker *The Geology of Parts of Oxfordshire and Berkshire (Sheet 13)* (Memoirs of the Geological Survey of Great Britain and of the Museum of Practical Geology 13), London, for HMSO, 1861.

7. *London and its Environs* district map (✣7).
   1. Solid edition, 1873 [▮Nbgs].
   2. Drift edition, 1873 [▮Nbgs].

Old Series mapping at original and enlarged scales was also used for a variety of official and military purposes.

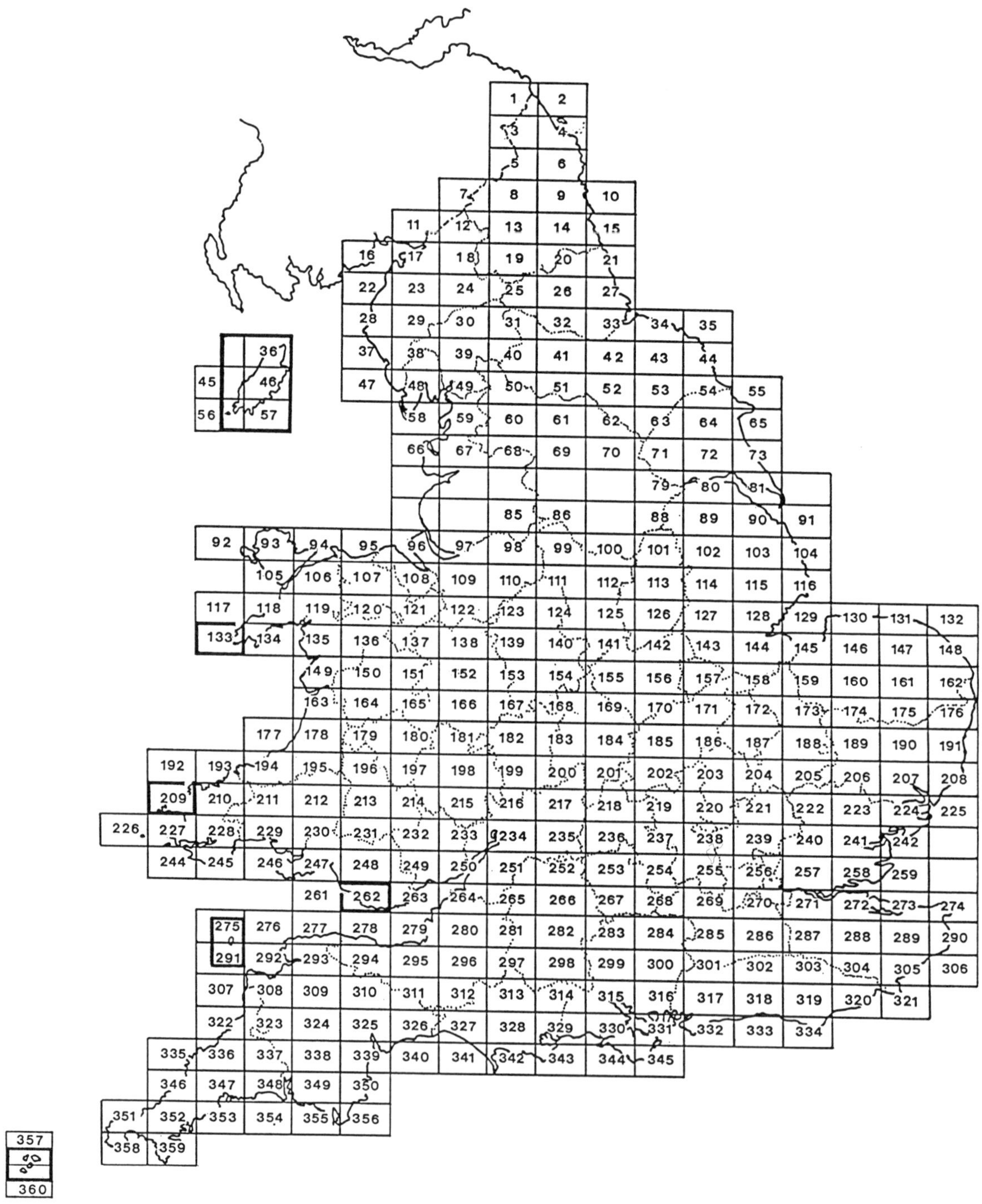

Sheets combined on publication are shown in bold

3. One-inch New Series Map of England and Wales

3. One-inch New Series Map of England and Wales

Surveyed 1842-93. Constructed on Cassini's Projection on the origin of Delamere. Laid out in 104 full sheets covering 36 by 24 miles numbered north to south, renumbered and published as 360 quarter sheets each covering 18 by 12 miles, sea areas being generally omitted. The total was reduced in this edition to a maximum of 349 sheets published in 340, some sheets being combined and Sheets 74-78, 82-84, 87, 243, 260 unpublished. Sheet 261 is included: although first issued as an unnumbered extrusion on Sheet 262 it was later recognised in a combined sheet number. Essentially the same sheet layout was used for four outline and two coloured editions [**✣3**, **4**, **5**, **6**, **7**, **9**]: Sheets 243 and 260 were published in none of them.

Sheets 1-73 are reissues, renumbered in the winter of 1881-82, of the relevant *Old Series* [**✣2**] quarters of sheets 91-99, 101-110 (which were numbered south to north), and [100] *Isle of Man* which remained a portrait full sheet and nominally required five landscape quarter-sheet numbers to accommodate it. This sheet alone carried its "full sheet series" sheet numbers 14 and 20 at the cutting line between those sheets. Late states of Sheets 1-73 carry the heading *Ordnance Survey of England.* Sheets numbered in the range 74 to 360 are headed *Ordnance Survey of England* or *England and Wales.* Sheets 7, 93, 96 (from 83), 262, 358, and 133, 209 in ✣1 only, have extrusions. The Scottish portions of Sheets 1, 3, 5, 7, 8, 11, 12, 16, 17 are blank. The words "New Series" appear only on some Geological Survey issues.

1. *Advance Edition published by Photozincography,* 1891-92. 87 sheets in 86: 92-94, 105, 106, 118-120, 133-136, 149-151, 153-155, 163-165, 167, 168, 177-183, 193-199, 209-217, 226-233, 244, 245, 266, 276-279, 281, 282, 292-298, 309-314, 324-328, 339, 340, 348, 350, 357/360.

   With contours. With a simple border graduated at 1' intervals. Available until the publication of engraved outline issues. Sheet 357/360 was not engraved until the Revised New Series [**✣4**.1], the other 85 appear in ✣2.4, wherein the extrusions on Sheets 133 and 209 from Sheets 117 and 192 respectively are recognised in combined sheet numbers. Hampshire and part of Wiltshire had previously been engraved on Sheet 314 [✣2.3]. Dorset and the remainder of Wiltshire is added to this issue by photozincography, prior to full engraving. Hand coloured by parish.

2. Outline edition, with contours, unless noted. By engraving. 343 sheets in 336.
   1. Reissues of *Old Series* sheets. 65 sheets: 91SE, 92-99, 101-110, renumbered in the range 1 to 73 (1881-82): 1-35, 37-44, 47-55, 60-65, 67-73.

      See **✣2**.2, and page 236 for a table of comparative sheet numbers. The area of England north of the River Tweed on Sheets 1 and 2 is filled.
   2. *Old Series* full Sheet [100]: 36/45/46/56/57 *Isle of Man.* Without contours.
   3. Published with blank areas, 1880-90. 16 sheets: 79-81, 85, 86, 88, 90, 95-101, 314, 329.
   4. Published complete, 1874-95 (published 1874-96). 262 sheets in 259 numbered in the range 74 to 360: 89-95, 101-116, 117/133, 118-132, 134-191, 192/209, 193-208, 210-242, 244-259, 262-274, 275/291, 276-290, 292-356, 358, 359; this includes reissues complete of 90, 95, 101, 314, 329 [✣2.3].

      See ✣1 for the temporary issue of 85 of these sheets by photozincography, also notes on Sheets 117/133, 192/209, 314. Sheet 226 (already photozincographed independently) was engraved as a separate sheet, also inset on Sheet 227. Sheet 261 appeared as an unattributed extrusion on Sheet 262, renumbered 261/262 by 1893; this increased the total to 263 numbered sheets in 259. Sheet 354 was apparently produced for mounting with its neighbours, with an attenuated border on all but the south side. A copy of Sheet 272, with manuscript "full sheet series" number 76SE, is recorded [▮PRO (T 1/7200B)].

   The following dependent issues are recorded:
   5. Sheet 285 *Country round Aldershot......,* 1886. Not found.
   6. IBWO 115: *Channel Tunnel schemes,* 1882. 2 sheets: 290, 306 [▮DGI].

      Sections and detail of proposed tunnel alignments are overdrawn.
   7. Facsimile reprints. 2 sheets: 247 (Educational Map Series 1009, 1978), 315.

3. *Advance,* later *Temporary Advance Edition with Hills.* 73 sheets.

Engraved outline sheets with contours were transferred to zinc, then brown hachures were added, first by photo-, later by heliozincography. They were available until the publication of engraved hill issues: Sheets 162, 224, 241, 242, 327, 328, 341-343 in ✣5.2, the others in the Revised New Series [**✣4**.3]. See also ✣6.

1. *Advance Edition with Hills Photozincographed,* 1892. Sheet 161 [▮PC].
   Probably an unpublished prototype. See also ✣3.3.
2. *Advance Edition with Hills,* 1892. Sheet 343.
3. *Temporary Advance Edition with Hills,* 1892-97. 72 sheets: 107-112, 121-132, 139-143, 145-148, 151, 153-162, 164, 165, 167-169, 171-176, 178, 179, 186-191, 205-208, 223-225, 240-242, 327-329, 341, 342.
   Sheet 161 [see ✣3.1] was here published in a new edition in 1894, with new hachures, by heliozincography. See also **✣4**.2.

4. Black hachured edition (outline and hills engraved in the same plate). 73 sheets in 69.

Reissues of *Old Series* sheets 91-110, renumbered in the range 1 to 73 during 1881-82. See **✣2**.1.5, **2**.1.6, and page 236 for a table of comparative sheet numbers.

1. Without contours. 67 sheets: 1-35, 37-44, 47-55, 59-73.
   The area of England north of the River Tweed outside Berwick is blank on Sheets 1 and 2.
2. With contours, and a graticule at 5' intervals. Sheet 58, reissued 1884.
3. Full sheet without contours. Sheet [100]: 36/45/46/56/57 *Isle of Man.*

5. Hachured edition, with contours. 73 sheets in 72 numbered in the range 74 to 360.

1. Black hachures (outline and hills engraved in the same plate), 1878-92 (published 1878-93). 12 sheets: 273, 274, 284-286, 289, 290, 300, 301, 304-306.
2. Black or brown hachures (outline and hills engraved in separate plates), 1892-1895 (published 1892-98). 61 sheets in 60: 92-95, 162, 200, 224, 237-239, 241, 242, 247, 254-258, 261/262, 263, 264, 268-272, 276, 280-282, 287, 288, 296-298, 302, 312, 313, 315-320, 327, 328, 330-334, 339-345, 350, 356.
   A prototype of Sheet 345 was made in this form in 1890 [▮RGS]. Sheet 313 was printed in 1898 but probably not published [▮RML]. See also ✣3.

6. Hachured edition, with contours. By zincography.

Outline sheets with contours were *engraved and transferred to zinc.* Hachures were then added by photozincography. Probably for military use.

1. Brown vertical hachures. 2 sheets ?only: 271 (1886), 272 (188x). Not found.
   Reissues of Sheets 271 (1892) [▮PC] and 272 (1893) [▮EH] are recorded.
2. Grey horizontal hachures, 1886. Sheet 273 [▮RML].

7. Outline edition, with water in blue, contours in red, 1887. 2 sheets: 255, 274 [▮RML].

Printed in colours from a transfer to Zinc in 1887. Apparently on public sale.

8. Outline edition, with water and contours in blue. By engraving. Sheet 274 [▮RGS].

This experimental printing was received on 7 June 1890 for an exhibition at the Royal Geographical Society.

9. Hachured edition in brown, with red contours. 2 sheets documented: 317, 332.

Presumably made by zincography. These experimental printings were received on 7 June 1890 for an exhibition at the Royal Geographical Society. Now mislaid.

10. *Index to the Ordnance Survey of the Isle of Man,* published c.1888. Sheet [36/45/46/56/57], with six-inch sheet lines and numbers added [▮BL, Og].

- For outline issues, hand-coloured by parish, see **✣4**.6.

11. District maps.
    1. By engraving: part or whole plates united by electrotype.
        Brighton, 1892.
        Derby, 1893 (published 1894).
        Isle of Wight, 1885. Another edition, 1889 [▮PC].
            The four sheets 330, 331, 344, 345 combined. This combined sheet was also used by the Geological Survey [✣G.1.2, G.2.2].
        Nottingham, 1894.
        Plymouth, 1894.
    2. By zincography.
        Cheltenham and Gloucester, 1894.
    3. Enlarged by photozincography.
        District round Aldershot (at scale 1:42,240).
            1. With grey horizontal hachures, 1878 [▮RML].
            2. With brown horizontal hachures, 1878, reprinted 1894 [▮Og].
        Aldershot and the Surrounding Country (at scale 1:31,680), 1889 [▮Og].
            In two sheets. With brown horizontal hachures. Reprints may be updated.

G. Geological Survey of England and Wales

Publication at the one-inch scale was never completed; the intention now (1999) is to publish the entire series at 1:50,000 [✣G.5, G.6].

New Series sheet lines are generally used. Sheets 1-73 were published as hachured maps, initially with *Old Series* [**✚2**] numbers in the range 91 to 110 (see page 236 for comparative sheet numbers). *Isle of Man* carries its *Old Series* sheet number 100 as well as its *New Series* equivalent. Some hachured base maps survive even at 1:50,000. Further south, *Old Series* mapping was superseded by outline issues of the *New Series,* supplemented by Revised New Series [**✚4**], *Third* [**✚6**] and *Fourth Edition* [**✚9**] base maps as they became available. Colour printing was introduced in 1902. In due course *New Popular Edition* [**✚19**] and *Seventh Series* [**✚20**] mapping on *New Series* sheet lines was used, both for new maps and new editions of existing ones. With them came the National Grid which was also applied to maps reprinted on earlier base material. Geological Survey and Ordnance Survey headings appear in tandem.

The sheet list offered here ignores the base mapping used. Revised editions are not listed.

For the purposes of the list below, drift editions are distinguished first by the hand colouring, then, in colour-printed editions, by the headings "Drift", "Solid and Drift", "Solid with Drift", or by indications of drift geology in the marginalia. The reclassification of 1996 does not affect matters here. However classified, one-inch drift editions also show solid geology.

One-inch mapping

1. Solid edition. 132 sheets in 121.
    1. Hand coloured issues on hachured originals. 71 sheets in 67: 1-15, 17-35, 36/45/46/56/57, 37-44, 47-55, 58-72.
        These are renumbered reissues of *Old Series* maps [**✚2**.G.3].
    2. Hand coloured issues on outline originals, 1893-1903. 21 sheets in 19: 155, 156, 231, 232, 248, 249, 261/262, 263, 268, 284, 325, 329-334, 330/331/344/345, 339.
        Sheet 330/331/344/345 (published 1893) derives from the *Isle of Wight* district map [✣11.1]. An 1888 solid edition is not recorded, even though listed in the Geological Survey catalogues of 1889 and 1891.
    3. Colour printed issues, 1902-71. 75 sheets in 69: 1-4, 6-10, 12, 14, 15, 18, 19, 22, 23, 27, 28, 32, 37, 40, 41, 50, 68-70, 75, 76, 78, 79, 83-86, 88, 92/93/94pt/105pt/106pt, 95-99, 108-110, 121-123, 137, 138, 143, 152-154, 166, 168, 169, 226/227, 228-232, 246-249, 261/262, 263, 327.
        Sheets 40 and 41 are headed *Provisional.* On Sheet 92/93/94pt/105pt/106pt only Anglesey is coloured. Sheet 95 solid and drift versions appear on the same sheet of paper.

4. Experimental production [with digital geology], 1971. Sheet 253.
   Printed by Cook, Hammond & Kell Ltd for the Institute of Geological Sciences.

2. Drift edition. 248 sheets in 232.
   1. Hand-coloured issues on hachured originals. 64 sheets in 60: 1-28, 30-35, 36/45/46/56/57, 37, 39-44, 47, 50, 52-55, 58-60, 63-68, 71-73.
      These are renumbered reissues of *Old Series* maps [**✢2**.G.4].
   2. Hand-coloured issues on outline originals, 1888-1901. 38 sheets in 36: 155, 187, 203, 231, 232, 248, 249, 261/262, 263, 267, 268, 282-284, 299, 300, 315, 316, 325, 328-334, 330/331/344/345, 339-343, 349, 350, 355, 356.
      Sheet 330/331/344/345 derives from the *Isle of Wight* district map [✢11.1]. It was issued in 1888 with only the island geology revised, and reissued in 1893 with mainland coverage added. Sheet 156 has a black plate which recognises drift geology, but no such version is recorded.
   3. Colour-printed issues, 1902-74. ?232 sheets in 216: 1-12, 14-18, 22, 23, 25, 27, 28, 32-34, 35 [inset]/44, 36/45/46/56/57, 37, 40-43, 50, 52-55, 62-65, 68-79, 83-88, 92/93/94pt/105pt/106pt, 95-101, 108-110, 112, 113, 121-123, 125, 126, 137-143, 152-157, 166-171, 182, 185-188, 201, 202, 204-208, 217, 218, 225, 226/227, 228-233, 235, 236, 238, 239, 244-252, 254-257, 261/262, 263-274, 280-290, 294-304, 305/306, 310-322, 324, 325, 326/340, 327-339, 341-343, 330pt/331pt/344/345, 346-350, 351/358, 352, 353/[354 inset], 355, 356, 357/360, 359.
      Sheets 35 and 44 were combined and colour printed in 1909. Sheets 40, 41, 294, 296, 297, 310 are headed *Provisional.* On Sheet 92/93/94pt/105pt/106pt only Anglesey is coloured. Sheet 95 solid and drift versions appear on the same sheet of paper. Sheets 208 and 225 were combined on reissue. The 1888 *Isle of Wight* sheet [✢G.2.2] was reduced and renumbered 330pt/331pt/344/345. It was colour printed in 1903 with a Second Edition in 1926.
   4. Experimental production [with digital geology], 1971. Sheet 253.
      Printed by Cook, Hammond & Kell Ltd for the Institute of Geological Sciences.

3. District maps. Drift edition.
   Bristol District, 1962.
      With National Grid.
   London District, 1904. In four sheets, numbered 1-4.
   London District, 1927. In one sheet.
      With an alpha-numeric squaring system.
   Nottingham District, 1910.
   Oxford, 1908.

4. All sheets published were available uncoloured.

1:50,000 mapping

Sheets were initially enlarged from one-inch issues, some of which were still on *New Series* hachured originals. Sheets first published at 1:50,000 may have one-inch *Seventh Series* [**✢20**] or 1:50,000 [**✢21**] base maps. Solid and drift editions and even Bouguer anomaly mapping may appear in the same sheet.

Known additional combined sheets at 1:50,000: 1/2, 37/47, 55/65, 145/129pt, 244/245, 258/259, 279/263pt/295pt, 292/275pt/276pt/291pt/308pt, 307/308, 318/333, 320/321, 335/336, 341/342, 343/342pt, 353/354, 355/356.

5. Solid edition, 1972- . Publication continues.

6. Drift edition, 1972- . Publication continues.

7. All sheets published are available uncoloured.

New Series mapping at original and enlarged scales was also used for a variety of official and military purposes which are not listed here.

4. One-inch Revised New Series Map of England and Wales

Laid out [as **✣3**] in 360 sheets, reduced on publication to 356 sheets in 346 as a consequence of unpublished and combined sheets. Produced from the first national revision of 1893-98. Heading: *Ordnance Survey of England* or *England and Wales.* The words "Revised New Series" do not appear.

Grassholm Island, The Smalls and Eddystone Rocks were not revised, thus Sheets 226 and 354 are not included in this edition. Sheets 243 and 260 remain unpublished. The area of England north of the River Tweed outside Berwick is filled on Sheets 1 and 2.

Sheets 58, 59, 66 were wholly re-engraved, and published in outline editions for the first time. Sheets 74-78, 82-84, 87 were published for the first time, 82 combined with 81. Sheets 79, 80, 81/82, 85, 86, 88, 96-100 [**✣3**.2.3] were published complete for the first time, with a legend, eg *Yorkshire portion added in 1895.* Sheet 357/360 was engraved for the first time.

Sheets 36/45/46/56/57, 81/82, 117/133, 192/209, 261/262, 275/291, 357/360 were issued combined. Sheet 227 was issued without the insets of 226 present in the **✣3**, **6** issues. Sheets 7, 93, 96 (from 83), 358 have extrusions. The Scottish portions of Sheets 1, 3, 5, 7, 8, 11, 12, 16, 17 are blank.

1. Outline edition. 356 sheets in 346.
    1. With contours, 1895-99. 351 sheets in 345 as described above.
    2. Full sheet without contours, 1898. Sheet 36/45/46/56/57 *Isle of Man.*

    The following dependent issue is recorded:

    3. Facsimile reprint, 1978. Sheet 21 (Educational Map Series 1111).

2. *Temporary Advance Edition with Hills.* 2 sheets: 147 (1894, reprinted 1901), 161 (1893, reprinted 1900) [▮BL].
   It would have been more correct to date these as new published editions rather than reprints, since they were produced from the first national revision of 1893-98. Furthermore the revision dates are lacking [see **✣3**.3].

3. Hachured edition in black or brown, with contours, 1895-99 (published 1895-1904). 344 sheets in 338: 2, 3, 6-35, 37-44, 47-55, 58-80, 81/82, 83-90, 92-116, 117/133, 118-132, 134-143, 145-191, 192/209, 193-208, 210-225, 227-242, 244-258, 261/262, 263-274, 275/291, 276-290, 292-320, 322-353, 355, 356, 357/360, 358, 359.
   However, Sheet 1 is listed in OSPR 9/03; Sheets 4 and 5 in OSPR 1/04. Sheet 6 was omitted from OSPR. It was apparently printed a month later than the *Third Edition* [**✣6**.2] equivalent, and, though there are no legal deposit copies, some record copies were certainly issued [▮BL, DRg, RML]. See also **✣3**.3.

4. *Index to the Ordnance Survey of Part[s] of [Countyname], on the Scale of Six Inches to 1 Mile (1/10560),* 1898-1904. 209 sheets in 207 [▮BL, RML].
   Colour printed by parish (not Scotland). Complex areas of Sheets 222, 253, 254, 299 are uncoloured. See also ✣6.
    1. With some parishes blank. 76 sheets recorded: 7, 12, 18, 25, 30-33, 38-40, 48, 49, 85, 86, 88, 96-101, 110, 121-123, 126, 141, 142, 157, 158, 170, 171, 185, 189, 200, 201, 204-206, 214, 216, 218, 220-224, 230-233, 238, 239, 246, 247, 251, 252, 256, 265, 267-270, 278, 281, 283, 285, 297, 299, 313-315, 326, 327, 329.
       Second states of Sheets 25, 204, 221, 233 show additional information but remain incomplete. Those reissued complete may be identified in ✣4.2.
    2. Showing complete information. 168 sheets in 166 recorded: 1-24, 26-30, 37, 47, 92-95, 99, 101, 105-113, 117/133, 118-126, 134-141, 149-155, 164-167, 172, 181, 185-188, 202-205, 217, 219-223, 225, 234-242, 248-255, 257-259, 261/262, 263, 265-269, 271-274, 279-290, 297, 298, 300-306, 312-321, 328-334, 341-345.

5. *Index to the Ordnance Survey of Part[s] of [Countyname], on the Scale of 25·344 Inches to 1 Mile (1/2500),* 1898-1904. 209 sheets in 207 [▮BL, RML].
Colour printed by parish (not Scotland). Complex areas of Sheets 222, 253, 254, 299 are uncoloured. See also ✢6.
   1. With some parishes blank. 80 sheets recorded: 7, 12, 15, 18, 20, 21, 25, 30-33, 38-40, 48, 49, 85, 86, 88, 96-101, 110, 121-123, 126, 141, 142, 157, 158, 170, 171, 185, 189, 200, 201, 204-206, 214, 216, 218, 220-224, 230-233, 238, 239, 246, 247, 251, 252, 256, 257, 265, 267-271, 278, 281, 283, 285, 297, 299, 313-315, 326, 327, 329.
   Second states of Sheets 25, 86, 204, 221, 233 show additional information but remain incomplete. Those reissued complete may be identified in ✢5.2.
   2. Showing complete information. 162 sheets in 160 recorded: 1-14, 16-19, 22-24, 26-30, 37, 47, 92-95, 99, 101, 105-113, 117/133, 118-126, 134-141, 149-155, 164-167, 172, 181, 185-188, 202-205, 217, 219-223, 225, 234-242, 248-255, 258, 259, 261/262, 263, 265-269, 272-274, 279-284, 286-290, 297, 298, 300-306, 312-321, 328-334, 341-345.
   Sheet 285 is also probable, though unrecorded.

6. Outline edition, hand coloured by parish [▮RML].
A set of maps survives which may have been masters or models for ✢4, 5. They were the property of the Board of Agriculture and are a mixture of *New Series* [**✢3**] and Revised New Series. They lack the large-scale sheet lines. Most sheets between 2 and 202 are present. Ten further sheets numbered in the range 308 to 338 are recorded in private collections. Official stamps suggest use between 1894 and 1910.

7. Outline edition, hand coloured by petty sessional division, 1904-05. 23 sheets recorded: 136-140, 200, 202-206, 223, 227-229, 235, 240, 241, 244-246, 258, 259 [▮PC].
The names of the petty sessional divisions were added by a stamp. These sheets are probably the remnant of much wider coverage. Each sheet was initialled and dated by the colourist in the bottom right-hand corner, but it is unclear whether the work was by the Ordnance Survey or another official body.

8. Colour printed edition, printed 1897. Sheet 315 [▮NLS].
Probably a Revised New Series sheet, colour printed by J. Bartholomew for purposes of comparison with their system of layer colouring (known at the time as contour colouring) introduced in 1880. See also **✢13**.7.

9. District maps. With an alpha-numeric border.
   1. *Wareham and Surrounding Country.*
   The land area is as on the 1906 map [**✢7**.3.2]; the sea area is greater.
      1. *Military Manoeuvre Map, 1898,* 1898 [▮PC].
      An outline map with no overprint.
      2. Outline with coloured hachures, contours and roads, 1898 [▮Cu, NLS].
   2. By engraving: the four plates 289, 290, 305, 306 united by electrotype.
   South East Kent, 1897.

10. District maps. With a simple border, from c.1900 graduated at 10' intervals.
   1. Outline editions, by lithography or zincography.
   Brockenhurst, 1898.
   Chatham, 1896 (published 1897).
   County of London : Diagram of the Metropolitan Boroughs, 1900 (✢9.3).
   With boundaries and names in red.
   Winchester, 1897 (**✢6**.3.2).
   2. Outline with coloured main roads and water.
   The Lake District, 1900 (**✢6**.3.1).
   The Lake District, West, 1902.
   3. Outline with coloured main roads.
   Banbury, 1901.
   Bath, 1900.
   Birmingham, 1900.

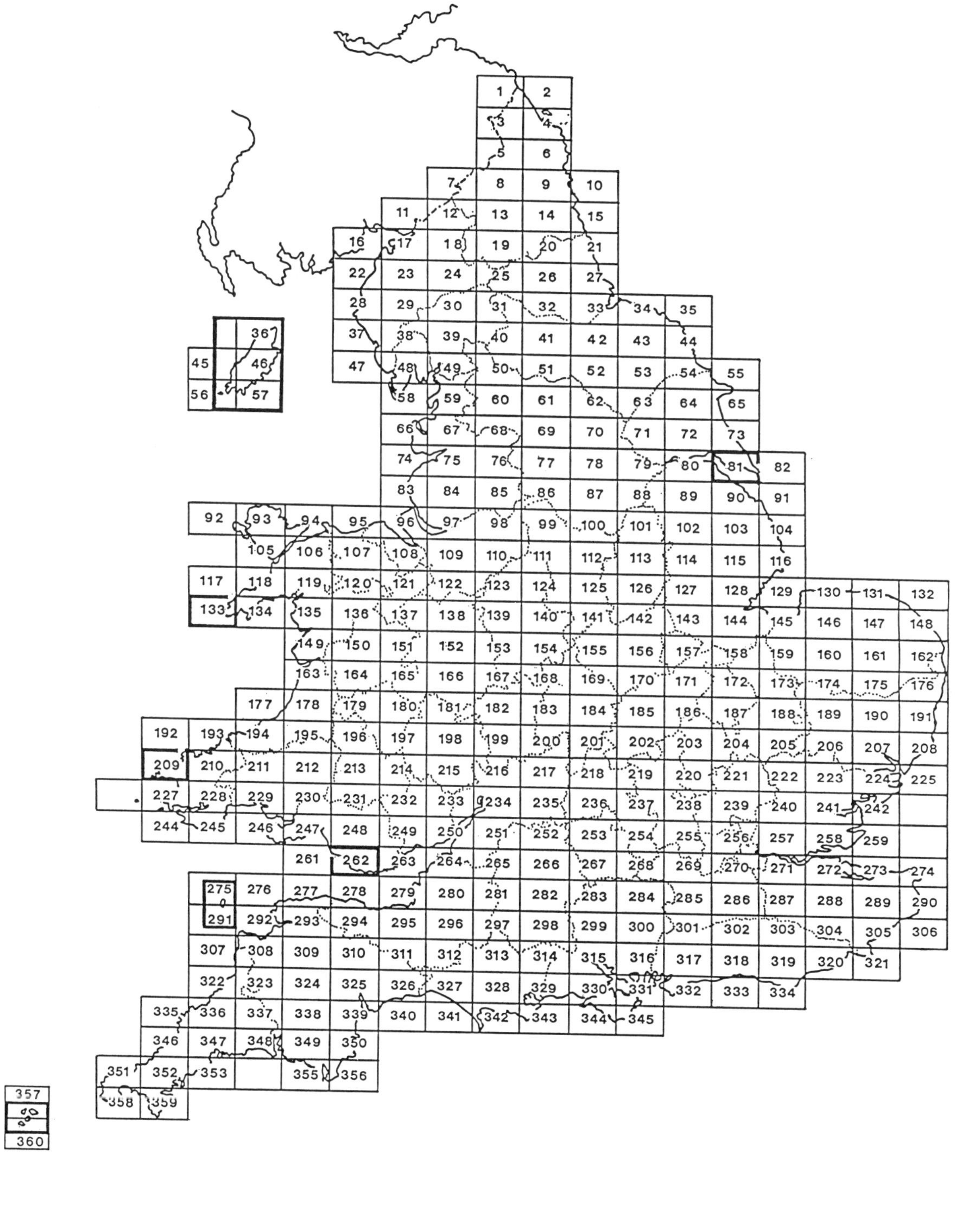

Sheets combined on publication are shown in bold

4. One-inch Revised New Series Map of England and Wales

Bolton and Wigan, 1902.
Bournemouth, 1900.
Bradford, 1899.
Bridlington, 1902.
Brighton and Worthing, 1899.
Bristol, 1900.
Bristol, 1900 (published 1903). With altered sheet lines (✣**6**.3.2).
Buxton, 1901.
Buxton District, 1901 (published by 1907). With altered sheet lines.
Cambridge District, 1903.
Cardiff, 1902.
Carlisle District, 1903.
Chatham, 1901.
Chelmsford District, 1903.
Clovelly and Surrounding Country, 1900.
With an inset of Lundy Island.
Cotswold Hunt Map, 1903 (✣**6**.3.2) [▮BL, NLS].
With the hunt overprint in green. The border has no graduation.
Darlington District, 1903.
Derby, 1899 (published 1900). Reprinted 1920.
Gloucester and Cheltenham, 1899.
Huddersfield, 1899 (✣**10**.12.3).
Isle of Wight, 1899. Another edition, 1904.
Leeds, 1899.
Leeds District, 1899 (published 1907). With altered sheet lines. Reprinted 1922.
Leicester, 1900. Renamed *Leicester District,* 1907.
Liverpool, 1899.
Llandovery, 1904.
Llandudno, 1902 (✣**6**.3.2).
London, 1899 (✣9.1).
Manchester, 1900 (✣**6**.3.2). Renamed and redated *Manchester District,* 1901 (published 1907).
Middlesbrough, 1902.
New Forest, 1900.
Newcastle upon Tyne, 1902.
North Devon, 1901. Another edition, 1906.
The land area is as in ✣**6**.3.2; the sea area is greater.
Nottingham, 1899.
Oxford, 1904 (✣**6**.3.2).
Plymouth, 1899.
Rugby, 1900.
Rugby District, 1900 (published by 1907). With altered sheet lines.
Salisbury, 1901.
Scarborough, 1902. Reprinted 1920.
Sheffield and the Peak, 1900.
Sheffield and the Peak, 1909. With altered sheet lines (✣**6**.3.2).
Southport, 1902.
Swansea, 1901. Another edition, renamed *Swansea District,* 1907.
Torquay, 1901 (✣**6**.3.2).
Tunbridge Wells, 1901.
Warrington, 1900.
Warwick and Leamington, 1900. Reprinted 1920.
Weymouth, 1899.
With an inset of the Isle of Portland.
Wolverhampton, 1901.

- For *War Department Land on Salisbury Plain,* an 1898 map with horizontal hachures enlarged from the one-inch to the two-inch scale, see ✣**122**.

Geological Survey of England and Wales: for series sheets see ✣**3**.G.

5. One-inch Revised New Series Map of England and Wales, in colour

Laid out [as **✤3**] in 360 sheets, reduced on publication to 351 sheets in 289 as a consequence of unpublished and combined sheets. Further sheets were combined when reissued. With an alpha-numeric border. All sheets were issued with a half-inch border; from 1905 some reprints in a quarter-inch border with reorganised marginalia were issued [✤1.4] (see page xxiii). Produced from the first national revision of 1893-98. Heading: *Ordnance Survey of England* or *England and Wales.* The words "Revised New Series" do not appear.

9 sheets in 4 were not published: 36/45/46/56/57, 243, 260, 357/360.

Sheets combined on publication: 16/17, 35/44, 47/48/58, 54/55, 64/65, 66/67, 74/83, 81/82, 83/96, 90/91, 92/93, 94/106, 95/107, 103/104, 105/118, 116/129, 117/133/134/118pt, 129/145, 130/146, 131/147, 132/148, 177/194, 192/209, 193/210, 224/225, 226 [inset]/227/244, 228/245, 229/246, 230/247, 248/261/262, 258/272, 259/273, 263/279, 264/280, 273/289, 273/274/289/290, 276/292/[275/291 inset], 277/293, 278/294, 279/295, 280/296, 282/281pt, 289/290/305/306, 289/305/321, 298/297pt/313pt/314pt, 304/320, 307/308, 317/332, 318/333, 319/334, 322/336, 324/338, 325/339, 326/340, 327/341, 328/342, 329/343, 330/344, 331/345, 335/346, 347/353, 348/[354 inset], 349/355, 350/356, 351/358, 352/359.

Sheets 258, 281, 297, 304, 313, 314 were also published independently.

Combined sheets 92/93, 94/106, 95/107, 105/118, 117/133/134/118pt, 317/332, 318/333, 319/334, 327/341, 328/342, 329/343 cover identical land areas to those in the *Third Edition,* small sheet series, in colour [**✤7**], the sheet lines of Sheet 117/133/134/118pt surviving to become those of Sheet 49 in the *Third Edition (Large Sheet Series)* [**✤8**].

The Scottish portions of Sheets 1, 3, 5, 7, 8, 11, 12, 16/17 are blank.

1. Coloured edition, with hachures and contours. 351 sheets in 289 as described above.
    1. With woods in green, 1901-04. 68 sheets in 61 numbered in the range 1 to 73.
    2. With uncoloured woods, 1897-1903. 283 sheets in 228, numbered in the range 74 to 359.

        Sheets 273/289, 273/274/289/290, 284, 289/290/305/306, 289/305/321, 300 were issued with photozincographed hachures, presumably because the hachures for some of the component sheets were still not available on duplicate engraved plates (see page xix). By 1900 Sheets 284, 289/305/321, 300 were duly reissued with engraved hachures: another issue of 273/289 is not recorded. For Sheets 273/274/289/290 and 289/290/305/306 see ✤1.3.
    3. Sheet combinations rearranged on reissue: 273/274/289/290/305/306 (superseding 273/274/289/290 and 289/290/305/306 in 1899), 282/281pt/297pt/298pt (superseding 282/281pt in 1900), 295/311 (added 1900).
    4. With a quarter-inch border, 1905-07. 35 sheets in 23 recorded: 125, 197-201, 206, 215, 216, 224/225, 248/261/262, 276/292/275/291, 280/296, 307/308, 309, 311, 312, 323, 335/346, 337, 347/353, 350/356, 352/359.

2. Outline edition, with water in blue, contours in red, 1907. Sheet 166 recorded [▮Bl].

3. District maps. Coloured with hachures and contours.

    Aldershot District Manoeuvre Map 1896, 1896.

    With photozincographed hachures [see ✤1.2]. In General Arthur *Report on Autumn Manoeuvres, 1896,* Aldershot, 1896.

    Aldershot District Manoeuvre Map, 1899 (**✤7**.3.1) [▮ALm].

    The 1896 map reissued with new hachures derived from the engraved plates.

    War Department Land on Salisbury Plain, 1898 [▮Mg, Og].

    The approximate boundary of the War Department property is overprinted.

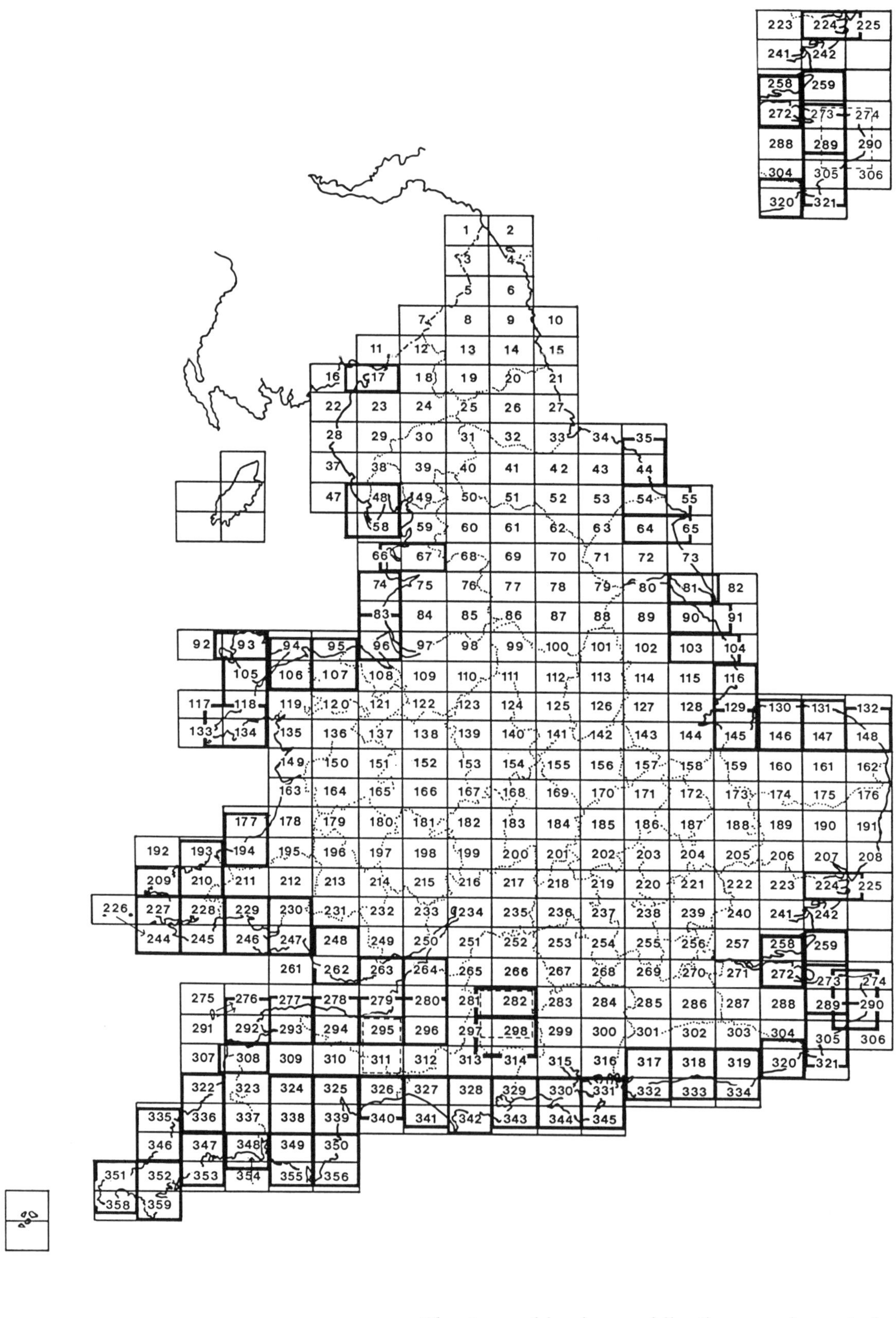

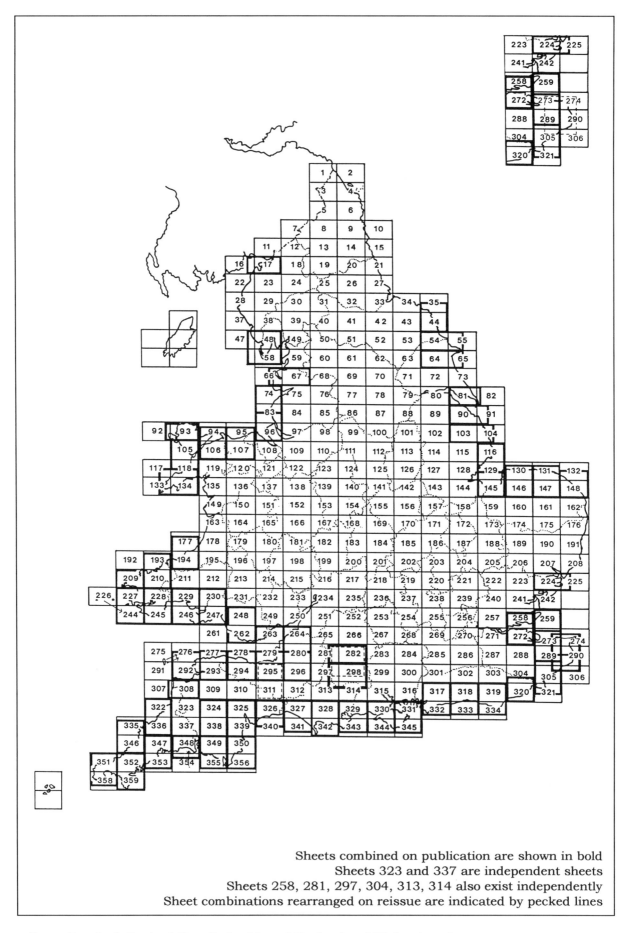

Sheets combined on publication are shown in bold
Sheets 323 and 337 are independent sheets
Sheets 258, 281, 297, 304, 313, 314 also exist independently
Sheet combinations rearranged on reissue are indicated by pecked lines

5. One-inch Revised New Series Map of England and Wales, in colour

6. One-inch Third Edition Map of England and Wales

Laid out [as **✣3**] in 360 sheets, reduced on publication to 357 sheets in 346 as a consequence of unpublished and combined sheets. Produced from the second national revision of 1901-12. Heading: *Ordnance Survey of England* or *England and Wales,* usually followed by *(Third Edition).*

Eddystone Rocks were not revised, thus Sheet 354 is not included in this edition. Sheets 243 and 260 remain unpublished.

Sheets 36/45/46/56/57, 81/82, 117/133, 192/209, 226 [inset]/227, 261/262, 275/291, 357/360 were issued combined. Sheets 7, 93, 96 (from 83), 358 have extrusions. The Scottish portions of Sheets 1, 3, 5, 7, 8, 11, 12, 16, 17 are blank.

1. Outline edition. 357 sheets in 346.
   Reissues were offered either by engraving or by lithography until about 1940.
   1. With contours, 1903-13. 352 sheets in 345 as described above.
   2. Full sheet without contours, 1906. Sheet 36/45/46/56/57 *Isle of Man.*

2. Hachured edition in black or brown, with contours, 1903-11 (published 1904-11). 332 sheets in 325: 1-35, 37-44, 47-55, 58, 63-65, 71-73, 78-80, 81/82, 86-90, 92-116, 117/133, 118-132, 134-143, 145-191, 192/209, 193-208, 210-225, 226/227, 228-242, 244-258, 261/262, 263-274, 275/291, 276-290, 292-320, 322-353, 355, 356, 357/360, 358, 359.
   Sheet 125 was offered only in brown; black was to special order [▮RML].

3. District maps. With a simple border graduated at 10' intervals.
   1. Outline with coloured main roads and water.
      The Lake District, 1909 (**✣4**.10.2).

   2. Outline with coloured main roads.
      Bath District, 1907.
      Birmingham, 1907. Renamed *Birmingham District,* 1914.
      With no reference to *Third Edition* in the heading.
      Bournemouth District, 1906 (published 1907). Reprinted 1920.
      Bristol District, 1907 (**✣4**.10.3).
      Cambridge District, 1907.
      Cardiff District, 1907. Reprinted 1920.
      Chatham District, 1907.
      Cotswold Hunt Map, 1912 (**✣4**.10.3) [▮BL].
      With the hunt overprint in red. The border has no graduation.
      Gloucester and Cheltenham, 1906.
      Leicester, 1909.
      Llandudno, 1908 (**✣4**.10.3).
      Manchester District, 1919 (**✣4**.10.3).
      New Forest, 1904.
      North Devon, 1909.
      The land area is as in **✣4**.10.3; the sea area is reduced.
      Oxford, 1906 (**✣4**.10.3).
      Salisbury, 1906 (published 1907). Renamed *Salisbury District,* 1911. Reprinted 1920.
      Sheffield and the Peak, 1911 (published 1912) (**✣4**.10.3). Reprinted 1920.
      Swansea District, 1911.
      Torquay, 1914 (**✣4**.10.3). Reprinted six times between 1920 and 1931.
      Tunbridge Wells District, 1907. Renamed *Maidstone and Tunbridge Wells* by 1914.
      Winchester, 1904 (**✣4**.10.1).
      Wolverhampton, 1910.

Geological Survey of England and Wales: for series sheets see ✢**3**.G.

Soil Survey of England and Wales

Third Edition mapping with National Grid was used, then *New Popular Edition* and *Seventh Series,* on *New Series* sheet lines. Other sheets in the series are on *New Popular Edition* and *Seventh Series* sheet lines. The earliest of these were given *New Series* combined sheet numbers. Finally some outline one-inch *Seventh Series* and 1:50,000 sheets were published carrying the normal sheet numbering systems of these series. See ✢**19**.8, **20**.14, **20**.15, **21**.B.9.

4. *Soil Survey,* 1952-74. 32 sheets in 29: 19, 66, 70, 74, 75, 83, 94, 95, 106, 107, 125, 138, 142, 163, 166, 173, 178, 181, 188, 238, 251/265, 253, 261/262, 263, 268, 279, 280, 296, 325/339.

5. *Land Use Capability.*
   1. Coloured edition, 1971. 2 sheets: 142, 253.
   2. Outline edition, 1966. Sheet 166.

6. *Post-glacial Mineral Deposits,* 1974. Sheet 173.

7. *Predicted Underdrainage Treatment for Arable Use,* 1973. Sheet 253.

Symbols **:** a **bold** number prefixed with ✢ is a cross reference to another section of the book; a number prefixed with ✣ is a cross reference within the current section; a reference number in ( ) at a district map identifies the next, or previous, such map listed with the same sheet lines; the ▮ symbol accompanies a source reference for maps rarely encountered (library sigla are listed on page 241); ❍ warns that there are noted exceptions to the information given in headings; ↑ identifies what is referred to here as War Office marginalia (for a description see page xxii); ⊛ refers to the exceptional use of the heading *Ordnance Survey of Great Britain.*

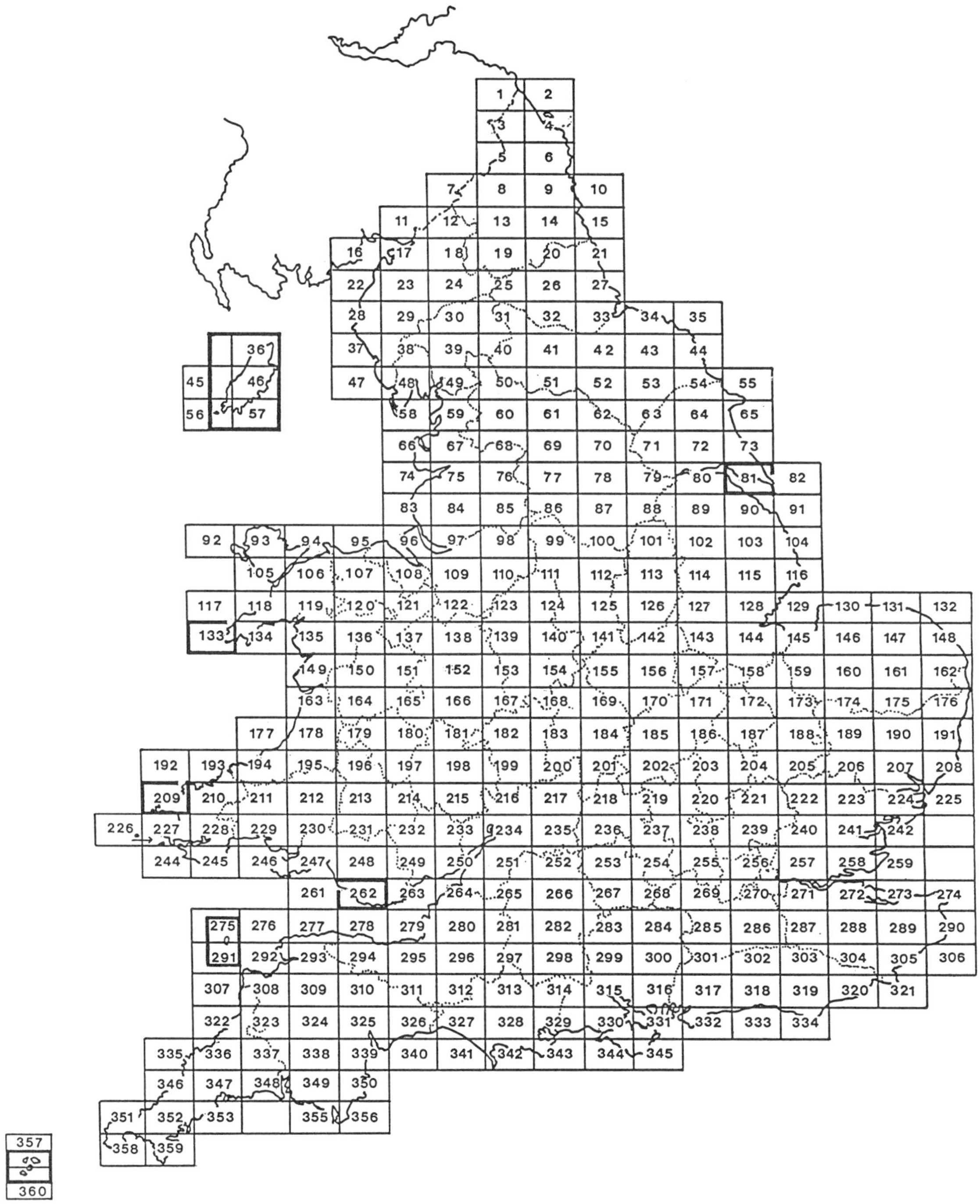

Sheets combined on publication are shown in bold

6. One-inch Third Edition Map of England and Wales

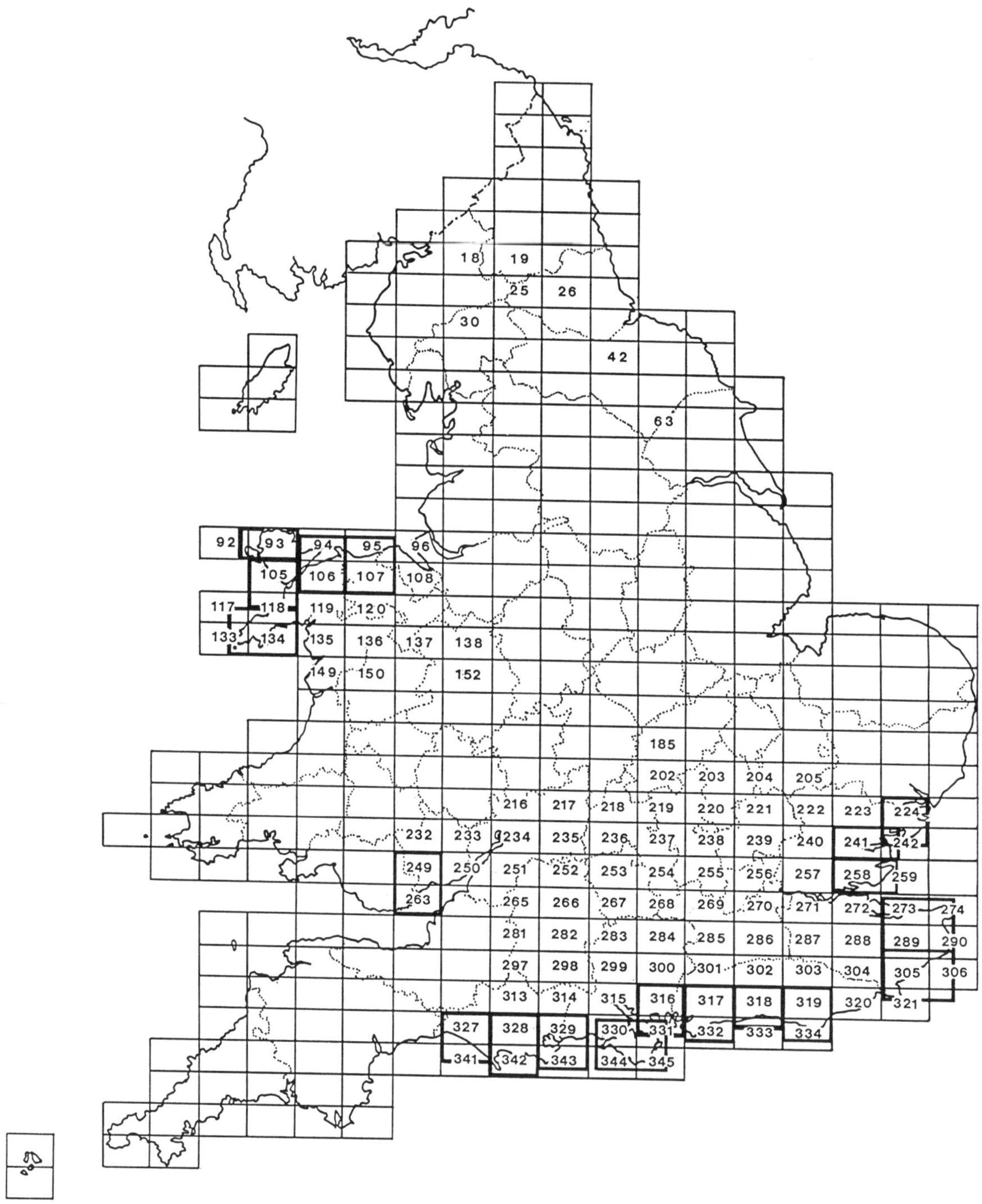

Sheets combined on publication are shown in bold

7. One-inch Third Edition Map of England and Wales, in colour : small sheet series

7. One-inch Third Edition Map of England and Wales, in colour : small sheet series

Laid out [as **✣3**] in 360 sheets, a number which would have been much reduced by sheet combinations and the non-publication of Sheets 243 and 260. Publication was discontinued before completion. Usually with an alpha-numeric border; the width was reduced from a half-inch to a quarter-inch in 1905 [✢1.2] (see page xxiii). Produced from the second national revision of 1901-05. Heading: *Ordnance Survey of England* or *England and Wales,* followed in most cases by *(Third Edition).* The words "small sheet series" do not appear.

Combined sheets 92/93, 94/106, 95/107, 105/118pt, 117/133/134/118pt, 317/332, 318/333, 319/334, 327/341, 328/342, 329/343 cover identical land areas to these combined sheets in the Revised New Series map, in colour [**✣5**]. Combined sheets which survived to be renumbered as members of the *Third Edition (Large Sheet Series)* [**✣8**]: 117/133/134/118pt as 49, 273/274/289pt/290pt as 118, 305/306/321/289pt/290pt as 128.

According to indexes published c.1908 combined sheets 1/2, 7/8, 9/10, 11/12, 14/15, 20/21, 22/23, 28/29, 36/45/46/57/58, 37/38, 72/73, 208/225, 264/263pt/279pt/280pt, 357/360 were also plotted, but they were never issued. For Sheet 36/45/46/57/58 see **✣8**.

1. Coloured edition, with hachures and contours. 118 sheets in 96.
    1. With a half-inch border, 1903-04. 27 sheets in 22: 253-255, 267-270, 283-286, 299-302, 315, 316/331, 317/332, 318/333, 329/343, 330, 344/345/330pt/331pt.
    2. With a quarter-inch border, 1905-07. 108 sheets in 90 recorded: 18, 19, 25, 26, 30, 42, 63, 92/93, 94/106, 95/107, 96, 105/118pt, 108, 117/133/134/118pt, 119, 120, 135-138, 149, 150, 152, 185, 202-205, 216-223, 224/242pt, 232-240, 241/242pt, 249/263, 250-257, 258/259pt, 265, 266, 268-272, 273/274/289pt/290pt, 281-288, 297-301, 303, 304, 305/306/321/289pt/290pt, 313-315, 317/332, 319/334, 320, 327/341, 328/342, 330.

        The sheets also listed in ✢1.1 are reprints here. Others will no doubt emerge. Sheet 205 is lacking in OSPR and legal deposit libraries [▮RML].

2. As ✢1.2, but with uncoloured woods, dated 1905. Sheet 286 recorded [▮Bl].

3. District maps. Coloured with hachures and contours.
    1. With a half-inch alpha-numeric border.

        Aldershot District Manoeuvre Map, 1904 (**✣5**.3).

    2. With a quarter-inch alpha-numeric border.

        Aldershot District Manoeuvre Map, 1905 (**✣10**.12.1). In two sheets, *(North)* and *(South).*

        With uncoloured woods. Command and other boundaries are overprinted.

        Salisbury Plain.
        1. Published 1906 with the War Department boundary overprinted.
        2. Published 1906 without overprint. For civilian use.
        3. Published 1909 (altered on some reprints to 1908).
           War Department information, updated to 1908, and on reprints to 1911 and 1914, is overprinted.
        4. Reprinted as *War Department Land on Salisbury Plain,* 1927 [▮PC].
           War Department information is updated to 1926.

        Wareham and Surrounding Country.

        The land area is as on the 1898 map [**✣4**.9.1]: the sea area is reduced.
        1. *Military Manoeuvre Map, 1906,* 1906 [▮BL, Cu, Bg]. With no overprint.
        2. Published for civilian use, 1907.

    3. With a simple border.

        Windsor and Neighbourhood, 1907 [▮PC].

        Prepared specially for Eton College Rifle Volunteer Corps.

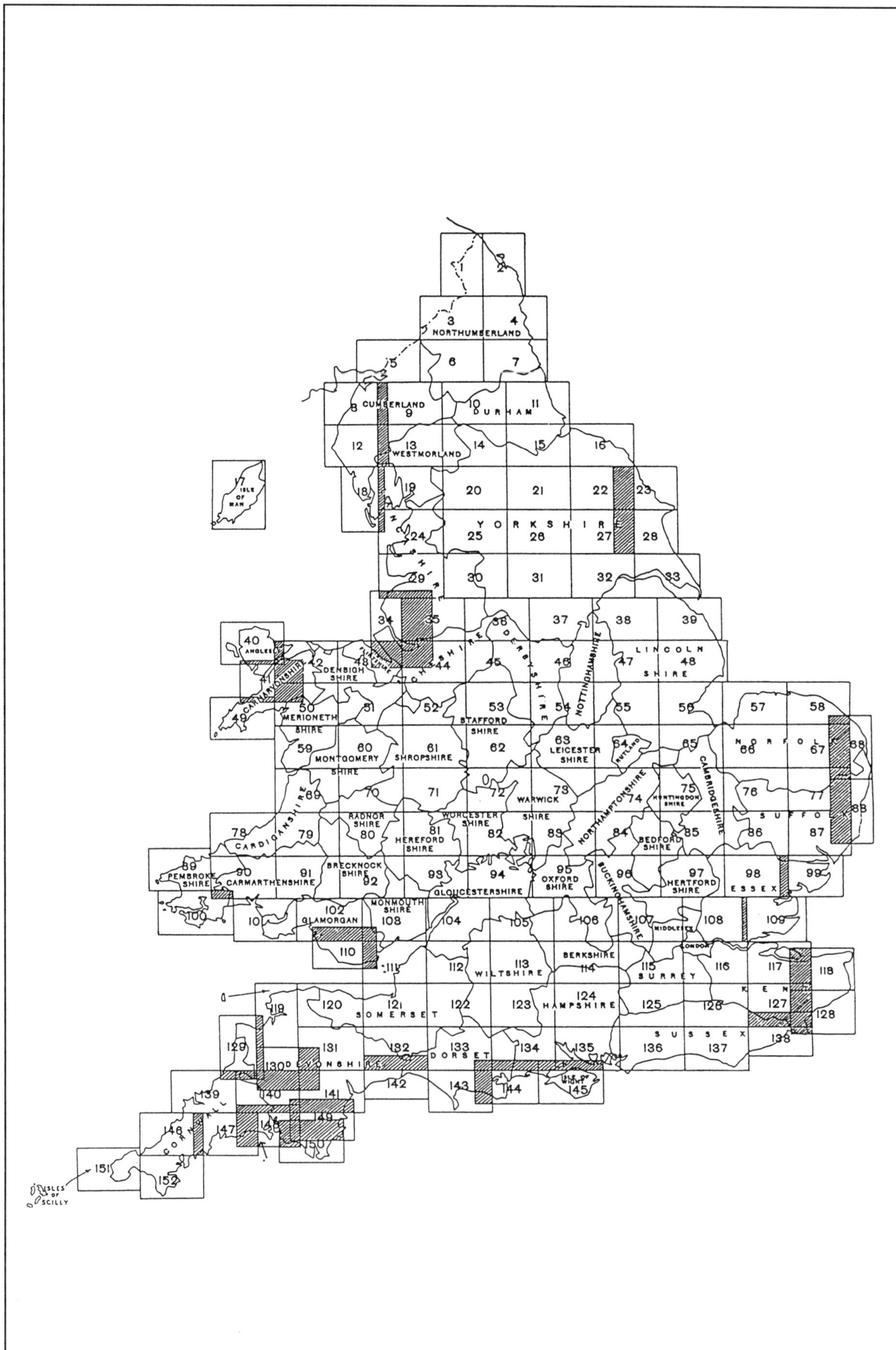

8. One-inch Third Edition Map of England and Wales (Large Sheet Series)

8. One-inch Third Edition Map of England and Wales (Large Sheet Series)

Constructed on Cassini's Projection on the origin of Delamere, and published in 152 sheets. Derived from the engraved one-inch map. The small sheet series [✚7] was abandoned in favour of one with standard sheet coverage of 27 by 18 miles, four sheets covering the same area as nine in its predecessor. Produced from the second national revision of 1901-12. Heading: *Ordnance Survey of England* or *England and Wales (Third Edition) : (Large Sheet Series).* When filled with Scotland mapping Sheets 1, 3, 5 carry the heading *Ordnance Survey of England and Scotland.*

Sheets which were first issued as members of the small sheet series [✚7]: 49 as 117/133/134/118pt, 118 as 273/274/289pt/290pt, 128 as 305/306/321/289pt/290pt. Sheet 17 was plotted as 35/45/46/57/58 in the small sheet series, but it was not issued there.

Sheet lines common with one-inch *Popular Edition* [✚**10**]: 1-3, 5-7, 23, 28, 29; also 39 with 40, 101-108 with 100-107, 111-117 with 110-116, 120-127 with 119-126, 131-138 with 128-135, 140 and 141 with 137 and 138 respectively. Congruity of the mapped detail is less precise in the north.

There are insets of Lundy Island on Sheet 119, Eddystone Rocks on 148 (their final appearance on mapping at this scale), Isles of Scilly on 151. Grassholm Island and The Smalls are not covered in this edition, though some indexes indicate they are on Sheet 100.

With an alpha-numeric border ❍

1. Coloured edition, with hachures. All sheets.
   1. Without contours, 1906. Sheet 17 only.
   2. With contours, and with Scotland blank, 1907. 4 sheets: 1, 3, 5, 8.
   3. Published complete, with contours, 1907-13. 150 sheets: 1-7, 9-16, 18-152.
      The new editions of Sheets 1, 3, 5 with coverage of Scotland were published in 1917. Sheet 74 was given a new publication date in 1913.

2. *Black Outline Edition,* without contours. 58 sheets.
   1. Published with Scotland blank, 1907 (published 1918). Sheet 8 only.
   2. Published complete, 1907-17 (published 1918-19). 57 sheets: 1-4, 6, 13-22, 27, 28, 36-38, 42-46, 48, 52, 53, 59, 66, 68, 73, 78, 79, 86, 93-96, 98, 99, 103-108, 111-116, 124-126, 150.
      Sheets 38 [▮Ob] and 48 [▮BL] are lacking in OSPR.

3. Outline edition, with water in blue, contours in red. 4 sheets recorded: 30, 31, 97, 124 [▮PC].
   Sheet 124 is recorded for use in Officers' Training Corps examinations, 1919 and 1920. The date, purpose and coverage of this edition remains unknown.

4. Coloured edition, with hachures and contours, dated 1909. Sheet 145.
   With military overprint. In *The Land Defence of the United Kingdom : Isle of Wight,* London, War Office A.1458, 1911 [▮PRO (WO 33/522)].

5. Coloured edition, with hachures and contours, overprinted with military grids.
   The only dates carried by these maps are the original civilian publication dates. Their issue is probably connected with the experimental gridding of maps for the western front during the First World War.
   1. With six-mile and quartered one-mile squares, in red. Sheet 115 [▮PC].
   2. With 12,000-yard and quartered 2000-yard squares, in red. Sheet 115 [▮PC].
   3. With 10,000-yard and quartered 2000-yard squares, in purple. Sheet 107 [▮PC].
   4. With a 2000-yard alpha-numeric squaring system, with 400-yard subdivisions, in red. Sheet 135 recorded [▮PC].
      Sheet 134 may also exist, with the numeric system commencing on 135 at "9".

6. Outline edition, with roads and contours in red, issued ?1915. Sheet 23 recorded [▮PC].

7. Coloured edition with contours, without hachures, issued after 1915. Sheet 71 recorded [▮PC].

8. District maps. Coloured with hachures and contours.
   1. With an alpha-numeric border.
      Brighton & Worthing District, 1912.
      Felixstowe District, 1911. Unnamed until reprinted. Renamed *Ipswich and Felixstowe*, 1914.
      Folkestone and Dover District, 1913.
      With a blue coastal tint.
      Hastings and Bexhill District, 1912.
      Land's End and Lizard District, 1912.
      Maidenhead, Windsor and Henley District, 1912.
      Newquay District, 1912.
      Pwllheli and Criccieth District, 1913.
      With a blue coastal tint. Lleyn Peninsula is inset.
      Reading and District, 1912.
      Rugby District, 1912. Reprinted 1920.
      Sidmouth, Budleigh Salterton & Exmouth District, 1912 (✢**10**.14.1). Reprinted 1920.
      Staffordshire Potteries and District, 1913. Reprinted 1923.
      Weston super Mare, 1911. Unnamed until reprinted.
      Winchester District, 1910.
      Worcester and Malvern District, 1912.

   2. With a simple border.
      Windsor and Neighbourhood, 1913 [▮Cu].
      Prepared specially for Eton College Officers Training Corps.

With an alpha-numeric squaring system

9. District maps. Coloured with hachures and contours.
   The borders of the Cambridge and Oxford maps include latitude and longitude values graduated at 1' intervals, perhaps a function of their use as training maps for the Officers' Training Corps of the two universities.
   Cambridge District, 1910.
   London, 1912. In two sheets, *(North)* and *(South)*.
   Oxford District, 1911. Renamed *Oxford and District*, 1912.

With a graduated and alpha-numeric border

10. District maps. Coloured with layers, hachures, hill shading and contours.
    Dorking and Leith Hill District, 1914. Reprinted 1922, 1925.
    Ilkley District, 1914. Reprinted 1920.

With a graduated border and alpha-numeric squaring system

11. *York District*.
    1. *Provisional Popular Edition*, 1919.
    2. *Popular Edition*, 1919, reprinted 1923 [▮PC].

12. Tourist Maps. Coloured with layers, hachures and contours.
    The Lake District, 1920 (✢**10**.13.2).
    Snowdon District, 1920.

13. Road Edition. Outline with water in blue, main roads in red, other roads in orange.
    The Lake District, 1920 [▮BL].
    With sheet lines different from both the 1909 district map [✢**6**.3.1] and the 1920 Tourist Map [✢12]. Contours are on the black plate.

9. One-inch Fourth Edition Map of England and Wales

Laid out [as ✣3] in 360 sheets. Produced from the third national revision of 1909-10 (abandoned). In the event only sixteen sheets, 271-274, 287-290, 304-306, 320, 321, 330, 344, 345, were revised, of which seven, 273, 274, 289, 290, 305, 306, 321, were published. Heading: *Ordnance Survey of England (Fourth Edition).*

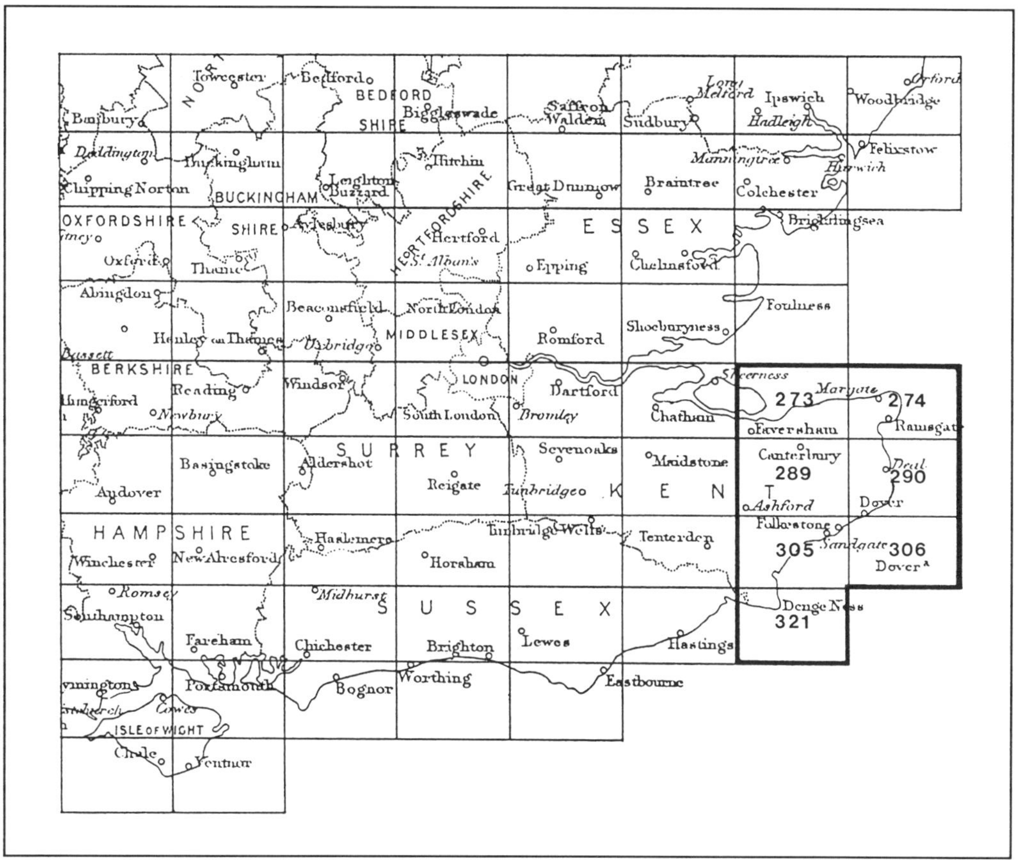

1. Outline edition, with contours, 1911-12. 7 sheets: 273, 274, 289, 290, 305, 306, 321. Reissues were offered either by engraving or by lithography.

2. Hachured edition in black or brown, with contours, 1911. 4 sheets: 273, 274, 289, 290.

Geological Survey of England and Wales: for series sheets see **✣3**.G.

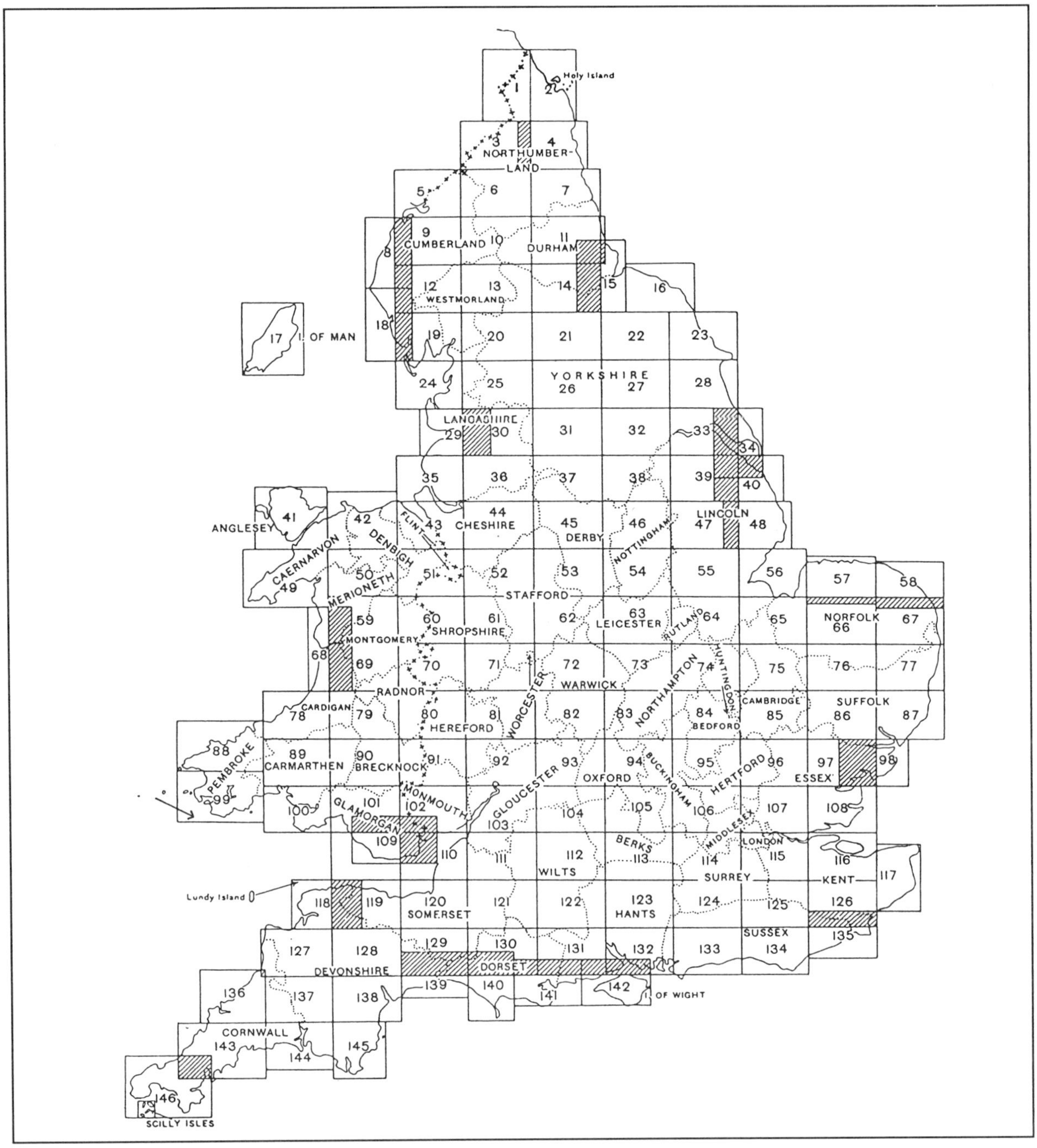

10. One-inch Popular Edition Map of England and Wales

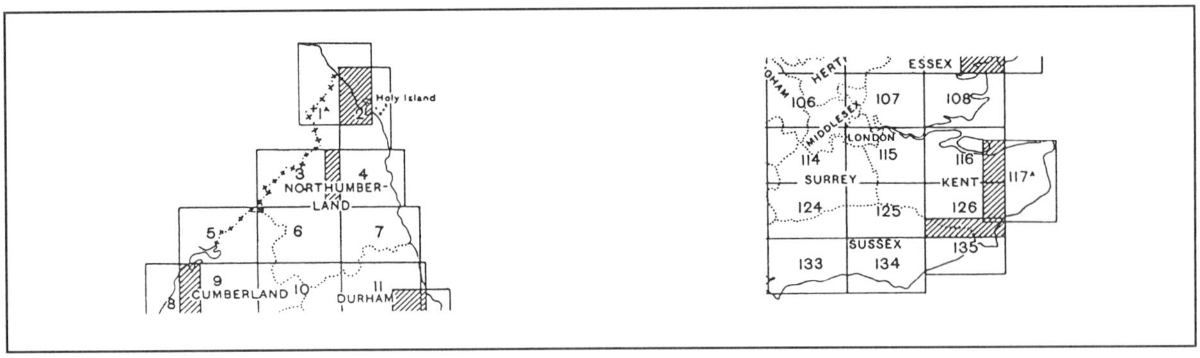

The position of Sheets 1A and 117A in the Second War Revision

10. One-inch Popular Edition Map of England and Wales

Constructed on Cassini's Projection on the origin of Delamere, and published in 146 sheets. Derived from the engraved one-inch map (except Sheets 1, 3, 5 which were newly drawn). Standard sheet coverage 27 by 18 miles. With an alpha-numeric squaring system unless noted. Produced from the third national revision of 1912-23. For the map border see page xviii. Heading: *Ordnance Survey of England,* or *England and Wales* : *Popular Edition One-inch Map* (*Great Britain* on Sheets 3, 5, 8, Sheet 107 in ✣M.5.4, M.8.3 and when marked ❂).

With its area covered by Scotland *Popular Edition* Sheets 75 and 81 [**✣18**], Sheet 1 was considered superfluous and unpublished in some editions. Sheets 3 and 5 are common with Scotland *Popular Edition* Sheets 86 and 89. *Isle of Wight* [✣13.1] and *Land's End & Lizard* [✣13.2] Tourist Maps are common with Sheets 142 and 146, but do have enhanced colouring.

Sheet lines common with one-inch *Third Edition (Large Sheet Series)* [**✣8**]: 1-3, 5-7, 23, 28, 29; also 40 with 39, 100-107 with 101-108, 110-116 with 111-117, 119-126 with 120-127, 128-135 with 131-138, 137 and 138 with 140 and 141 respectively. Congruity of the mapped detail is less precise in the north. With insets of Grassholm Island and The Smalls on Sheet 99, Lundy Island on 118, Isles of Scilly on 146. The Scottish portion of Sheet 6 is blank.

1. Coloured edition, 1918-26 (published 1919-26). All sheets.

2. *Outline Edition.* All sheets.
   Until c.1924 sheets are headed *One-inch Outline Edition,* thereafter usually *Popular Edition One-inch Map,* with *(Outline)* on the contour plate.
   1. With contours in red, 1920-23 (published 1921-23). 50 sheets: 17, 41, 42, 49-69, 71, 72, 76, 77, 86-89, 97-99, 101, 106-109, 114-117, 123, 125, 126, 133-135. Sheet reprints may have water in blue, as in ✣2.2.
   2. With water in blue, contours in red, 1919-26 (published 1923-26). Probably most sheets; 107 sheets recorded: 1-16, 18-40, 43-48, 54, 60, 70, 72-75, 78-85, 90-98, 100, 102-107, 110-116, 118-122, 124, 127-132, 134, 136-146.
      The sheets also listed in ✣2.1 are reprints here with water features coloured. Others will no doubt emerge, notably Sheets 42, 53, 55, 61, 62, 64, 71, 77, 101, 123, 126 (listed in OSR 1936-37 *et seq*).

   The following dependent issue is recorded:
   3. Showing War Department lands, 1925. 2 sheets recorded: 116, 132 [▮Ob].

3. Outline edition, with water in blue, 1941-42. Without grid. ?124 sheets: 1-105, 109, 111-113, 115-117, 120-122, 125, 126, 130, 131, 134, 135, 139, 142, ?144.
   The above sheets, other than 115, are listed in the unpublished wartime OSRs. For complementary coverage of southern England see **✣11**.4, **12**.4. Sheet 144 is the only one in the south not recorded. Additional sheets cannot be discounted since there was some duplication of coverage between *Popular* and *Fifth Edition* sources. Alpha-numeric values survive in the borders of some sheets. At least eleven sheets, 7, 21, 31, 32, 35, 36, 44, 46, 53, 54, 72, were reprinted in 1946.

4. Water and contour issues.

5. *London Passenger Transport Map,* 1934. 12 sheets.
   Outline issues with an alpha-numeric border, with overprint showing:
   1. Boundaries and roads. 12 sheets: 84, 85, 95, 96, 106-108, 114-116, 124, 125.
   2. Boundaries, roads and railways. 9 sheets recorded: 85, 95, 96, 106, 107, 114, 115, 124, 125.
      The base map has uncoloured main roads in ✣5.1, 5.2.
   3. Boundaries and roads. 12 sheets: 84, 85, 95, 96, 106-108, 114-116, 124, 125.
   4. Boundaries, roads and railways. 9 sheets recorded: 85, 95, 96, 106, 107, 114, 115, 124, 125.
      The base map has main roads in red in ✣5.3, 5.4.

6. *Land Utilisation Survey of Britain.* 145 sheets in 134.
   Published by the Land Utilisation Survey of Britain except the sheets in ✣6.1. Sheet 1 was not issued, the area being covered by Scotland Sheets 75 and 81 [✚**18**.A.5]. With alpha-numeric borders, lacking on Sheets 67, 77, 99, 107, 109, 125. Sheet 35 has an alpha-numeric squaring system. In 1943 a quarter-inch atlas *Coloured Maps of England & Wales* was published, containing in 38 plates three-colour prints of all the sheets still not published. A pioneer *Land Utilization Map of the County of Northampton* was published in 1929 by the Ordnance Survey for Northamptonshire Education Committee, in three sheets: *NW, NE, SW* [▮Bg].
   1. Printed and published by the Ordnance Survey, 1932-35 (published 1933-35). 14 sheets: 11, 12, 35, 44, 55, 58, 66, 67, 72, 87, 95, 114, 142, 146.
   2. Printed by J. Bartholomew, 1935. 2 sheets: 57, 63.
      Ten sheets, 11, 12, 35, 44, 55, 67, 72, 87, 95, 142, were reprinted in 1942.
   3. Printed by Greycaine, 1935. Sheet 103.
   4. Printed by Martin, Hood & Larkin, 1935. Sheet 54.
   5. Printed by Waterlow, 1935. 4 sheets: 106, 107, 112, 115.
      Three sheets, 106, 107, 114, were reprinted in 1942.
   6. Printed by G.W. Bacon, 1935-40. 66 sheets in 62: 7, 16, 22, 28-32, 33/34pt, 36-39, 43, 45-47, 52, 53, 56, 61, 62, 64, 65, 71, 73, 75-77, 81, 82, 84-86, 88, 95, 96, 97/98, 99-102, 105, 108, 109, 111/110pt, 113, 116, 117, 120-125, 126/135, 132-134, 138, 141, 142.
      Some copies of Sheet 29 (1936) were designated *British Association for the Advancement of Science : Blackpool Meeting.....1936.* Sheets listed earlier are reprints here: there may be others. Sheets 23, 27, 40/48, 74, 83, 92, 94, 104 were being printed in 1941 but were destroyed by enemy action.
   7. Printed by Baynard Press for G.W. Bacon, 1942. 3 sheets: 74, 83, 94.
   8. Printed by E. Stanford, 1942-47. 49 sheets in 42: 2-4, 6, 8pt/18pt with 15pt, 9/8pt, 10, 13, 14/15pt, 17, 19/18pt, 20, 21, 24-26, 40/48, 41, 49, 50, 59/68pt, 69/68pt, 70, 78-80, 89-93, 118/119, 127, 128, 129/139, 130 with 131, 136, 137, 140, 143-145.
      The Scottish portion of Sheet 9/8pt is not overprinted.
   9. Printed by W. & A.K. Johnston, 1942-49. 7 sheets: 5, 23, 27, 42, 51, 60, 104.

7. Experimental coloured issues. With an alpha-numeric border.
   1. With layers, hachures and hill shading, 1914. Sheet 145 [▮RGS].
   2. With grey hachures and yellow ground tint, 1916. Sheet 120 [▮PC].

8. Monochrome outline issues (perhaps unpublished).
   1. With an alpha-numeric border.
      1. *Black Outline Edition,* 1919. Sheet 96 recorded [▮RGS].
      2. Outline edition in black, 1928. Sheet 142 recorded [▮PC].
      3. Outline edition in grey, 1930. Sheet 142 [▮PC].
         Probably for the Le Play Society.
   2. With an alpha-numeric squaring system.
      1. *Early Popular Outline : transferred from copper (engraved),* 1919. Sheet 144.
      2. *Latest Popular Outline : transferred from copper (engraved),* 1920. Sheet 133.
         The above two maps are experimental outline issues, with headings in red, presumably in some way related to a series of similar such issues in the quarter-inch *Third Edition* [✚**54**.4]. Copies ▮Sg.
      3. Outline edition. 3 sheets recorded: 98 (1932), 132 (1935), 141 (1935) [▮PC].

9. Coloured edition, with unspecified straight line overprint, 1930. Sheet 31 recorded [▮PC].

10. Coloured edition, with hachures, 1919 (published 1931). Sheet 112 only [▮BL].
    For Marlborough College use.

11. *Anglesey,* overprinted with the sites of ancient monuments, 1936. Sheet [41].
    In *An Inventory of the Ancient Monuments in Anglesey* (The Royal Commission on Ancient & Historical Monuments in Wales & Monmouthshire), London, HMSO, 1937.

• For Sheet 17 in *Popular Edition Style with National Grid* see ✣M.13, M.14.

12. District maps.
    1. With an alpha-numeric border.
        Aldershot District, 1914 (**✣7**.3, ✣12.2). In two sheets, *(North)* and *(South).*
        1. Coloured edition, with layers, hachures and contours. Both sheets.
        2. Coloured edition. Both sheets.
        3. Coloured edition, overprinted with a military grid divided into twelve-mile and quartered two-mile squares, in red. Both sheets [▮PC].
    2. With an alpha-numeric squaring system. Coloured editions.
        The Aldershot Command, 1920 (✣M.2).
            Showing the Command boundary.
        Aldershot District, 1919 (✣12.1). In two sheets, *(North)* and *(South).*
        Salisbury Plain, 1920 (✣M.2).
    3. With a simple border and no grid. Coloured editions.
        Bolton, Bury & District, 1930.
        Central Chilterns, 1929 (✣15) [▮BL].
        Huddersfield, 1930 (**✣4**.10.3).

- For *York District* Provisional Popular Edition see **✣8**.11.

13. Tourist Maps. With an alpha-numeric squaring system.
    1. Coloured with layers, hachures and contours.
        Isle of Wight, 1921 (altered on reprints to 1919).
            A fully coloured version of Sheet 142.
        London, 1921 (published 1922) (✣13.2).
        New Forest, 1920 (altered on some reprints to 1921) (✣M.2).
    2. Coloured with layers.
        Brighton & District, 1922. ?Also proved post-war.
        Cheltenham and District, 1922.
        Chichester, 1922.
        Dartmoor, 1922 (altered to 1928 on 1934 reprint).
        Dorking & Leith Hill, 1929. Also proved in 1945 [▮BSg].
        Exmoor Forest, 1921.
        Hertford & St Albans, 1922.
        The Lake District, 1925 (**✣8**.12). Reprinted 1945.
        Land's End & Lizard, 1922 (altered on reprints to 1919).
            A coloured version with layers of Sheet 146.
        London, 1921, reprinted 1927 (✣13.1, M.2).
        The Middle Thames, 1923 (altered on reprints to 1926). ?Also proved post-war.
        Norfolk Broads, 1932 (published 1936) (✣14.1).
        The Peak District, 1924.
        Snowdon District, 1925 (✣13.3). With altered sheet lines.
    3. Coloured with relief.
        Ilkley District, 1935❊. Also proved in 1945 [▮BSg].
        Snowdon District, 1925 (published 1938) (✣13.2). Also proved in ?1945 [▮BSg].

14. Special Sheets.
    1. Coloured editions, with an alpha-numeric squaring system.
        Birmingham & Wolverhampton, 1927 (altered on some reprints to 1921).
        Bristol District, 1922.
        The Chilterns, 1932.
        Derby and District, 1934❊.
        Forest of Bowland, 1934❊.
        Hastings & Bexhill, 1928. Headed *Special Popular Edition One-inch Map.*
        Leeds District, 1930 (altered on reprint to 1925).
        Leicester District, 1936❊.
        Liverpool District, 1924.
        London, 1925. In two sheets, *(North)* and *(South).*
        Maidstone & Tunbridge Wells, 1928.
        Manchester District, 1924 (✣15).
        Norfolk Broads, 1932 (✣13.2).

North East Wales, 1931 (published 1932).
North Staffordshire, 1930 (✣15).
Oxford and District, 1921.
Sidmouth, Budleigh Salterton & Exmouth District, 1927 (published 1928) (**✣8**.8.1). Headed *Special Popular Edition One-inch Map.*
Southampton, 1928.
Weston super Mare, 1918-19 (published 1929); (corrected on reprints to 1929).
Worcester & Malvern District, 1924 (published 1925).
Wye Valley, 1929. ?Also proved post-war.

2. Coloured edition, with a simple border and no grid.
   Barnsley & District, no date (published 1931).

15. Outline issues of the above.
   Central Chilterns, with main roads in red, 1929 (✣12.3) [▮PC].
   Manchester District, 1924 (✣14.1) [▮Mg].
   North Staffordshire, with water in blue and contours in red, 1930 (✣14.1) [▮BL, Ob].

M. Military issues with War Office Cassini Grid ❍

Overprinted with War Office Cassini Grid (British System) in purple ❍

The grid letters were initially hatched. From about 1925 they were open and larger.

1. *Popular Edition.* All sheets.
   1. With woods in green, 1923-?27. All sheets.
      Special printings of Sheets 45 and 125 appear in *Report on War Office Exercise Nos.1,2,4 (1930)* and *No.3 (1930) Crowborough...* [▮PRO (WO 279/71, 279/72)].
   2. With uncoloured woods. 1931-32 reprints.

   The following dependent issue is recorded:
   3. Untitled: [Sussex Manoeuvres], 1928. 4 sheets: 124, 125, 133, 134 [▮ALm].

2. District maps on sheet lines square with Cassini's Projection.
   The Aldershot Command, 1923 (✣12.2, M.6.1).
      Showing the Command boundary. Used for training in the Staff College. Later issues appear in *Report on War Office Exercise No.1 (1929) Aldershot...* [▮PRO (WO 279/66)], and A.H.C. Kearsey *Tactical Schemes,* Third Edition, Aldershot, 1930.
   Blandford, 1924 (✣M.6.1) [▮PC].
   London (Tourist Map), 1928 (✣13.2) [▮PC].
      Lacking the hill depiction of the civilian issues.
   New Forest, (✣13.1, M.6.1).
      Lacking the hachures of the civilian edition.
      1. Without grid, 1924 [▮PC].
      2. With grid, 1924.
   Salisbury Plain, 1925 (✣12.2, M.6.1).
      Showing War Department information.

3. District map on War Office Cassini Grid sheet lines.
   Catterick Area, 1925 (✣M.7.1) [▮PC].
      Showing the War Department property boundary. The map border lacks the graduation of degrees of latitude and longitude.

Overprinted with War Office Cassini Grid (Modified British System) in purple ❍

4. [Military exercise map], 1928. Sheet 26.
   Referencing is by a variant of the War Office Cassini Grid (Modified British System), already introduced on some overseas series, prior to its introduction in Great Britain. The grid is in black, square with the sheet lines, and springs from a false origin situated near Atherton. Grid values are overprinted in purple. In *Report on War Office Exercise No.5 (1928) Harrogate...* [▮PRO (WO 279/64)]. See also **✣54**.M.5.

5. GSGS 3907: *Popular Edition.* All sheets.
    1. With uncoloured woods, preceding application of GSGS number, 1931. 4 sheets recorded: 106, 107, 115, 132.
       Other sheets covering military areas in the south are also probable.
    2. With uncoloured woods, 1931-33. Up to 146 sheets.
       Sheets 31, 106, 107, 115 are improbable, and many others are unrecorded.
    3. With woods in green, 1934- . All sheets.
    4. *Fifth Edition* mapping, 1938. Sheet 107 only.
    5. *Fifth Edition* mapping and *Popular Edition* marginalia, 1940. Sheet 114 only.

    The following dependent issues are recorded [all ▮PC]:
    6. Untitled, showing restricted and out of bounds areas, 1936. Sheet 126 recorded.
       Apparently as *East Kent Special Sheet* [✣M.7.2].
    7. Untitled: [Metropolitan Police Divisions]. 4 sheets: 106, 107, 114, 115.
       Issues dated 1939 are recorded, with up to two overprints, showing:
        1. Boundaries and divisional letters of Metropolitan Police Divisions (purple).
        2. Boundaries of the London Area (Metropolitan Police Area) (red).

6. District maps, usually on sheet lines square with Cassini's Projection.
    1. With uncoloured woods.
       GSGS 3907: *The Aldershot Command,* 1931 (✣M.2).
         Showing the Command boundary. In A.H.C. Kearsey *Tactical Schemes,* Fourth and Fifth Editions, Aldershot, 1932 and 1934.
       GSGS 3907: *Blandford,* 1931 (✣M.2, M.6.2) [▮DGI].
       GSGS 3907: *East Kent,* 1931 [▮DGI].
         With a neat line border. The map is the south-west corner of Sheet 117, to 673 km E, 170 km N. It is thus curiously shaped, with south and west sides square with the projection and north and east with the grid.
       GSGS 3907: *New Forest,* 1931 (✣M.2, M.6.2). Not found.
       GSGS 3907: *Salisbury Plain,* 1931 (✣M.2, M.6.2).
        1. Showing War Department information [▮PC].
        2. Overprinted *Training Area Aug-Sept 1933,* 1933 [▮Mg].
    2. With woods in green.
       GSGS 3907: *Blandford,* 1931, reprinted 1936 (✣M.6.1).
       GSGS 3907: *New Forest,* 1931, reprinted 1936 (✣M.6.1).
       GSGS 3907: *Salisbury Plain,* 1931, reprinted 1934 (✣M.6.1).
        1. Showing War Department information, updated to 1934, 1937, 1939.
        2. Overprinted as *Southern Command Manoeuvre Area, 1934 (Southern Section),* 1934.
       GSGS 3907: *Salisbury Plain,* 1940.
         Showing War Department information to 1939.

7. District maps on War Office Cassini Grid sheet lines.
    1. With a border lacking the graduation of degrees of latitude and longitude.
       GSGS 3907: *Catterick Area* (✣M.3).
         War Department detail is overprinted.
        1. With uncoloured woods, 1932.
        2. With woods in green, 1932, reprinted by 1939.
           The Second Edition is on National Grid sheet lines [✣**19**.M.2].
       GSGS 3907: *Colchester Area,* 1933 (issued 1934).
    2. With a neat line border only.
       GSGS 3907: *Builth Wells,* 1939 [▮DGI].
       GSGS 3907: *East Kent Special Sheet.*
         The sheet lines were used for Sheet 117A in *Second War Revision* [✣M.12].
        1. First issue, 1935 [▮Lk].
        2. Overprinted with restricted and out of bounds areas, 1937 [▮PC].
           Apparently as Sheet 126 [✣M.5.6].
       Llandrindod Wells, 1940.
       Ripon Special One-inch Sheet, 1941 [▮PC].
         Printed by the 13th Corps Field Survey Company, Royal Engineers.
       Sennybridge Artillery Ranges, 1943. Reprinted 1947.
         With ranges revised to 1942.

War Revision. 137 sheets, 1-5, 7-20, 22-44, 46, 47, 49-56, 58-105, 107, 109-113, 116-146, are recorded. Of these eleven, 118, 119, 127, 128, 136-138, 143-146, are on *Fifth Edition* sheet lines [✣**11**.M.2]. OSR 1940-41 states that all sheets were being revised, so there is no certainty that those not recorded do not exist.

8. GSGS 3907: *War Revision,* 1940. 126 sheets recorded.
   War Office publication dates (some *First Published*) as in ✣M.5 may be disregarded.
   1. With *Popular Edition* marginalia, 1940-41. 125 sheets recorded: 1-5, 7-20, 22-44, 46, 47, 49-56, 58-105, 109-113, 116, 117, 120-126, 129-135, 139-142.
   2. With War Office marginalia↑, 1942. 4 sheets recorded: 37, 90, 93, 112.
      Issues in this style have the heading *Popular Edition Style.*
   3. *Fifth Edition* mapping, 1941. Sheet 107 only.
   4. *Sales Copy,* without grid, 1942-43 (published 1943). 12 sheets: 41, 44, 52, 61, 81, 82, 90, 92, 93, 99, 100, 109.
   5. *Sales Copy,* with grid, published 1943- . 32 sheets recorded: 12, 13, 17-19, 24, 25, 29, 41, 42, 44, 49-52, 59, 61, 62, 68, 70, 78, 79, 81, 82, 88, 89, 92, 93, 99-101, 109.

   The following dependent issue is recorded:
   6. *Trigonometric Station Data Map,* [1943]. 2 sheets: 92, 93 [▮Wn].
      Compiled by HQ SOS OCE and reproduced by 660th Engineers, US Army. For Sheet 94 see ✣M.12.8.

With War Office Cassini Grid (Modified British System) in black, numbered in blue

9. District map on War Office Cassini Grid sheet lines.
   Netheravon, 1933 [▮BL].
   Outline edition, with water in blue, contours in red. With a neat line border only. Showing the War Department property boundary, updated on reprints to 1935.

10. GSGS 3907[Z]: *Yorkshire Manoeuvre Area,* 1939. ?6 sheets: 22, 23, 27, 28, 32, 33 [▮PC].

Second War Revision. 129 sheets, 1A, 2-23, 25-43, 45-50, 52-77, 79-87, 90-116, 117A, 120-126, 129-135, 139-142, were issued. *Fifth Edition* material [✣M.12] was used when available, otherwise *Popular Edition* [✣M.11]. *Popular Edition* sheet lines remained in use for all sheets with the exception of Sheets 1A and 117A, which replaced 1 and 117 respectively. Eleven sheets, 29, 41, 42, 52, 61, 62, 81, 82, 92, 100, 109 [✣M.11.4], are recorded only in outline editions. There is evidence that a coloured edition of Sheet 109 at least was proved (copy received by the War Office on 25 October 1943) but it was apparently not issued.

11. GSGS 3907: *Second War Revision,* 1940 : *Popular Edition Style.* 83 sheets.
   The *Popular Edition Style* heading is only on issues with War Office marginalia↑. See also ✣M.12.
   1. Coloured edition, with *Popular Edition* marginalia, 1940-41. 25 sheets: 1A, 4-6, 9, 10, 16, 19, 21, 22, 26, 33, 34, 39, 40, 45-48, 55-58, 64, 66.
      A printing of Sheet 33 lacks the War Office publication data.
   2. Coloured edition, with War Office marginalia↑, 1940-42 (issued 1941-44). 72 sheets: 1A, 2-23, 25-28, 30-40, 43, 45-50, 53-60, 63-72, 76, 77, 79, 80, 90, 91, 99, 101, 102.
      Some copies of Sheets 4, 11, 14 are erroneously headed *5th Edition Style.* Sheet 17 was reprinted in 1948. For National Grid versions see ✣M.13, M.14.
   3. *Sales Copy,* coloured, published 1943-44. 72 sheets: 1A, 2-23, 25-28, 30-40, 43, 45-50, 53-60, 63-72, 76, 77, 79, 80, 90, 91, 99, 101, 102.
   4. *Sales Copy,* outline with water in blue, 1932/1940-43 (published 1943-45). 33 sheets: 4, 7, 11, 19, 20, 25, 26, 29-31, 35-37, 41-43, 45, 49, 52, 54, 60-62, 71, 72, 80-82, 91, 92, 100, 102, 109.

   The following dependent issues are recorded:
   5. *Redesdale & Otterburn Ranges,* dated 1942. Sheet 3 [▮DRg].
   6. *Plan from Radar fixed Air Photo's,* 1947. Sheet 41.
      In Major C.A. Hart *Mapping by Remote Control with the Aid of Radar* (Directorate of Military Survey, Air Research Paper 19), War Office, 1946.

12. GSGS 3907: *Second War Revision,* 1940 : *5th Edition Style.* 46 sheets.
    The *5th Edition Style* heading is only on issues with War Office marginalia↑. Sheet 117A is unique in being on grid sheet lines; they are identical with those of *East Kent Special Sheet,* 1935 [✣M.7.2]. Sheets 93, 96, 103 retain some *Popular Edition* drawing. See also ✣M.11.
    1. Coloured edition, with *Fifth Edition* marginalia, 1940-41. 36 sheets: 73-75, 83-87, 94, 96-98, 104-106, 108, 110, 113-116, 117A, 121, 123, 125, 126, 130-136, 139, 141, 142.
    2. Coloured edition, with War Office marginalia↑, 1940-42 (issued 1941-44). 46 sheets: 73-75, 83-87, 93-98, 103-108, 110-116, 117A, 120-126, 129-135, 139-142.
       5 sheets, 111, 112, 114, 121, 122, were reprinted 1947-48.
    3. Coloured edition, with layers, 1941-42 (issued 1947). 6 sheets: 104, 105, 112, 113, 122, 123 [▮PC].
       For the Staff College. Combined sheets 105/113, 113/114 (both 1947) are also documented, but not found.
    4. *Sales Copy,* coloured, published 1943-44. 46 sheets: 73-75, 83-87, 93-98, 103-108, 110-116, 117A, 120-126, 129-135, 139-142.
    5. *Sales Copy,* outline with water in blue, published 1943-44. 15 sheets: 83-85, 93-95, 97, 103, 105, 111-113, 115, 116, 120.
    6. *Sales Copy,* outline with water in blue, woods in grey, published 1944-45. 4 sheets: 106, 107, 110, 125.

    The following dependent issues are recorded or documented:
    7. GSGS 3907: *South Downs Training Area,* 1942. 2 sheets: 133, 134 [▮DGI].
    8. *Trigonometric Station Data Map,* 1943. Sheet 94 [▮Wn].
       Compiled by HQ SOS OCE and reproduced by 660th Engineers, US Army. For Sheets 92 and 93 see ✣M.8.6.
    9. GSGS Misc.516: *SADE Decca Chart,* 1946. 2 sheets recorded: 87, 107 [▮NLS].
       Proof sheets. The overprint in green and red was computed by the War Office and drawn by GSGS (AM) in July 1946. There are four versions of each sheet, cumulatively one to four colour plates (outline, blue sea, brown, green).
    10. GSGS 3907: *Experimental Gee Chart* : *Eastern Chain,* 1947. Sheet 122 [▮DGI].
    11. GSGS Misc.302: *Exercise Ubique II,* 1947. Sheet 122 [▮Ob].
        See also **✣56**.M.8.5.
    12. GSGS 3907A: Colchester Training Areas, 1949. Sheet 97. Not found.
    13. GSGS Misc.363 Sheet 121, GSGS Misc.364 Sheet 122: *Exercise Viking,* 1949.
        See also **✣56**.M.8.6.
        1. GSGS Misc.363/1 and 364/1: *Exercise Viking* : *23 Corps Plan* [▮BL, Mg].
        2. GSGS Misc.363/2 and 364/2: *Exercise Viking* : *8 Corps Plan* [▮BL].

Military and civilian issues with National Grid

The *Second War Revision* : *Popular Edition Style* issue of Sheet 17 [✣M.11.2] served instead of the never published *New Popular Edition* Sheet 87 [**✣19**].

13. Coloured editions overprinted with National Grid (Military System) in purple.
    1. GSGS 4620: *War Office Edition,* 1949 (issued 1950). Sheet 17, overprinted *National Grid Sheet 87.*
    2. GSGS 4620: Second Edition-GSGS, 1952. Sheet [17], renumbered 87.
       Reference to *Second War Revision* is deleted. Reprinted in 1955.

14. With National Grid.
    1. Coloured edition, 1950. Sheet 17.
    2. *Outline Edition,* 1950. Sheet 17 [▮RML].
    3. Water and contour issue [without grid]. Sheet 17 [▮EXg].

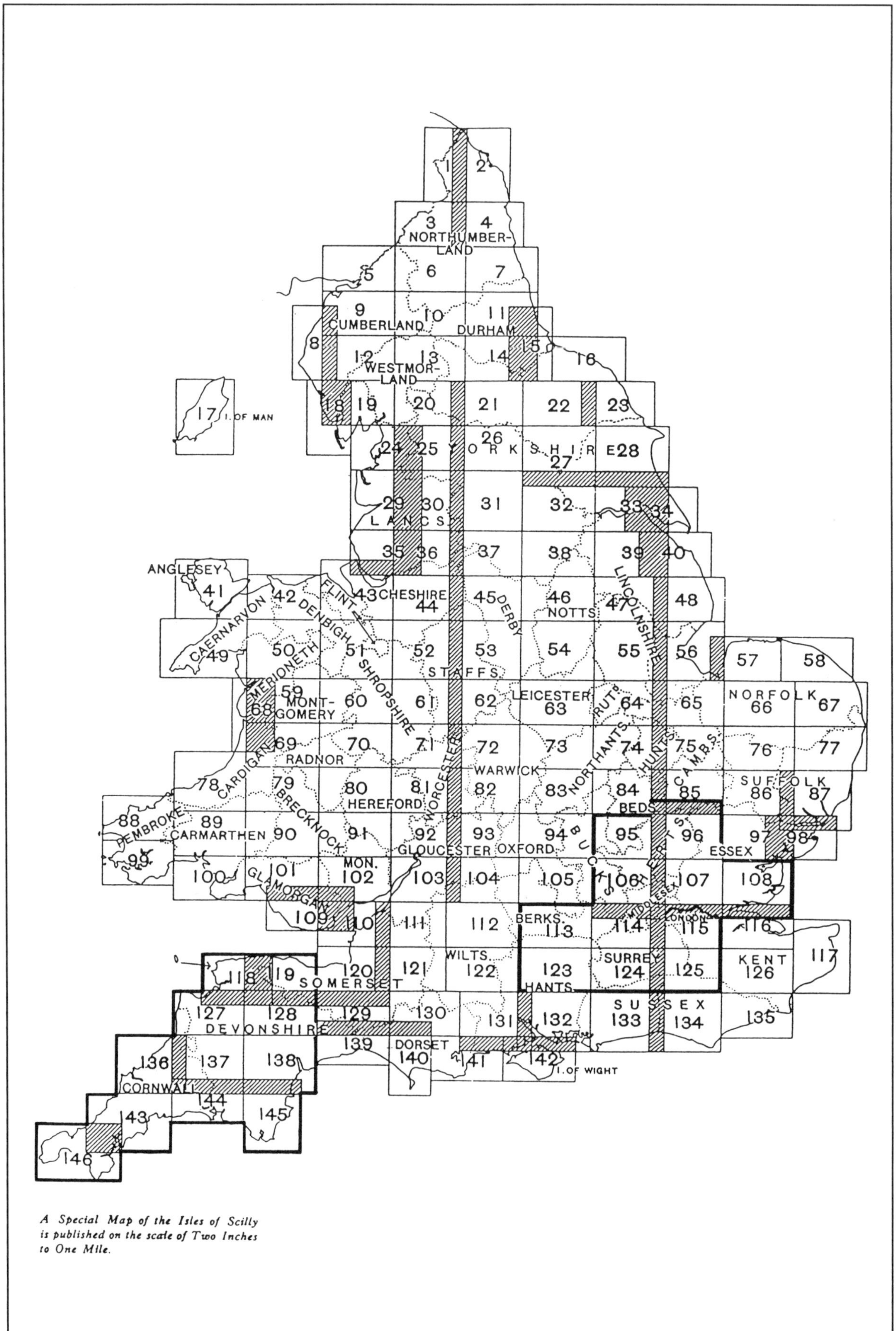

11. One-inch Fifth Edition Map of England and Wales : small sheet series

11. One-inch Fifth Edition Map of England and Wales : small sheet series

Constructed on the national Transverse Mercator Projection on the origin of 49°N,2°W. Laid out on National Yard Grid sheet lines in 146 sheets of which only 22 were published. Standard sheet coverage 52,000 by 32,000 yards, including 2000 yard overlaps with sheets adjoining east and north. With National Yard Grid at 5000 yard intervals except where noted. Produced from the fourth national revision beginning in 1928 and compiled from drawings at the two-inch scale. Heading: *Ordnance Survey of Great Britain : Fifth Edition, England & Wales.* Sheet 144 in ✣1, 3, 5, 6 has *Ordnance Survey of England & Wales : Fifth Edition.* The words "small sheet series" do not appear. See also **✣12**.

22 sheets published: 95, 96, 106-108, 113-115, 118, 119, 123-125, 127, 128, 136-138, 143-146. Sheet gazetteers are recorded for Sheets 114, 118, 144, 145.

There is an inset of Lundy Island on Sheet 118. The Isles of Scilly are excluded here, but covered by a special sheet at the two-inch scale [**✣129**].

1. *Relief* edition, 1931-36. 22 sheets as listed above.
   Sheet 137 has ruled water. Printings of Sheet 137 with screened water and of Sheet 144 with ruled water were made [▮PRO (OS 1/48): 144].

2. Coloured edition, 1932-36 (published 1934-36). 22 sheets as listed above.

3. *Black* [outline] edition. 22 sheets as listed above.
   1. With contours in black, 1932-34. 14 sheets: 113, 114, 118, 119, 123, 127, 128, 136-138, 143-146.
   2. Without contours, 1934-35. 6 sheets: 95, 96, 106, 107, 115, 124.
   3. With woods in grey, 1936- . ?9 sheets: 95, 96, 106-108, 114, 115, 124, 125.
      Sheets 96, 124 are unrecorded, though listed in OSR 1936-37.

4. Outline edition, with water in blue. Without grid. ?14 sheets.
   The word "Black" is often left unmasked on the black plate. For complementary coverage of southern England see **✣10**.3, **12**.4.
   1. London area, 1942. ?3 sheets: 107, 108, 125.
      Sheet 115 appears in OSR 1941-42, but its existence must be regarded as doubtful. It was probably listed in error for *Popular Edition* Sheet 115, issued in January 1942 but lacking in OSR. Full coverage is achieved without it.
   2. South-west area, 1942. All 11 sheets: 118, 119, 127, 128, 136-138, 143-146.

5. *Physical Features alone,* 1932-36. 22 sheets as listed above.

6. *Outline* edition, with water in blue, contours in red, 1931. Sheet 144 only.
   Two copies are recorded [▮PRO (OS 1/48), RML]. This edition was probably experimental, not intended for publication, though the War Office also received a copy.

7. Special District (Relief) Maps.
   Aldershot, 1932. In two sheets, *North,* and *South.*
   For the combination of the two sheets as the *Aldershot Command* district map see ✣M.3.
   Dartmoor, 1936 (✣M.4).
   Exmoor Forest, 1936.

M. Military issues

Overprinted with War Office Cassini Grid in purple ○

1. GSGS 3907: *Fifth Edition.* 11 sheets.
    1. Coloured edition, 1940. 11 sheets: 118, 119, 127, 128, 136-138, 143-146.
       The word "Relief" is often left unmasked on the black plate.
    2. *Sales Copy,* published 1943-44. 7 sheets recorded: 127, 136, 138, 143-146.

2. GSGS 3907: *War Revision,* 1940 : *5th Edition Style.* 11 sheets.
   See page 34. References to *5th Edition Style* do not appear in ✣M.2.1, and irregularly later. For the remainder of GSGS 3907 *War Revision* see **✚10**.M.8, also ✣M.6.
    1. With *Fifth Edition* marginalia, 1940-41. 4 sheets: 118, 119, 136, 138.
    2. With War Office marginalia↑, 1940-41 (issued 1941-42). 11 sheets: 118, 119, 127, 128, 136-138, 143-146.
    3. *Sales Copy,* without grid, 1942-43 (published 1943). 3 sheets: 143, 144, 146.
    4. *Sales Copy,* with grid, published 1943-44. 11 sheets: 118, 119, 127, 128, 136-138, 143-146.

3. GSGS 3907: *Aldershot Command* district map (✣M.7).
   The combination of the *Aldershot North* and *South* Special District (Relief) Maps [✣7].
    1. Coloured edition, without relief, 1934 (issued 1935).
       The Command boundary is overprinted in red.
    2. Outline edition in grey, 1934 (issued 1940) [▮DGI].
       All detail, including grid and water, is monochrome. Without contours or the Command boundary.

4. Special District Map. Coloured without the relief of the civilian edition.
   Dartmoor, 1936 (issued 1937) (✣7) [▮BL].

5. District maps on War Office Cassini Grid sheet lines.
   Outline editions, with water in blue, contours in ?brown. With a neat line border.
   Bordon, ?1934. Not found.
   Shown on mid-1930s military adjoining sheet diagrams. Plotted south of, and overlapping (by ?4 km), *Farnborough,* with the same west and east sheet limits. But there is no evidence that the map was issued.
   Farnborough, 1933 (issued 1934) [▮ALm].
   With sheet co-ordinates 527 km E to 545 km E, 166 km N to 189 km N.

With War Office Cassini Grid in black, numbered in blue

6. GSGS 3907: *War Revision,* 1940 : *5th Edition Style.* 5 sheets.
   With War Office marginalia↑. See also ✣M.2.
    1. Coloured edition, 1941 (issued 1947). Sheet 143.
    2. *Sales Copy,* outline with water in blue, 1933 (published 1944). Sheet 145.
    3. *Sales Copy,* outline with water in blue, woods in grey, 1941 (published 1944-45). 3 sheets: 118, 119, 138.
       These sheets lack the reference to *5th Edition Style.*

7. District map.
   GSGS 3907: *Manoeuvre Area, 1939* : *Aldershot Command* (✣M.3) [▮Lk].
   The northern part of this manoeuvre area appeared on a specially produced map GSGS 3907 *Thames Valley* [**✚12**.M.2.1].

12. One-inch Fifth Edition Map of England and Wales : large sheet series

Constructed on the national Transverse Mercator Projection on the origin of 49°N,2°W. Laid out on National Yard Grid sheet lines. Standard sheet coverage 62,000 or 67,000 yards by 47,000 yards, including 2000 yard overlaps with sheets adjoining east and north. With National Yard Grid at 5000 yard intervals except as noted. Produced from the fourth national revision beginning in 1928. Heading: *Ordnance Survey of Great Britain* : *Fifth Edition, England & Wales,* except as noted. The words “large sheet series” do not appear.

Sixteen sheets were published: 93, 94, [95] *St Albans,* 102, 111-113, [114] *London,* 129-132, 139-142. Sheets 106, 113, 114, 123, 124 in the small sheet series [✚**11**] were superseded. *London* and *St Albans* were classified Special District Maps but in due course they were to receive the sheet numbers noted here. Sheet lines for Sheets 97, 98, 101, 116, 117, 134, 135 were determined, and those for 115 and 133 may have been, but the full layout was never plotted. An area of England north to Coventry had been drawn, but mapping unpublished here appeared later in *Second War Revision* [✚**10**.M.12] and *New Popular Edition* [✚**19**].

1. Coloured edition, 1937-39. 16 sheets as listed above.

2. *Black* [outline] edition. 16 sheets as listed above.
    1. With woods in grey, 1937-39. 16 sheets as listed above.
       St Albans is lacking in OSPR and is not recorded in legal deposit collections [▮BL, Ng].
    2. With uncoloured woods, 1937 (published 1944). Sheet [114] *London* [▮NLS].

3. Outline edition, with water in blue, 1937 (published 1944). Sheet [114] *London* [▮PC].

4. Outline edition, with water in blue. Without grid. 13 sheets.
   The word “Black” is often left unmasked on the black plate. For complementary coverage of southern England see ✚**10**.3, **11**.4.
    1. With uncoloured woods, 1942. 13 sheets: 94, [95] *St Albans,* 111, 113, [114] *London,* 129-132, 139-142.
    2. With woods in grey, 1944. 2 sheets recorded: [95] *St Albans,* 139.
       Unusually for a wartime map the words “Outline Edition” appear on *St Albans.*

5. *New Forest* Tourist Map (✣M.1).
   Coloured with relief. On National [metric] Grid sheet lines.
    1. With National Yard Grid, 1938.
    2. With National [metric] Grid, 1945. Proved but not published [▮BSg].

- For the Special District Maps *London* and *St Albans* (both dated 1937) see the references to Sheets [114] and [95] above.

M. Military issues

Overprinted with War Office Cassini Grid in purple

1. *New Forest* Tourist Map (✣5).
   Coloured without the relief of the civilian map. On National [metric] Grid sheet lines.
   The civilian publication date is altered to 1939.
    1. GSGS 3907: *New Forest,* 1940 [▮DGI].
    2. GSGS 3907: *New Forest Training Map, 1941,* 1941 [▮DGI].
       With overprint. The military legend covers the south-east corner of the map.
    3. GSGS 3907: *New Forest Training Area Map, 1943,* 1943 [▮DGI].
       With overprint. The military legend covers the south-east corner of the map.

With War Office Cassini Grid in black, numbered in blue ❍

These maps have a neat line border only.

2. Coloured district maps on War Office Cassini Grid sheet lines.
   GSGS 3907: *Thames Valley.*
   With heading: *Ordnance Survey of England and Wales.*
   1. Overprinted *Manoeuvre Area, 1939,* 1939 [▮Lk].
      The southern part of this manoeuvre area was overprinted on a special printing of GSGS 3907 *Aldershot Command* [✚**11**.M.7].
   2. Without overprint, 1939 [▮Lk].

   GSGS 3907: Untitled: [London], 19xx. Not found.

   The following issues dependent on *London* are recorded:
   1. Untitled: showing boundaries of the London District and of Metropolitan Police Divisions, 1941 [▮Ob].
   2. OR 1527: *London Region Civil Defence Groups,* 1944 [▮DGI].
   3. OR 1527B: *Metropolitan Police Boundaries,* 1944 [▮DGI].
   4. OR 1527C: *London District Anti Tank Groups,* 19xx. Not found.
   5. OR 1527D: *London District Training Areas,* 1943. Not found.
   6. *London District Boundaries and Defence Zones,* 19xx. Not found.
   7. *London District Bridge Classification,* 1943. Not found.
      Printed by the Ordnance Survey.

3. Outline district maps on War Office Cassini Grid sheet lines. Without grid.
   GSGS 3994: *Territorial Drill Halls in and around London and Zones of Influence within the County of London,* 1937. Not found.
   GSGS 3994: *Territorial Army and Auxiliary Air Force Headquarters in the Greater London Area : also Zones of Influence within the County of London,* 1939 [▮Ob].

***Symbols* :** a **bold** number prefixed with ✚ is a cross reference to another section of the book; a number prefixed with ✣ is a cross reference within the current section; a reference number in ( ) at a district map identifies the next, or previous, such map listed with the same sheet lines; the ▮ symbol accompanies a source reference for maps rarely encountered (library sigla are listed on page 241); ❍ warns that there are noted exceptions to the information given in headings; ↑ identifies what is referred to here as War Office marginalia (for a description see page xxii); ❂ refers to the exceptional use of the heading *Ordnance Survey of Great Britain.*

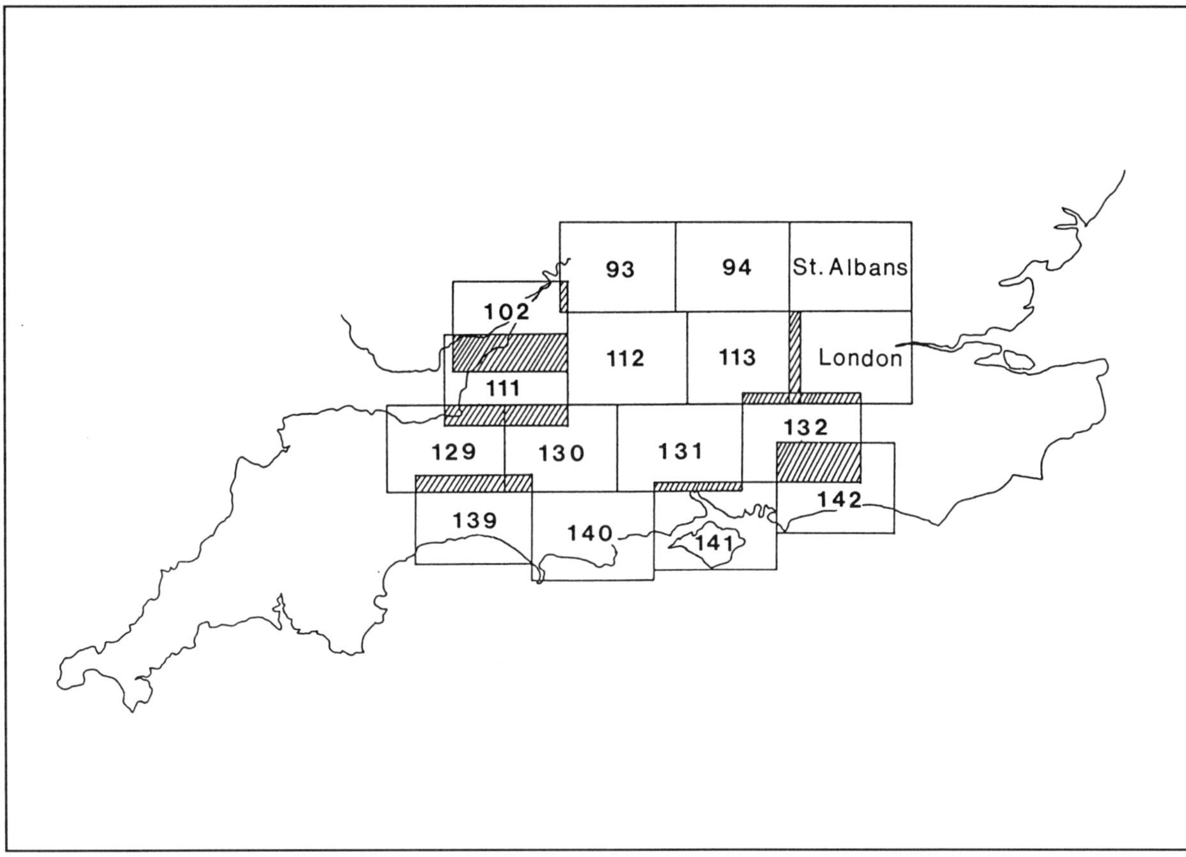

12. One-inch Fifth Edition Map of England and Wales : large sheet series

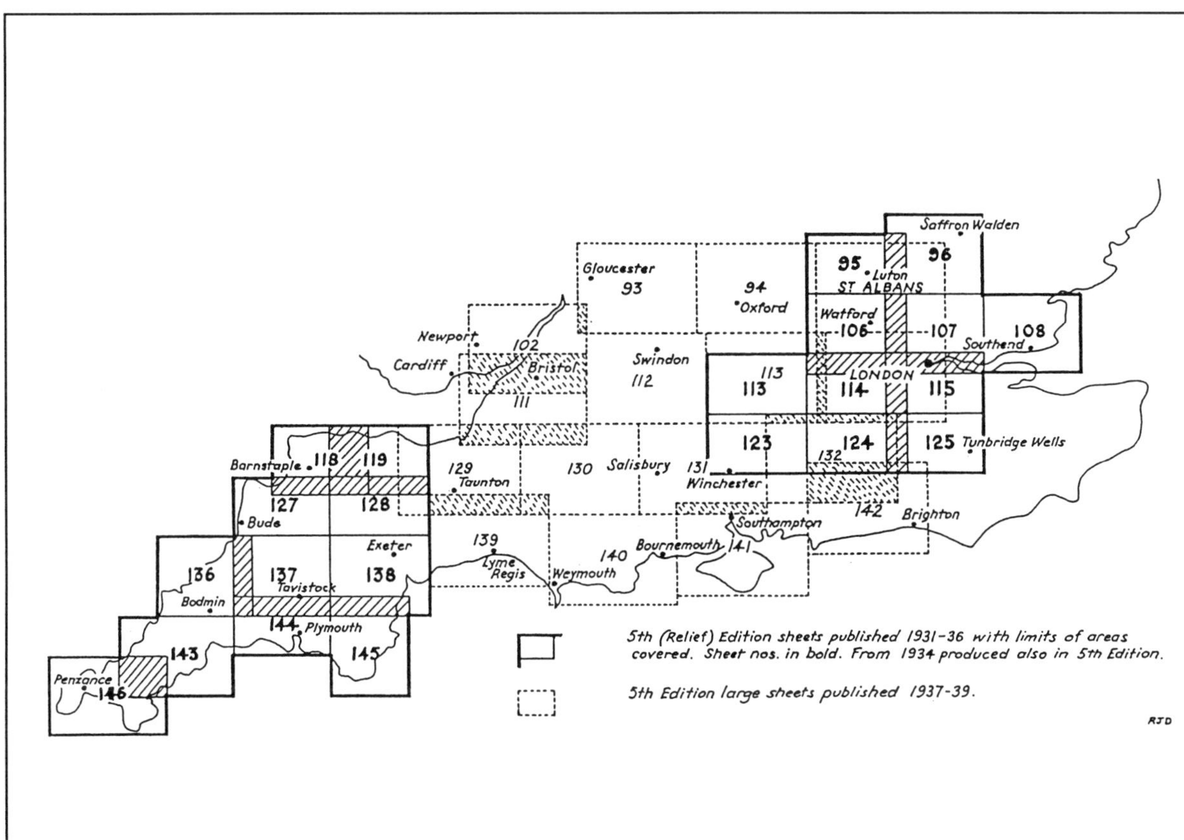

Sheets in the large sheet series set against those published in the small sheet series

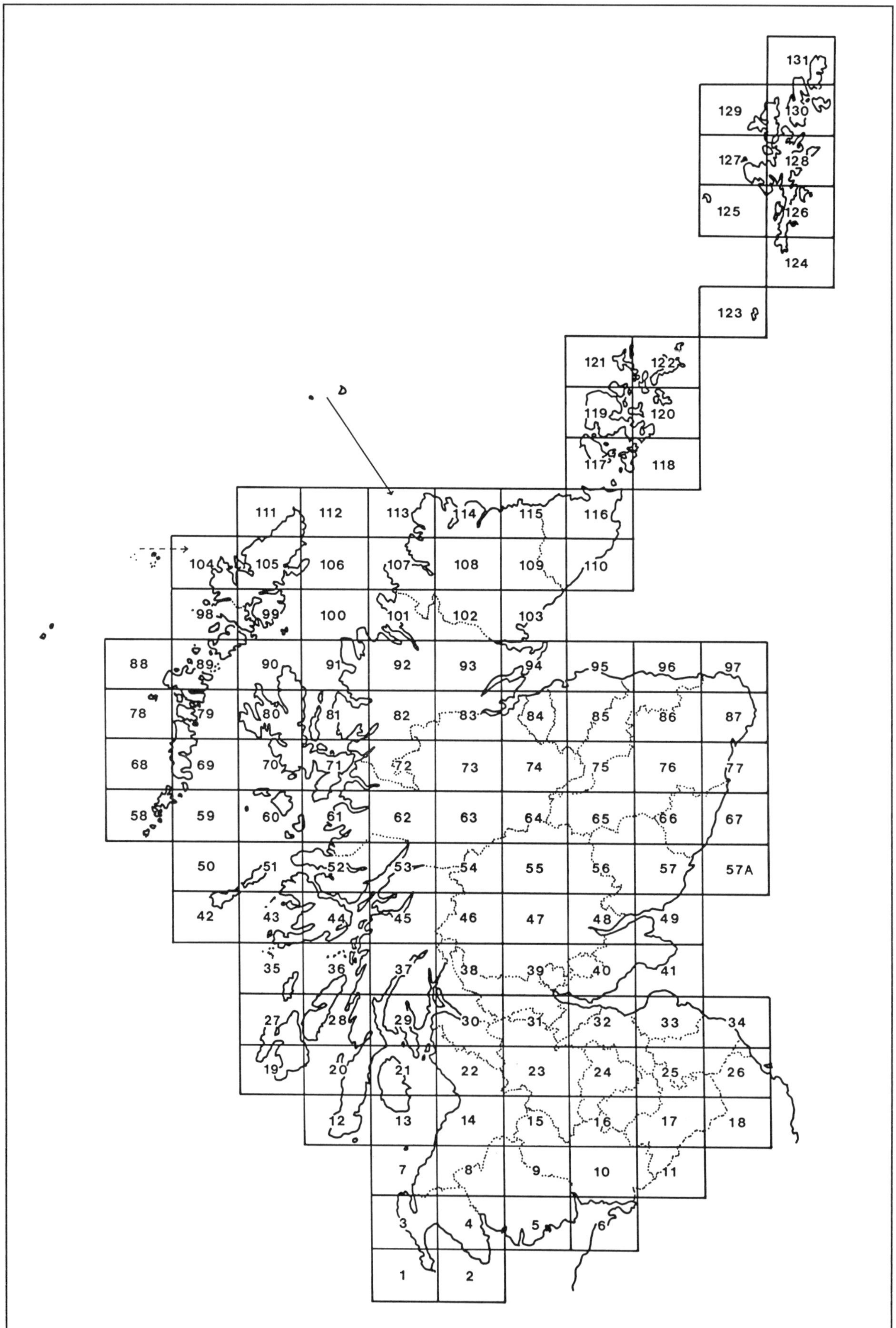

13. One-inch Map of Scotland : First Edition

13. One-inch Map of Scotland : First Edition

Surveyed 1845-78. Constructed on Bonne's Projection on the origin of 57°30'N,4°W, and published in 132 sheets: 1-57, 57A, 58-131, numbered south to north. Sheets 111, 112, 104-106, 98, 99 were at first independently numbered Isle of Lewis 1-7 respectively, a system apparently abandoned in 1862. Standard sheet coverage 24 by 18 miles. The same sheet layout was used, with variations, for four outline and one coloured editions [**✚13**, **14**, **15**, **16**, **17**]. Heading: *Ordnance Survey of Scotland*. The words "First Edition" do not appear.

There are insets of Flannan Isles on all but early outline issues of Sheet 104. Sula Sgeir and Rona are inset on Sheet 113. Tiree appears complete on Sheet 42 by means of extrusions from 43 and 50: Sheet 50 was also issued independently. Likewise the Mull portion of Sheet 36 appears as an extrusion on 44, Eigg and Canna appear complete on 60 as extrusions from 61 and 70, South Uist on 69 from 68, Pentland Skerries on 117 from 118, Holm of Huip on 120 from 122. Sheets 58 and 128 also have extrusions.

The English portions of Sheets 6, 10, 11, 17, 18, 26, other than the Berwick area, are blank.

St Kilda and Boreray do not appear on mapping at this scale until the one-inch *Popular Edition* [**✚18**].

1. Outline edition, with contours. All sheets.
    1. Published with blank areas, 1858- . ?4 sheets: ?13, ?20, 98, 99.
       Sheets 98 and 99 were initially numbered Isle of Lewis Sheets 6 and 7 respectively. Issues of Sheets 13 and 20 with blank areas have not been recorded. The mainland part of Sheet 13 is depicted as engraved in OSR 1859 and of Sheet 20 in OSR 1870. They were published complete in 1870 and 1882. Partially completed states of some fifteen sheets have also been recorded. They are undated, usually lack contours, and may have incomplete topography.
    2. Published complete, 1856-87. All sheets.
       Sheets 111, 112, 104-106 were initially numbered Isle of Lewis Sheets 1-5 respectively. Sheet 63 and part of 62 also appear in Sir Henry James *Notes on the Parallel Roads of Lochaber,* Southampton, Ordnance Survey, 1874.

2. Black hachured edition, without contours. All sheets.
    1. Published with blank areas, 1861-75. 4 sheets: 13, 20, 98, 99.
       Sheet 99 was initially numbered Isle of Lewis Sheet 7. Sheet 98 [▮NLS] is not recorded in legal deposit collections.
    2. Published complete, 1856-94 (published 1856-95). All sheets.
       Sheets 111 and 112 were initially numbered Isle of Lewis Sheets 1 and 2.

3. *Hill edition, with shaded zones of altitude,* 1858. Sheet 32 only [▮NLS].
   Effectively the same technique as the *shaded contours* of the Lake District sheets of 1867 [**✚2**.4]. The contour interval increases from 200 to 250 feet above 1000 feet.

4. Hachured edition in brown, with contours, 1898. By zincography. Sheet 123.
   This edition covered the whole of Scotland. For the remainder see **✚14**.2.

5. *Index to the Ordnance Survey of Part of the County of Zetland, on the Scale of Six Inches to 1 Mile (1/10560),* 1901. Sheet 123.
   Coloured by parish. This edition covered most of Scotland. For the remainder see **✚14**.4.

6. *Royal Commission (Highlands and Islands, 1892).* By lithography. 72 sheets: 12, 19-21, 27-29, 35-37, 42-46, 51-53, 58-64, 69-75, 79-84, 88-94, 98, 99, 101-105, 107-111, 113-122, 124, 126, 128, 130, 131.
   Colour lithographed by Wyman for issue in BPP(HC) 1895 [C.7668-II], XXXIX Part II, ie Appendix 2 of the *Report of the Royal Commission (Highlands and Islands, 1892)* (BPP(HC) 1895 [C.7681], XXXVIII).

7. Colour printed edition, with layers, 1892. Sheet 38 [▮NLS].
   The work was done experimentally for the Government by J. Bartholomew. See also **✣4**.8.

8. District map.
   Glasgow and its Environs, 1885. Not found.
   Listed in OSPR (Scotland) 8/85, so it would be curious if it were not published.

G. Geological Survey of Scotland

Publication at the one-inch scale was never completed: the intention now (1999) is to publish the entire series at 1:50,000 [✣G.7, G.8].

Hachured issues of one-inch First Edition mapping were used initially, superseded by outline issues from 1882. Second [**✣14**] and *Third Edition* [**✣15**] base maps were employed as they became available. Colour printing was introduced in 1910. In due course *Popular Edition (with National Grid)* [**✣18**.C] and *Seventh Series* [**✣20**] mapping, on the original sheet lines, was used. With them came the National Grid which was also applied to maps reprinted on earlier base material. Geological Survey and Ordnance Survey headings appear in tandem.

The sheet list offered here ignores the base mapping used.

Geological editions may be encountered in various forms. Hand-coloured issues were usually solid editions which sometimes included drift elements. A hand-coloured drift edition was begun in 1906, such sheets being distinguished by the hand colouring. The words "Solid" or "Drift" do not appear as headings on hand-coloured sheets, though these words may appear stamped or handwritten.

For the purposes of the list below, colour-printed issues in the drift section combine those distinguished by the headings "Drift", "Solid and Drift", "Solid with Drift", or by indications of drift geology in the marginalia. The reclassification of 1996 does not affect matters here. However classified, one-inch drift editions also show solid geology.

One-inch mapping

1. Solid edition. 91 sheets in 83.
   1. Hand-coloured issues on hachured maps, 1859-84. 32 sheets: 1-7, 9-11, 13 (mainland only), 14, 15, 17, 18, 22-26, 30-34, 39-41, 49, 57A, 67, 97.
      A new edition was published of Sheet 40 (1898), also revised editions of Sheets 41 (1889) and 67 (1898).
   2. Hand-coloured issues on outline maps, 1882-1909. 42 sheets: 7, 8, 12, 13 (complete), 16, 19-21, 27, 29, 32, 36-38, 45-48, 55-57, 60, 65, 66, 70, 75-77, 81, 85, 87, 91, 94-96, 100, 101, 103, 107, 113-115.
      Sheets 7 (1898), 13 (1898 and 1902), 32 (1892) are new editions of sheets first published in ✣G.1.1. Sheet 57 was reissued *with additions* in 1897 and Sheet 114 published in a revised edition, 1893.
   3. Colour-printed issues, 1924-81. 41 sheets in 33: 11, 14, 15, 22-24, 27, 30-32, 37, 39-41, 44, 45, 52, 61, 71, 80/81pt/90pt/91pt, 82-84, 86, 94-96, 103, 116, 126/123pt [inset]/124pt, 127/125pt/126pt/128pt [Foula inset], 128, 129pt/130pt/131pt.
      Sheet 94 (1973) is headed *Provisional.*

2. District maps. Solid edition.
   Arran, 1947.
   Glasgow District, 1931.

3. Drift edition. 85 sheets in 77.
    1. Hand-coloured issues on outline maps, 1906-09. 6 sheets: 13, 21, 36, 37, 45, 55.
    2. Colour-printed issues, 1910-82. 83 sheets in 75: 1-5, 7-9, 11, 14-17, 19, 22-24, 26-33, 35-37, 39-41, 42/50, 43-45, 51-55, 60, 61, 64, 65, 67, 70, 71, 74, 80/81pt/90pt/91pt, 81-84, 86, 92-96, 102, 103, 108-110, 116-122, 126/123pt [inset]/124pt, 127/125pt/126pt/128pt [Foula inset], 128, 129pt/130pt/131pt.
    Sheets 26, 29, 60, 94 are headed *Provisional.*

4. District maps. Drift edition.
    Arran, 1910. Another edition, 1948.
    Assynt District, 1923. Another edition, 1965.
    Glasgow District, 1911. Another edition, 1931.

5. All sheets published were available uncoloured.

6. *Soil Texture Map.* 2 sheets: 14 (1932), 22 (1929).
    On *Third Edition* base maps [**✢15**]. Published by the Ordnance Survey.

1:50,000 mapping

With the enlargement of scale came the decision to divide many, particularly inland, sheets into eastern and western halves. Some sheets are enlarged from one-inch originals, some of which were still on *Third Edition* [**✢15**] base maps. Sheets first published at 1:50,000 may have one-inch *Seventh Series* [**✢20**] or 1:50,000 [**✢21**] base maps.

Known additional combined sheets at 1:50,000: 5E/6Wpt, 30W/29Ept, 33W/41pt, 33E/41pt, 44W/41pt, 80E/81pt, 90/91pt, 130pt/131pt.

7. Solid edition, 1974- . Publication continues.

8. Drift edition, 1968- . Publication continues.

9. All sheets published are available uncoloured.

10. District maps enlarged from the one-inch.
    Arran.
    1. Solid edition, 1972.
    2. Drift edition, 1971 (*recte* 1974). Experimentally enlarged.
    Assynt District, 1997.

11. District maps on National Grid sheet lines.
    Arran.
    1. Solid edition, 1987.
    2. Drift edition, 1985.
    The Rhins of Galloway, 1992. Solid edition.

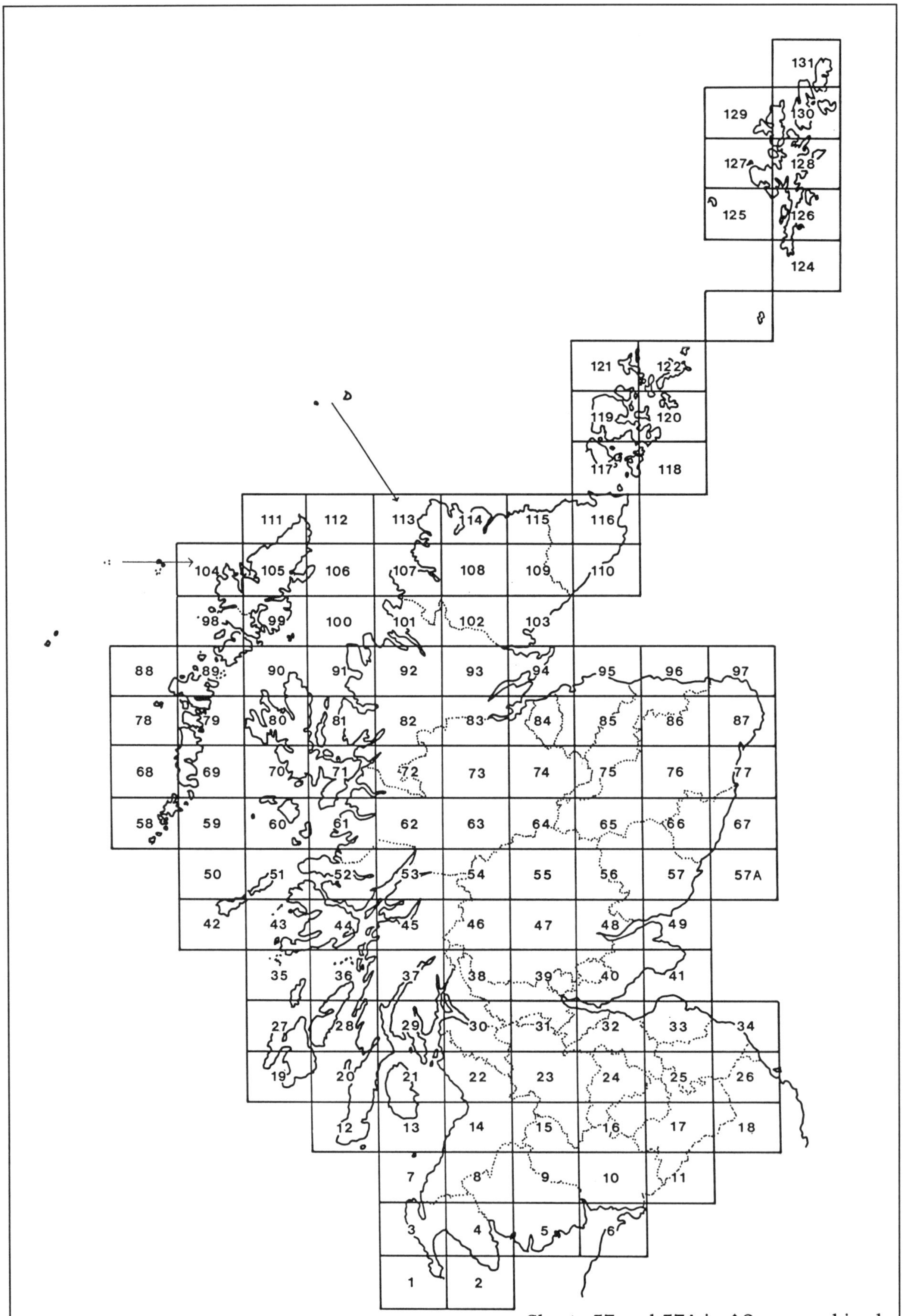

Sheets 57 and 57A in ✢2 are combined

14. One-inch Map of Scotland : Second Edition

14. One-inch Map of Scotland : Second Edition

Laid out [as **✣13**] in 132 sheets, of which 131 were published: 1-57, 57A, 58-122, 124-131. Produced from the first national revision of 1894-95. Fair Isle was not revised, thus Sheet 123 was not published in this edition. Heading: *Ordnance Survey of Scotland*. The words "Second Edition" do not appear.

There are insets of Flannan Isles on Sheet 104, Sula Sgeir, Rona on 113. The Mull portion of 36 appears as an extrusion on 44, Eigg and Canna appear complete on 60 as extrusions from 61 and 70, South Uist on 69 from 68, Pentland Skerries on 117 from 118, Holm of Huip on 120 from 122. Sheets 58 and 128 also have extrusions. The English portions of Sheets 6, 10, 11, 17, 18, 26, other than the Berwick area, are blank.

1. Outline edition, with contours, 1896-98. 131 sheets: 1-57, 57A, 58-122, 124-131.
   Tiree appears complete on Sheet 42 by means of extrusions from 43 and 50.

2. Hachured edition in brown, with contours, 1898-1903. By lithography or zincography. 131 sheets in 129: 1-41, 42/50, 43-49, 51-56, 57/57A, 58-122, 124-131.
   Sheets 50 and 57A are discontinued, 57A being combined with 57. Sheet 42 is physically unaltered with extrusions completing Tiree from 43 and 50, with only the latter recognised in the combined sheet number 42/50. See **✣13**.4 for Sheet 123.

3. Hachured edition in ?black or brown, with contours, dated 1896. By engraving. 5 sheets recorded: 1-3 [▮BL]; 83, 84 [▮Eg].
   Sheets 1-3 were published in late 1903 or early 1904; Sheets 83 and 84 were printed, but probably not published, in 1910. No black copies are as yet recorded.

4. *Index to the Ordnance Survey of Part[s] of the County[ies] of [Countyname], on the Scale of Six Inches to 1 Mile (1/10560)*, 1898-1904. 104 sheets recorded [▮BL, Ebgs].
   Colour printed by parish (not England). There are insets of Flannan Isles on Sheets 99 and 104, Sula Sgeir on 111, Rona on 112. Tiree appears complete on Sheet 42 by means of extrusions from 43 and 50. See **✣13**.5 for Sheet 123 in this style.
   1. With some parishes blank. 20 sheets recorded: 9, 15-17, 39, 40, 48, 49, 52, 53, 66, 72, 74, 75, 81, 82, 86, 98, 99, 117.
      Those reissued complete may be identified in ✣4.2.
   2. Showing complete information. 93 sheets recorded: 1-39, 41-51, 53-56, 58-65, 68-70, 76-80, 87, 88, 90, 97, 98, 104-106, 111, 112, 118-122, 124-131.

5. *Index to the Ordnance Survey of Part[s] of the County[ies] of [Countyname], on the Scale of 25·344 Inches to 1 Mile (1/2500)*, 1898-1904. 100 sheets recorded [▮BL, Ebgs].
   Colour printed by parish (not England). There are no insets on Sheets 99, 111, 112. Tiree appears complete on Sheet 42 by means of extrusions from 43 and 50.
   1. With some parishes blank. 18 sheets recorded: 9, 15-17, 39, 40, 48, 49, 52, 53, 66, 74, 75, 81, 86, 98, 99, 117.
      Those reissued complete may be identified in ✣5.2.
   2. Showing complete information. 92 sheets recorded: 1-39, 41-51, 55, 56, 58, 60-65, 68-70, 74-80, 87, 88, 90, 97, 98, 104-106, 111, 112, 118-122, 124-131.

6. *Manoeuvre Map, Scotland*, 1899. Sheet 33. Not found.

7. District maps. With a simple border graduated at 10' intervals.
   1. Outline with coloured main roads and water.
      Edinburgh, 1901.
   2. Outline with coloured main roads.
      Aberdeen, 1900.
      Dundee, 1900 (**✣15**.5).
      Glasgow, 1900.

Geological Survey of Scotland: for series sheets see **✣13**.G.

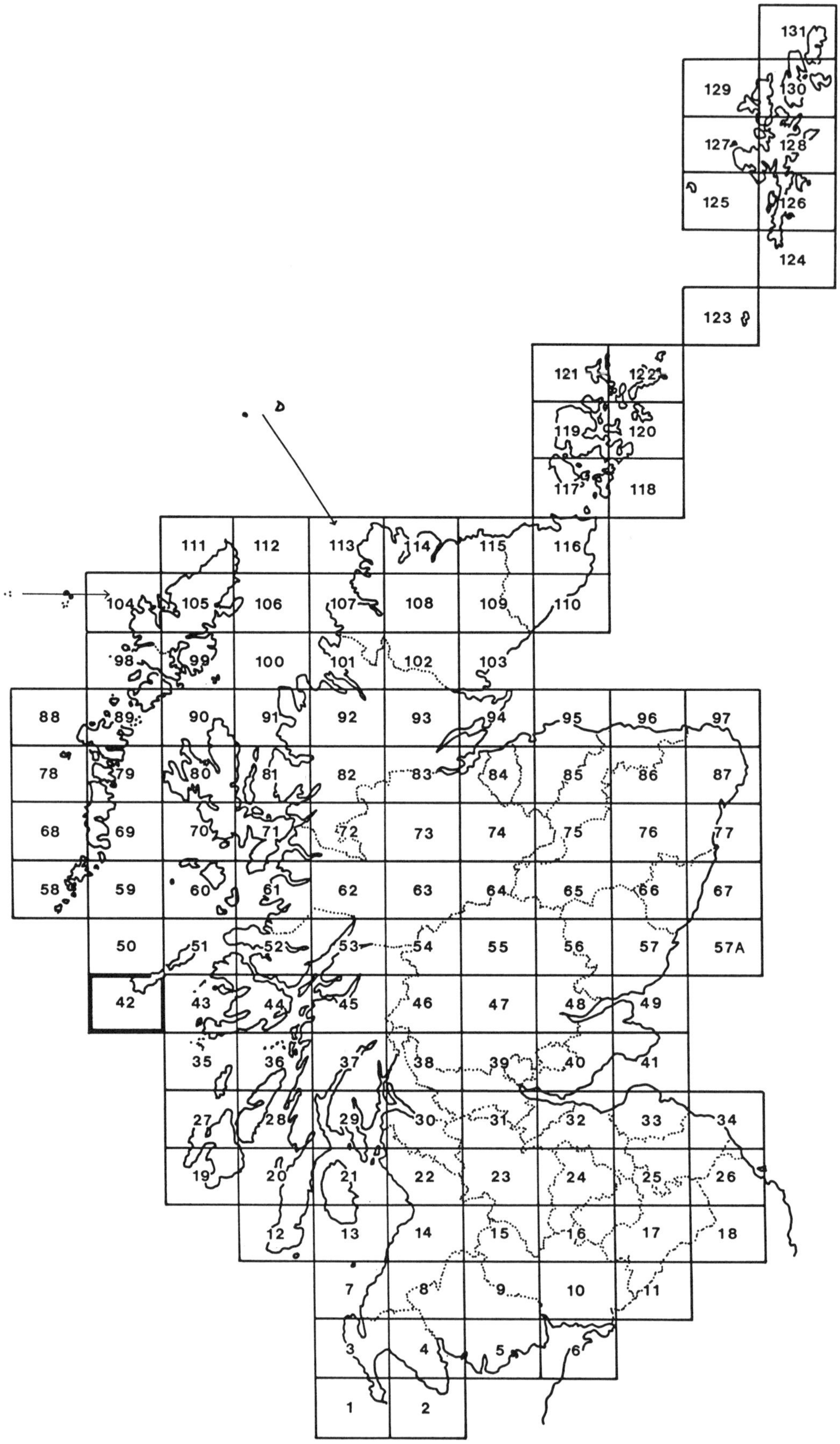

Sheets combined on publication are shown in bold

15. One-inch Third Edition Map of Scotland

15. One-inch Third Edition Map of Scotland

Laid out [as **✣13**] in 132 sheets: 1-57, 57A, 58-131, reduced on publication to 131 with the combination of Sheets 42 and 50. Produced from the second national revision of 1901-10. Heading: *Ordnance Survey of Scotland,* followed in most cases by *(Third Edition).*

There are insets of Flannan Isles on Sheet 104, Sula Sgeir, Rona on 113. The Mull area of 36 appears as an extrusion on 44, Tiree appears complete on 42/50 by means of an extrusion from 43, Eigg and Canna on 60 from 61 and 70, South Uist on 69 from 68, Pentland Skerries on 117 from 118, Holm of Huip on 120 from 122. Sheets 58 and 128 have extrusions. The English portions of Sheets 6, 10, 11, 17, 18, 26, other than the Berwick area, are blank.

1. Outline edition, with contours, 1902-12 (published 1903-12). All 132 sheets in 131: 1-41, 42/50, 43-49, 51-57, 57A, 58-131.
   Reissues were offered either by engraving or by lithography.

2. *Black Outline Edition,* with contours, 1903-12 (published 1918-20). By lithography. 71 sheets in 70 recorded: 1, 2, 8, 11, 14, 17-19, 21-25, 27, 29-41, 42/50, 43-49, 51, 55-57, 57A, 59, 60, 63, 64, 70, 72, 73, 75, 77, 79, 85, 87, 91, 92, 94-98, 102-110, 113, 114.
   For Sheet 26 in this style see **✣17**.2. Two sheets, 35 [▮PC] and 79 [▮Cu], are recorded that do not form part of legal deposit collections, and there may well be others.

3. Hachured edition in black or brown, with contours, 1903-11 (published 1905-11). 110 sheets in 109 recorded: 1-41, 42/50, 43-49, 51-57, 57A, 58-78, 80-82, 85-101, 104-109, 111-114, 118.
   Sheets 99, 104, 105, 109, 118 were issued but may not have been published [▮Eg]. For 1910 issues of Sheets 83 and 84 see **✣14**.3. By engraving: for issues in this style printed by lithography see ✣4.

4. Hachured edition in brown, with contours, dated 1911 (issued ?after 1914). By lithography. 2 sheets recorded: 88, 89 [▮PC].
   The cover title on the copies recorded is *Scotland in outline and hills.* The extent of coverage is unknown; perhaps hachured editions of those sheets not available in colour were required for military use, presumably after 1914 [see **✣16**]. See also ✣3.

5. District maps. Outline with coloured main roads. With a simple border graduated at 10' intervals.
   Dundee District, 1909 (**✣14**.7.2).
   Glasgow District, 1907.

Geological Survey of Scotland

For series sheets see **✣13**.G; for the *Soil Texture Map* see **✣13**.G.6.

Soil Survey of Scotland

Base maps are *Third Edition* with National Grid, then *Seventh Series.* English areas are blank.

6. *[Systematic] Soil Survey,* 1954-83. 49 sheets in 28: 1/2/3/4/7pt, 8/7pt, 14/13pt, 17, 18, 22/21pt, 24/32pt, 25, 26, 31, 33/34/41pt, 35pt/36pt/43pt/44pt/51pt/52pt, 39/31pt, 40/41pt/32pt, 47, 48/49, 57/57A, 66/67, 75-77, 83pt/84pt/93pt/94pt, 84/94pt, 85/95, 86, 87/97, 94-96, 110/116/117pt.

7. *Land Use Capability,* 1967-83. 40 sheets in 19: 1/2/3/4/7pt, 8/7pt, 24/32pt, 25/26, 31, 33/34/41pt, 35pt/36pt/43pt/44pt/51pt/52pt, 39/31pt, 40/41pt/32pt, 47, 48/49, 57/57A, 66/67, 76/77, 83pt/84pt/93pt/94pt, 84/94pt, 87/97, 94, 110/116/117pt.
   Some printings of Sheets 39/31pt and 48/49 lack the heading *Land Use Capability.*

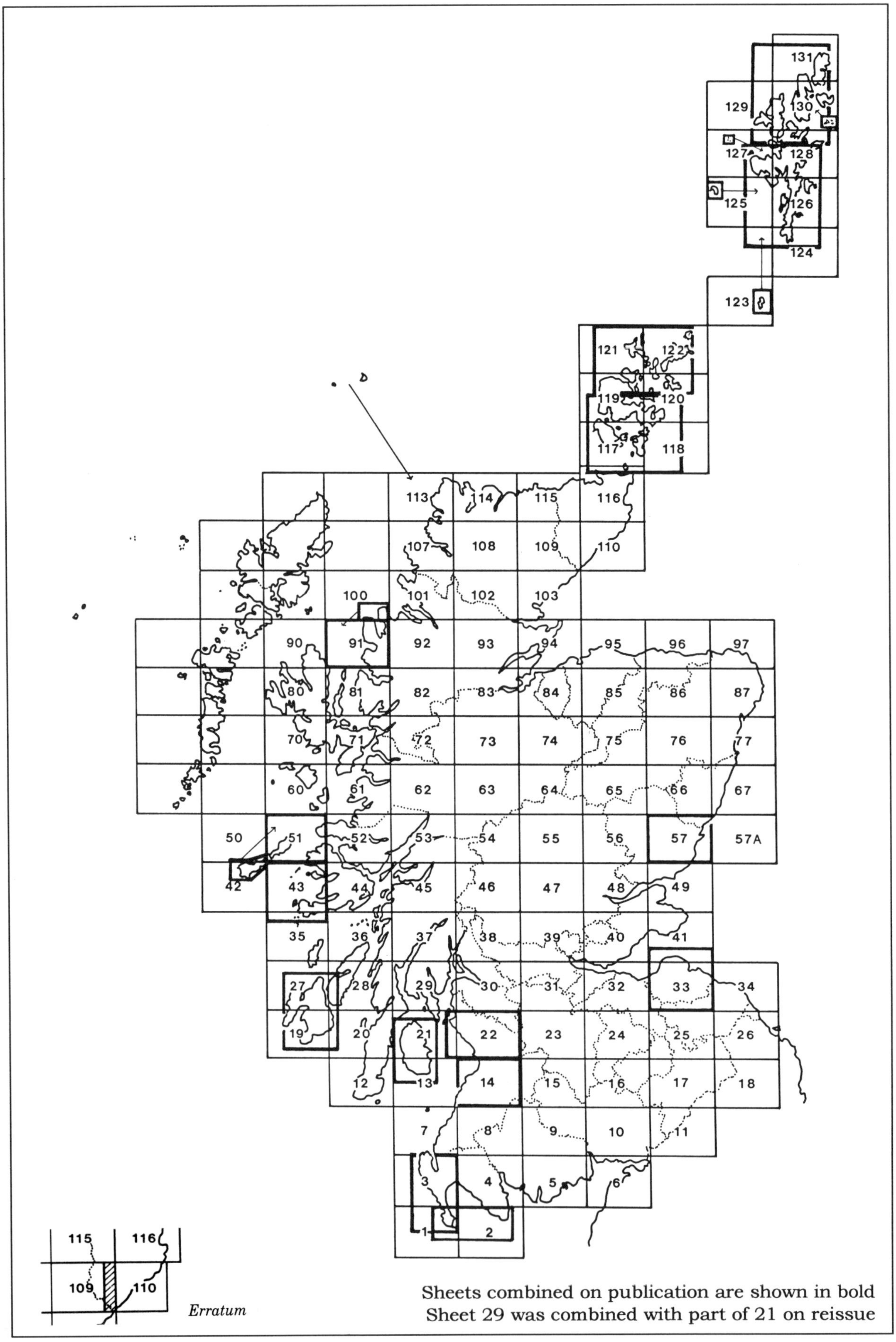

Sheets combined on publication are shown in bold
Sheet 29 was combined with part of 21 on reissue

16. One-inch Third Edition Map of Scotland, in colour

16. One-inch Third Edition Map of Scotland, in colour

Laid out [as ✣**13**] in 132 sheets: 1-57, 57A, 58-131. This number would have been much reduced by sheet combinations. Publication was discontinued before completion. Produced from the second national revision of 1901-10. For the map border see page xxiii. Heading: *Ordnance Survey of Scotland,* followed in most cases by *(Third Edition).*

Coverage of the Outer Hebrides and Colonsay is lacking, and Sheets 58, 59, 68, 69, 78, 79, 88, 89, 98, 99, 104-106, 111, 112 were unpublished. The Islay area of Sheet 27 and the Mull area of 35 were issued as parts of combined sheets. The Mull area of Sheet 36 also appears as an extrusion on 44. The Tiree portions of Sheets 42, 43, 50 are combined inset on 51. Sheet 100 is inset on 91. Sheet 60 has extrusions from 61 and 70 to complete Eigg and Canna. Sheet 116 was extended two miles north to complete coverage of the mainland. There are insets of Sula Sgeir, Rona on Sheet 113, Foula and Ve Skerries on 123/124/125/126/127pt/128pt (Sheet 123 *Fair Isle* is itself inset), Out Skerries on 129/130/131/127pt/128pt.

Combined sheets: 1/2, 1/3/7pt, 14/13pt, 19/20pt/27pt/28pt, 21pt/13pt, 22/21pt, 33/41pt, 42/50/51/43pt, 43/35pt, 57/57A, 91/100, 117/118/119pt/120pt, 121/122/119pt/120pt, 123/124/125/126/127pt/128pt, 129/130/131/127pt/128pt.

Sheets 7, 20, 28, 41 were also published independently, but not Sheets 27 and 35 (Colonsay).

The English portions of Sheets 6, 10, 11, 17, 18, 26, other than the Berwick area, are blank.

With an alpha-numeric border

1. Coloured edition, with hachures and contours. 117 sheets in 98.
    1. First issues, 1905-13. 117 sheets in 98 as described above.
    2. Sheets combined on reissue, 1908. Sheet 29/21pt.
       A six-mile extension covering the entire Island of Bute was made to the south of Sheet 29. That part falling on Sheet 21 was otherwise not fully covered.

2. District maps. Coloured with hachures and contours.
   Aberdeen District, 1913.
   Loch Lomond District, 1908.
   With a quarter-inch border. The north end of the loch is inset.

With a graduated and alpha-numeric border

3. District map. Coloured with layers, hachures and contours.
   Glasgow District, 1914 (✣4).

With a graduated border and alpha-numeric squaring system

4. District map. Coloured with layers, hachures and contours.
   Glasgow District : Edition of 1921, 1914 (published 1921) (✣3).

5. Tourist Maps. Coloured with layers, hachures and contours.
   Burns' Country, 1921.
   Deeside, 1920.
   Lower Strath Spey, 1921.
   Oban, 1920.
   Rothesay & Firth of Clyde, 1920 (published 1922).
   Scott's Country, 1921.
   The Trossachs & Loch Lomond, 1920.

The notes for OSR 1943-44 mention "97 (Hills and Outline) Original Cadestral *(sic)* Sheets", which, if made, could possibly have been reprints from the outline and hill plates of this issue, though there is a discrepancy of one in the sheet total.

17. One-inch Fourth Edition Map of Scotland

Laid out [as ✛**13**] in 132 sheets, 1-57, 57A, 58-131. Produced from the third national revision of 1910 (abandoned). In the event only eight sheets, 1-5, 26, 33, 34, were revised, of which only Sheet 26 was published. Heading: *Ordnance Survey of Scotland (Fourth Edition).*

The English portion of Sheet 26, other than the Berwick area, is blank.

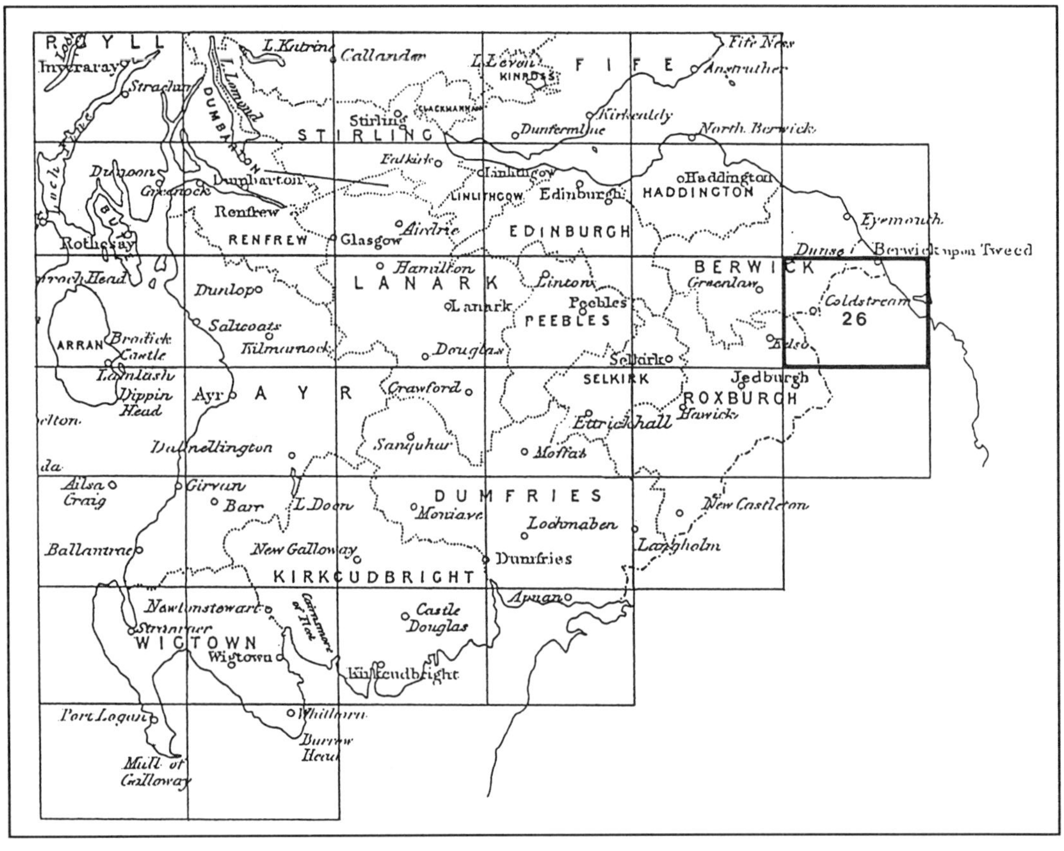

1. Outline edition, with contours, 1912. Sheet 26.
   Reissues were offered either by engraving or lithography.

2. *Black Outline Edition,* with contours, 1912 (published 1918). By lithography. Sheet 26.
   See also ✛**15**.2.

18. One-inch Popular Edition Map of Scotland

Constructed on Cassini's Projection on the origin of Delamere, and published in 92 sheets numbered north to south. Standard sheet coverage 28 by 19 miles, including one-mile overlaps with sheets adjoining east and south. Produced from the third national revision of 1921-30. Newly drawn at the two-inch scale. For the map border see page xviii. Heading: *Ordnance Survey of Scotland,* with *Ordnance Survey of Great Britain* on Sheets 86 (not ✣C) and 89, and as noted. At first issue Sheets 71, 72, 78, 79, 81-92 were headed *Popular Edition One-inch Map,* 1-70, 73-77, 80 had *Popular Edition.*

Sheets 86 and 89 are common with England *Popular Edition* Sheets 3 and 5 [**✣10**].

There are insets of Ve Skerries on Sheet 2, Foula on 3, Fair Isle on 4, Sule Skerry, Stack Skerry on 6, Sula Sgeir, Rona, Flannan Isles on 8, Gasker on 13, St Kilda and Boreray (making their first appearance on mapping at the one-inch scale) on 22, Oigh-sgeir on 34.

A. With an alpha-numeric squaring system ○

1. Coloured edition, 1924-32. All sheets.

2. *Outline Edition,* with water in blue, contours in red, 1924-32. All sheets.
   The heading is *One-inch Outline Edition* on Sheets 80, 90, 91, thereafter *Popular Edition One-inch Map,* with *(Outline)* on the contour plate.

3. Outline edition, with water in blue. Without grid. All sheets.
   Alpha-numeric values survive in the borders of Sheets 79, 86, 89.
   1. With *Popular Edition* marginalia, 1941-42. 4 sheets: 28, 47, 86, 89.
   2. With War Office marginalia↑, 1941-42. 88 sheets: 1-27, 29-46, 48-85, 87, 88, 90-92.

4. Water and contour issues.

5. *Land Utilisation Survey of Britain.* 38 sheets in 37.
   Published by the Land Utilisation Survey of Britain except the sheets in ✣5.1. All sheets have alpha-numeric borders, except Sheet 4 which has an alpha-numeric squaring system.
   1. Printed and published by the Ordnance Survey, 1933-35. 5 sheets: 4, 53, 59, 60, 68.
   2. Printed by G.W. Bacon, 1935-40. 9 sheets: 6, 12, 28, 29, 45, 72, 73, 74, 78.
   3. Reprinted by J. Bartholomew, 1942. Sheet 53.
   4. Printed by W. & A.K. Johnston, 1944-51. 23 sheets in 22: 30/[31pt], 40/[31pt], 51, 58, 63, 64, 66, 67, 75, 79-85, 87-92.
   5. Printed by E. Stanford, 1947. Sheet 86.

6. Tourist Maps.
   1. Coloured with layers.
      The Cairngorms, 1922.
      The Trossachs & Loch Lomond, 1930 (altered to 1929 on reprint).
   2. Coloured with relief.
      Invergordon to Loch Ness, 1933 (published 1934).

B. With National Yard Grid at 5000 yard intervals

1. Tourist Maps. Coloured with relief. On National Yard Grid sheet lines (see page xiii).
   The Cairngorms, 1936❂.
   Oban, 1936❂.

C. With National Grid

Heading: *Popular Edition One-inch Map (with National Grid).* Sheet 89 was discontinued, with its area covered by *New Popular Edition* Sheets 75 and 76 [✤**19**].

1. Coloured edition, 1925-48 (published 1945-48). 91 sheets: 1-88, 90-92.
   Pre-war publication dates as in ✤A.1 survived on sheets published before mid-1947.

2. *Outline Edition,* 1925-48 (published 1945-48). 91 sheets: 1-88, 90-92.
   Pre-war publication dates as in ✤A.2 survived on sheets published before mid-1947.

3. *Diagram to show relationship of National Grid to old style 6" sheets and 25" plans,* 1946. Sheet 72 only.
   Dunbartonshire, Lanarkshire and Stirlingshire sheet lines are blue, Renfrewshire green and Ayrshire purple. The National Grid is red.

4. *Index to the Ordnance Survey 1/2,500 and 1/1,250 Scale Plans on National Grid Sheet Lines,* 1951-56. 8 sheets: 45, 64, 67, 68, 72-74, 78.
   In brown outline with index details overprinted in purple.

- For *The Trossachs & Loch Lomond* Tourist Map see ✤**19**.7.

Geological Survey of Scotland: for the use of *Popular Edition* mapping see ✤**13**.G.

M. Military issues with War Office Cassini Grid ❍

Overprinted with War Office Cassini Grid (British System) in purple

1. *Popular Edition.* Coverage unknown.
   Full coverage of the Outer Hebrides, Orkney and Shetland Islands is unlikely because Sheets 1-8, 11-14, 18, 22, 23, 32, 33 were all published in 1931-32, and thus possibly not in time for issue in this style.
   1. With woods in green, 1925-30. Number of sheets unknown.
   2. With uncoloured woods, 1931-33. Number of first issues or reprints unknown.

Overprinted with War Office Cassini Grid (Modified British System) in purple ❍

2. GSGS 3908: *Popular Edition.* All sheets.
   1. With uncoloured woods, ?1933. ?All sheets.
   2. With woods in green, 1934- . All sheets.
      A printing of Sheet 61 is erroneously classified GSGS 3907.
   3. *Sales Copy.* Sheet 21 recorded [▮PC].
      So far the only pre-*War Revision* sales copy recorded on a *Popular Edition* base in either Scotland or England and Wales.

3. GSGS 3908: *War Revision,* 1940. All sheets.
   War Office publication dates as in ✤M.2 may be disregarded here.
   1. With *Popular Edition* marginalia, 1940-41. 85 sheets recorded: 1-3, 5-7, 9-17, 19-29, 31-50, 52-64, 66-91.
      Some other sheets not so far recorded almost certainly also exist in this form.
   2. With War Office marginalia↑, 1941-42. 90 sheets: 1-85, 87, 88, 90-92.
      A printing of Sheet 90 is erroneously classified GSGS 3907.
   3. *Sales Copy,* without grid, 1942-43 (published 1943). 42 sheets: 1, 7, 8, 12-14, 17, 18, 25, 28-30, 33, 34, 37, 38, 44, 48-53, 55, 61, 62, 67, 68, 70-76, 78-81, 84, 85, 87.
   4. *Sales Copy,* with grid, published 1943-45. 73 sheets recorded: 2-7, 9-11, 14-16, 19-24, 26-29, 31, 32, 34-36, 38-43, 45-49, 51-54, 56-69, 72-75, 77-85, 87, 88, 90, 91.

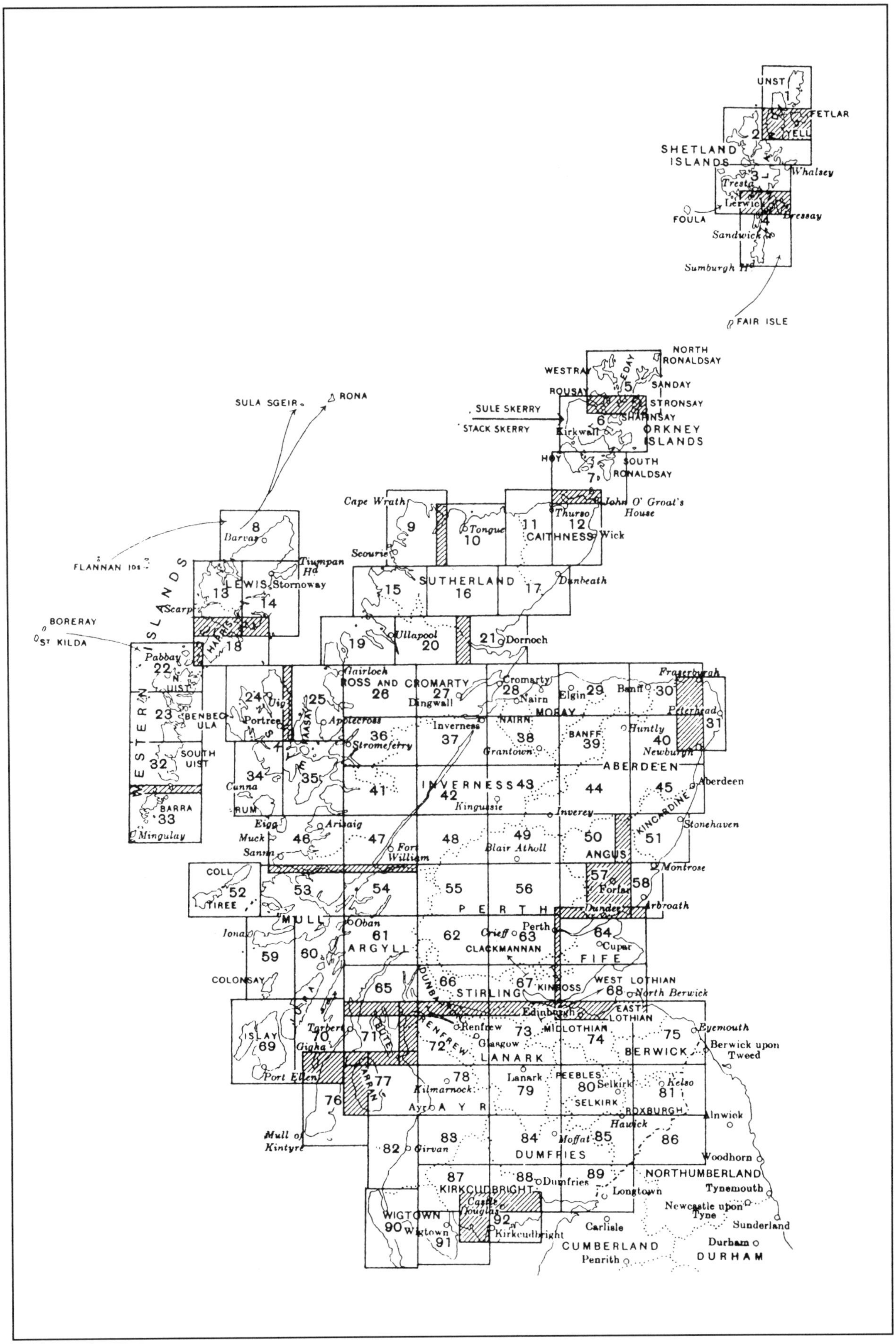

18. One-inch Popular Edition Map of Scotland

With War Office Cassini Grid (Modified British System) in black, numbered in blue

4. GSGS 3908: *Second War Revision,* 1940/1942 : *Popular Edition Style.* 4 sheets.
   At the request of the Director of Surveys, Home Forces, Sheets 45 and 92 were revised in 1942. Only issues with War Office marginalia↑ are headed *Popular Edition Style.*
   1. With *Popular Edition* marginalia, 1941. Sheet 89.
   2. With War Office marginalia↑, 1941-43 (issued 1942-43). 4 sheets: 45 (still dated 1933), 86, 89, 92.
   3. *Sales Copy,* published 1943. 4 sheets: 45, 86, 89, 92.

5. District map on War Office Cassini Grid sheet lines.
   GSGS 3908: *Inveraray,* 1941 [▮RGS].
   A 736 code inside the map frame could be evidence of a 1936 printing, but this has yet to be confirmed.

Military issues overprinted with National Grid (Military System) in purple

6. GSGS 4639 coloured edition. 91 sheets.
   1. *War Office Edition,* 1947-50 (issued 1950). 91 sheets: 1-88, 90-92.
      Sheet 43 lacks the heading. The base maps display the numerical reference system of the National Grid, blocked out by overprinting.

   The pattern of later issues is complex and its logic has yet to be fully exposed. This is the record of sheets located so far:
   2. Second Edition-GSGS, 1953. 2 sheets: 74, 80.
      Using base maps displaying the letter reference system of the National Grid. Sheet 74 was reprinted in 1955.
   3. Edition 1-GSGS, 1947-49 (issued 1955). 8 sheets: 63, 64, 66, 67, 73, 75, 78, 85.
      These sheets continue to carry the publication dates of the *War Office Edition,* but use base maps displaying the letter reference system of the National Grid.
   4. *War Office Edition,* 1947-49, reissued 1957. 6 sheets: 52, 59, 87, 88, 91, 92.
   5. Edition 2-GSGS, 1957. Sheet 72: this was reprinted in 1960.
   6. Edition 1-GSGS, 1957-58 (issued 1958). 3 sheets: 29, 68, 79.
   7. *War Office Edition,* 1948-49, reissued 1960. 4 sheets: 28, 57, 58, 65.

   The following issue dependent on ✣M.6.1 is recorded:
   8. GSGS Misc.421: *Exercise Backstop,* 1950. 4 sheets recorded: 80, 81, 85, 86 [▮Ob].

7. District map.
   GSGS Misc.406: *Redesdale and Otterburn Artillery Ranges,* 1955 (✚**20**.M.4) [▮PC].
   With some *New Popular Edition* mapping [✚**19**]. The number Misc.406 suggests 1949-50 usage, but no such issue is yet recorded.

Symbols : a **bold** number prefixed with ✚ is a cross reference to another section of the book; a number prefixed with ✣ is a cross reference within the current section; a reference number in ( ) at a district map identifies the next, or previous, such map listed with the same sheet lines; the ▮ symbol accompanies a source reference for maps rarely encountered (library sigla are listed on page 241); ❍ warns that there are noted exceptions to the information given in headings; ↑ identifies what is referred to here as War Office marginalia (for a description see page xxii); ❁ refers to the exceptional use of the heading *Ordnance Survey of Great Britain.*

19. One-inch New Popular Edition Map of Great Britain

National Grid series, also known as *One-inch Sixth Edition.* Laid out in 190 sheets of which the 114 covering England and Wales, 64, 71, 75-78, 82-86, 88-190, were issued. Standard sheet coverage 40 by 45 km. The English part of Sheet 70 is on Scotland *Popular Edition* Sheets 81 and 86 [✣**18**.C]. Coverage of the Isle of Man was provided by *Second War Revision* Sheet 17 [✣**10**.M.13, M.14]. *Fifth Edition* mapping was used where available, *Popular Editions* elsewhere. Heading: *Ordnance Survey of Great Britain.*

64 sheets were published headed *New Popular One-inch Map with National Grid (Provisional Edition)* using *Popular Editions* source material: 64, 71, 75-78, 82-86, 88-131, 138-142, 151-154. Sheet 126 was a pilot sheet: early printings had orange contours and solid blue water.

Fifty sheets were published headed *New Popular One-inch Map with National Grid,* using *Fifth Edition* style material: 132-137, 143-150, 155-190. Eleven of these, 157, 158, 161, 167, 169, 171, 172, 179, 182-184, had been printed in 1940-41 in five colours, including contours in orange, with the heading *New Popular One-inch Map,* when the expression *Ordnance Survey Grid* was used. They were not published until 1945. Sheets 156 and 159 were proved in this form. Prototype Sheets 160, 162, 169 were printed before the war. Some issues of Sheets 136 and 137 erroneously make reference to *Provisional Edition.*

There are insets of Grassholm Island and The Smalls on Sheet 151, Lundy Island on 163, Isle of Portland on 178, Isles of Scilly on 189.

1. Coloured edition, 1940-47 (published 1945-47). 114 sheets as listed above.

2. *Outline Edition.* 114 sheets as listed above.
   1. With woods in black, 1945-47. 64 Provisional Edition sheets using *Popular Edition* source material.
   2. With woods in grey, 1940-47 (published 1945-47). 50 sheets using *Fifth Edition* style material.

3. *Outline Edition,* with contours in orange. ?114 sheets as listed above.
   Printed for the Ministry of Town and Country Planning. The departmental catalogue of 1 May 1947 implies that all sheets were being made: "A special edition of the New Popular, showing contours in brown *(sic),* is available for departmental use." Sheets 126, 157, 158, 161, 167, 169, 171, 172, 179, 182-184 also have orange second class roads because these were coloured by the contour plate. The heading is lacking on some sheets.

4. *Index to the Ordnance Survey 1/2,500 and 1/1,250 Scale Plans on National Grid Sheet Lines,* 1950-56 (published 1951-56). 75 sheets recorded: 78, 82, 85, 86, 88, 89, 94-97, 99-105, 107-112, 118-122, 126, 130-133, 135, 137, 142, 143, 148-150, 153-184, 186-188.
   In brown outline with index details overprinted in purple. National Grid 100 km squares are identified by letters. A 1948 prototype of Sheet 179 showing these squares still identified by figures is in PRO OS 1/279. An index in PRO OS 1/421 implies the intention of issuing Sheet 98, but it has not been recorded.

5. Water and contour issues.

6. *London District* (✣M.2).
   See ✣M.2 for title details. The map was printed in separate west and east sections which in this format were untitled. Made at the behest of New Scotland Yard for a general base map of London.
   1. Outline edition, with woods in grey, published 1947.
   2. Outline edition in grey, reprinted 1948 [▮Bg].

7. Tourist Maps.
   The Lake District.
   1. Coloured edition, with layers, 1948 (✢**20**.12.1).
   2. Physical issue, without black plate [▮EXg].
   The Trossachs & Loch Lomond, 1949.
   Coloured edition, with layers. The only wholly Scottish member of the *New Popular Edition* to be published. It has the standard height of a series sheet, but covers an area 15 km wider.

Soil Survey of England and Wales. See also ✢**6**.4.

8. Coloured edition, 1958. Sheet [106], numbered 93/105/92pt/94pt/106pt/118pt/119pt.

Geological Survey of England and Wales: for use of *New Popular Edition* mapping see ✢**3**.G.

M. Military issues with War Office Cassini Grid

Issues of Sheet 167 in ✢M.1, M.3, M.4 have an extrusion covering the western portion of the War Department property between Westbury and Warminster.

With War Office Cassini Grid in black, numbered in blue

1. GSGS 4620: *6th Edition Style,* 1946. 2 sheets: [167] *Salisbury Plain,* [169] *Aldershot* [▮PC].
   Revised by the Ordnance Survey. Reprints were issued in 1947 and 1949. Adjoining sheet diagrams still relate these maps to GSGS 3907 sheets on *Popular Edition* sheet lines [✢**10**.M.12] which continued in military use until the conversion to National Grid in 1950. This presumably explains the absence of sheet numbers here. With War Office marginalia↑. War Department information is overprinted in red on *Salisbury Plain,* revised to 1946 and updated on the reprints.

Overprinted with War Office Cassini Grid in purple

2. District maps.
   GSGS 3907: *Catterick Area,* 2nd Edition, 1948 (✢M.5).
   Laid out on National Grid sheet lines in readiness for the forthcoming National Grid edition, GSGS 4620, issued some two years later [see ✢M.5]. The War Department property boundary is overprinted. Superseding ✢**10**.M.7.1.
   OR 1826: *London District,* 1947 (✢6) [▮Ob].
   Showing boundaries of police divisions (purple), garrisons (red).

Military issues overprinted with National Grid (Military System) in purple ❍

3. GSGS 4620, later M722, coloured edition. 114 sheets.
   The series adopted *Seventh Series* material as it became available. Sheet edition numbers continue sequentially therein [✢**20**.M.1].
   1. *War Office Edition,* 1947-49 (issued 1950). 114 sheets as listed above.
      Sixteen sheets are recorded that were reprinted by [No.1] Survey Production Centre, Royal Engineers.
   2. First Edition-GSGS. 25 sheets recorded.
      1. Issued 1950-51. 19 sheets recorded: 120, 121, 129, 147, 160-164, 167, 169, 170, 173-175, 178, 180, 183, 184.
         With *War Office Edition* publication dates, and on base maps that continue to display the numerical reference system of the National Grid.
      2. Issued 1954-55 (as Edition 1-GSGS). ?6 sheets: 64, 75, 85, 146, 150, 188.
         Using base maps displaying the letter reference system of the National Grid. This issue follows that of the Second Edition-GSGS [✢M.3.3]. Sheets 64, 75, 188 still carry *War Office Edition* publication dates.

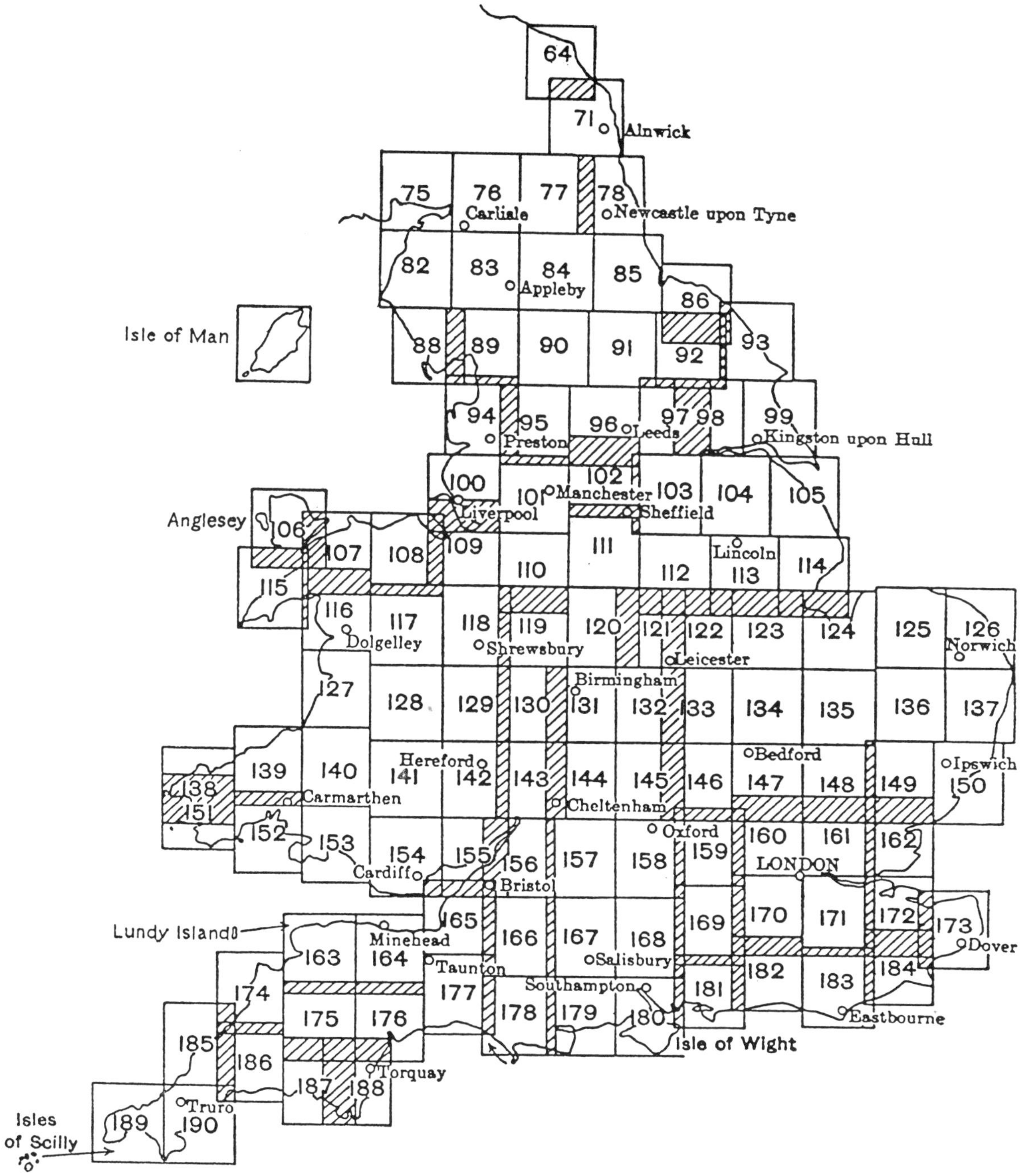

19. One-inch New Popular Edition Map of Great Britain

3. Second Edition-GSGS, 1951-53. 87 sheets recorded: 71, 82, 84, 86, 88, 90-93, 95-119, 122-126, 130-137, 143, 144, 147-149, 155-187, 189, 190.
   Using base maps displaying the letter reference system of the National Grid. Sheets 163 and 164 were issued exceptionally late, in 1957-58.
4. Edition 3-GSGS, 1957-58 (issued 1958-59). 3 sheets recorded: 167, 179, 187.
   Sheet 187 is still dated 1951, though issued in 1959.
5. Edition 4-GSGS, 1951 (issued 1959). Sheet 187.
   Reclassified Edition 4 with the correction of the Edition 3 true north data.

The following dependent issues are recorded [unless noted ▮Ob or PC]:

6. GSGS 4620: Overprinted *...for training purposes only...* 10 sheets recorded: 100, 127, 128, 149, 150, 162, 168, 169, 173, 180 [▮DGI, Ob, PC, Wc].
7. GSGS Misc.433: *Salisbury Plain PTA,* ?1950. Sheet 167.
   The first edition is not found. Thereafter Second Edition, 1953, Third Edition, 1959, Fourth Edition, 1961.
8. GSGS Misc.490: *Exercise Hereward,* 1950. ?3 sheets: ?126, 136, ?137.
   See also **✣56**.M.9.7.
9. GSGS Misc.491: *Exercise Father Tiber,* 1951. ?4 sheets: 155, 156, 165, 166.
10. GSGS Misc.1560: *Exercise Surprise Packet,* 1951. 15 sheets: 155-159, 165-169, 177-181.
    See also **✣56**.M.14.
11. GSGS Misc.1585: *Stanford Training and Gun Areas,* 1952. Sheet 136.
12. GSGS Misc.1605: *Exercise Ballista III,* 1953. ?2 sheets: 109, 118.
13. GSGS Misc.1618: *Exercise Noahs Ark,* 1953. ?4 sheets: ?101, ?109, 110, 118.
14. GSGS Misc.1622: *WD Land and Training Areas, Home Counties.* Sheet 173.
    The First Edition (not found) was probably issued in 1953, the Second Edition, 1955. This edition remained in print as a *Seventh Series* map [**✣20**.M.1.3].
15. GSGS Misc.1663: *Exercise Quicksilver,* 1954. ?4 sheets: 91, 92, 96, 97.
    See also **✣56**.M.9.8.

4. GSGS 4620A coloured edition, with layers. 13 sheets.
   For the Staff College.
   1. *War Office Edition,* 1947-49 (printed 1949-50, issued 1950). 13 sheets: 144-146, 157-159, 166-169, 178-180 [▮DGI].
   2. Second Edition-GSGS, 1951-52 (issued 1952-54). 7 sheets: 144, 157 (issued 1962), 158, 159, 166, 168, 169 [▮DGI].
      See **✣20**.M.2 for Sheet 158 Edition 3-GSGS on a *Seventh Series* base map.
   3. Edition 1-GSGS, 1954. 2 sheets: 145, 146 [▮DGI].
      Sheet 145 still carries its *War Office Edition* publication date.

5. District maps.
   GSGS 4620: *Catterick Area,* First Edition-GSGS, 1948 (issued ?1951) (✣M.2).
   The War Department property boundary is overprinted.
   GSGS 4620A: *Parts of Sheets 158, 159, 168, 169,* 1949 [▮DGI].
   Coloured edition, with layers. For the Staff College.
   GSGS 4620A: *Reading - Basingstoke Area,* 1949 [▮DGI].
   Coloured edition, with layers. For the Staff College. Reissued in 1954 and 1962.
   London.
   1. M924, later (or earlier) M722, later GSGS 4692: First Edition-GSGS, ?1949.
      The map was compiled by the Ordnance Survey in 1949. As GSGS 4692 it was first published in 1951. The earlier versions, if made, have not been recorded. Edition 2-GSGS was M725, a *Seventh Series* map [**✣20**.M.4].
   2. GSGS Misc.1513, overprinted *London District Boundaries Map 1:63,360,* 1951.

   GSGS Misc.1522: *Sennybridge Artillery Ranges,* ?First Edition, 1951. Not found.
   GSGS Misc.1881: *Dartmoor Training Areas,* 1960 [▮Cu].
   Outline edition, overprinted in red.

- For GSGS Misc.406 *Redesdale and Otterburn Artillery Ranges* see **✣18**.M.7.

6. *Experimental Graticule Reference,* no date. Sheet 167 recorded [▮PC].
   Without grid, but overprinted with a graticule at 1' intervals in purple.

20. One-inch Seventh Series Map of Great Britain

National Grid series. Published in 190 sheets, reduced in 1965 to 189 by the combination of Sheets 138 and 151. Standard sheet coverage 40 by 45 km. Produced from 1944-58 revision. Newly drawn at the 1:40,000 scale from reductions of the 1:25,000 map and, where lacking, enlargements of the Scotland one-inch *Popular Edition* [**✣18**]. Heading: *Ordnance Survey of Great Britain* : *One Inch to One Mile Map (Seventh Series).*

In England and Wales *New Popular Edition* sheet lines were used except Sheets 106, 160, 161, 185, 189 [**✣19**].

There are insets of Foula, Fair Isle on Sheet 4, Sule Skerry, Stack Skerry on 6, Rona, Sula Sgeir on 8, Flannan Isles, Gasker on 12, St Kilda and Boreray, Haskeir Island on 17, Puffin Island on 106, Grassholm Island and The Smalls on 151 (Grassholm Island only on 138/151), Lundy on 163, Isle of Portland on 178, Isles of Scilly on 189.

1. Coloured edition. All sheets.
   Prototypes were issued of Sheet 142 (1949) with the heading *Seventh (Great Britain) Edition,* and Sheet 154 (1950) with *Seventh Edition* [▮CCS]. Some issues of Sheets 3, 26, 82, 83, 121, 135, 152 were printed by the Hydrographer of the Navy.
   1. In ten colours, 1952-61. All sheets.
   2. In six colours, 1961-72. All sheets.
      Sheet 137 was last reprinted in 1991 to provide stock for Ordnance Survey commemorative boxed sets of their final one-inch map.
   3. Sheets combined on reissue, 1965. Sheet 138/151.

2. *Outline Edition.* All sheets.
   1. With grey building infill, 1952-60 (published 1952-61). 169 sheets: 5-162, 164-166, 168-173, 178, 184.
   2. With black stipple building infill, 1960-65 (published 1961-74). 188 sheets: 1-31, 33-56, 58-190.
   3. Sheets combined on reissue, 1965. Sheet 138/151.
   4. With stippled water, 1962. Sheet 105 is documented, but not found.

3. *Index of Large Scale National Plans.* 153 sheets in 152 recorded.
   1. With sheet index overprinted in purple, 1952-68 (published 1958-68). 124 sheets in 123 recorded: 6, 8, 9, 27, 43, 50, 53, 55, 56, 59-64, 68, 70-79, 82-86, 89-95, 97-100, 102-133, 135-137, 138/151, 139-146, 148-150, 152-154, 156, 157, 159-181, 183-185, 187, 188, 190.
      The further numbers listed in ✣3.2 probably exist in this form.
   2. With additional orange overprint showing published plans, 1958-66. 124 sheets in 123 recorded: 10, 11, 16, 24, 25, 28-31, 33-35, 40, 46, 49, 50, 54-56, 59-62, 64, 65, 67, 69, 71, 72, 75-78, 82, 84-86, 88, 89, 91, 93-97, 99-103, 105-113, 117-123, 126, 127, 130-137, 138/151, 141-144, 147-150, 152-184, 186-190.
      The further numbers listed in ✣3.1 may exist in this form.

4. *Index showing Sheet Lines of the 1:2500 County Series related to the National Grid,* 1960-66 (published 1967). 14 sheets: 40, 43, 50, 53-56, 59-63, 67, 72.

5. Water and contour issues.

6. Coloured edition, with hill shading, 1970. Sheet 87, edition *C.*
   Hill shading was added only to civilian, not military printings.

7. Outline edition, overprinted with the sites of ancient monuments, 1960. Sheet 106.
   In *An Inventory of the Ancient Monuments in Anglesey* (The Royal Commission on Ancient & Historical Monuments in Wales & Monmouthshire), London, HMSO, reprinted 1960.

8. Experimental coloured issues, with metric heights.
   1. At scale 1:62,500, 1968. Sheet 170 [▮RML].
   2. At scale 1:63,360, 1968. Sheet 170 [▮RML].
   3. At scale 1:66,667, 1968. Sheet 170 [▮RML].
   4. At scale 1:75,000, 1968. Sheet 170 [▮RML].

9. Experimental coloured issues (at scale 1:50,000), 1970. ?3 sheets: 47, 170, 180 [▮OS].
   Issues concerned with line gauge and colour experiments which four years later would result in the production of the 1:50,000 *First Series* [✣**21**.A].

10. *1:50,000 scale metric map (Special edition for educational purposes),* 1970-71. 8 sheets: 47(M), 50(M), 91(M), 107(M), 135(M), 154(M), 170(M), 180(M).
    With heights and contours relabelled in metres.

11. *Greater London* Special Map (✣M.4).
    1. Coloured with black stipple building infill, 1967.
    2. Coloured with orange stipple building infill, 1971.

12. Tourist Maps.
    Some issues lack reference to *Tourist / Touring Map* except on the covers provided.
    1. Coloured with layers and hill shading.
       Cairngorms, 1964.
       Dartmoor, 1967. Another edition, 1973 (✣**21**.B.7.1).
       Exmoor, 1967. Another edition, 1973.
       Lake District, 1958. Another edition, 1966 (✣**19**.7.1, **21**.B.7.1).
       Loch Lomond and the Trossachs, 1961. Another edition, 1967.
       Lorn and Lochaber, 1959. Renamed *Ben Nevis and Glen Coe,* 1964.
       North York Moors, 1958. Another edition, 1966 (✣**21**.B.7.1).
       Peak District, 1957.
       Peak District, 1963, edition *B.* With new sheet lines (✣**21**.B.7.1).

    2. Coloured with hill shading, without contours.
       New Forest, 1966. Another edition, 1972 (published 1973) (✣**21**.B.7.2).

    3. Coloured with layers.
       Wye Valley and Lower Severn, 1961.

    4. Coloured.
       Cambridge, 1965.

- For one-inch Tourist Maps compiled from 1:50,000 *Second Series* mapping see ✣**21**.B.7.

13. *1:50,000 Channel Tunnel (UK),* 1969 [▮BL, Wc].
    For the Ministry of Transport. Parts of *Seventh Series* Sheets 172, 173, 184 enlarged to scale 1:50,000. With Universal Transverse Mercator Grid (sheet co-ordinates 347 km E to 395 km E, 5650 km N to 5678 km N), and National Grid intersections at 10 km intervals. A sheet overlapping mid-channel to the south-east completed the set.

Soil Survey of England and Wales. See also ✣**6**.4.

14. Coloured edition, 1958. Sheet [115], numbered 105pt/117pt/118pt/133pt/134pt.

15. *Outline Edition,* 1968-69. 3 sheets: 135, 147, 148.

Agricultural Land Classification of England and Wales

16. *Provisional* edition, 1965-75. 115 sheets in 113: 64/70, 71, 75-78, 82-86, 88-137, 138/151, 139-150, 152-190.
    Issued by the Ministry of Agriculture, Fisheries and Food, and printed on Ordnance Survey base maps by Her Majesty's Stationery Office.

For use of *Seventh Series* mapping: by **Geological Survey of England and Wales** see ✣**3**.G, by **Geological Survey of Scotland** see ✣**13**.G, by **Soil Survey of Scotland** see ✣**15**.6.

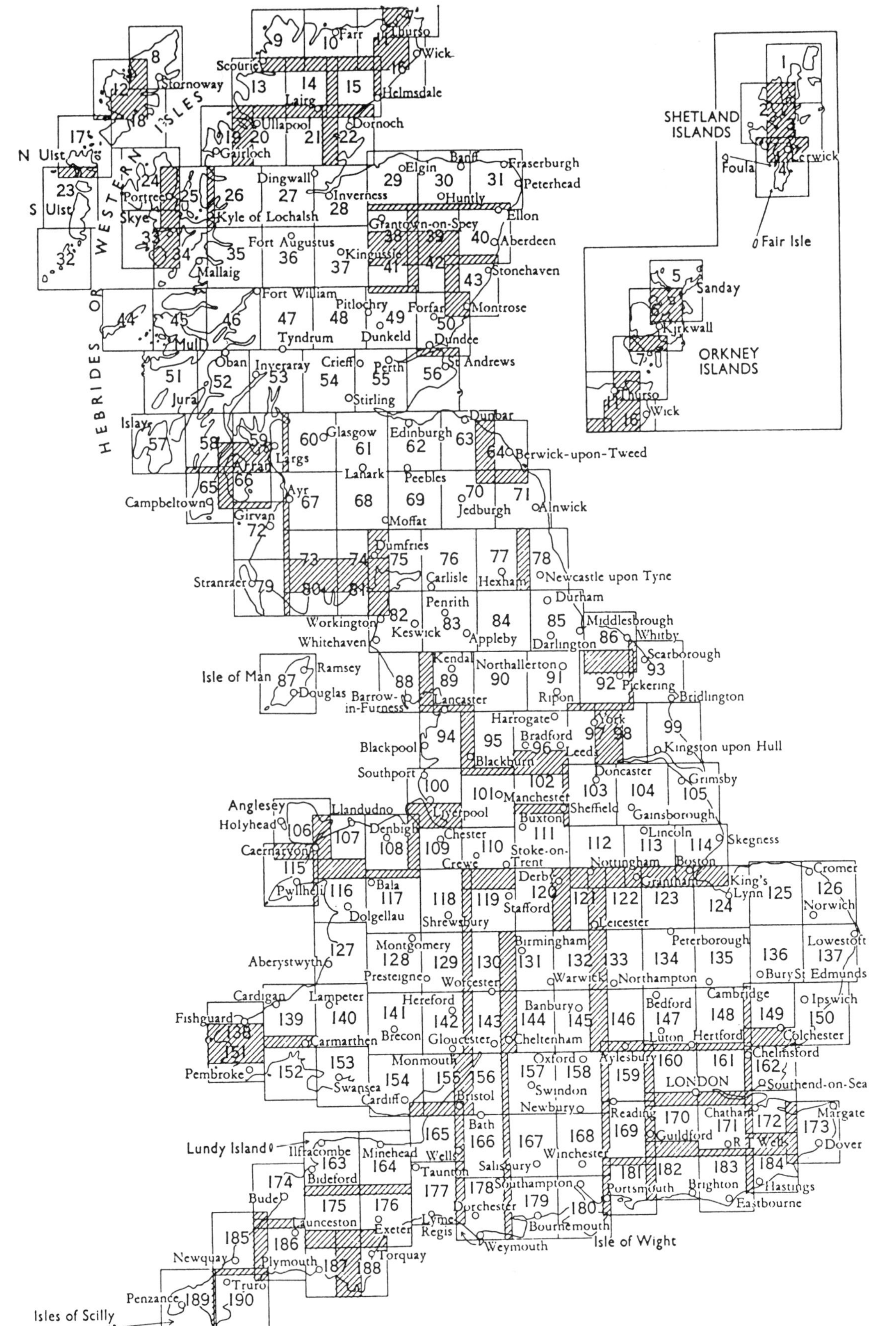

Sheets 138 and 151 were combined in 1965

20. One-inch Seventh Series Map of Great Britain

M. Military issues, with National Grid (Military System)

1. GSGS 4620, later M722, coloured edition. All sheets.
   Issued in numbered GSGS editions, in sequence from those in ✢**19**.M.3.
   1. With the grid numbered in blue, 1952. 5 sheets: 141, 142, 151, 152, 154.
      These are second editions of sheets issued as *War Office Edition* in ✢**19**.M.3.
   2. With the grid numbered in red, 1952-63. All sheets.
      Nineteen sheets are recorded as reprinted by [No.1] Survey Production Centre, Royal Engineers, eighteen by their British Army of the Rhine subsection in 1966, and nine by the Hydrographic Department, Admiralty in 1961.

   The following dependent issues are recorded:
   3. GSGS Misc.1622: *WD Land and Training Areas, Home Counties,* Second Edition-GSGS. Sheet 173 [▮PC].
      Transferred to the *Seventh Series* base, ?1961. See also ✢**19**.M.3.14.
   4. GSGS Misc.1974: *RAF Decca Aeronautical Charts,* 1963. 3 sheets: 167-169.
   5. GSGS Misc.1999, 1963. 6 sheets (at scale 1:50,000): 166-168, 178-180 [▮Wc].
   6. GSGS Misc.2000, 1963. 6 sheets (at scale 1:100,000): 166-168, 178-180 [▮Wc].
   7. *Showing CCF Arduous Training Areas (cleared by DLA(A)).*
      1. GSGS Misc.2132: *Area Number Three,* 1966. Sheet 116 [▮Ob].
      2. GSGS Misc.2133: *Plynlimmon,* 1966. Sheet 127 [▮Ob].
      3. GSGS Misc.2134: *Brecon Beacons,* 1966. Sheet 141[▮Ob].
   8. GSGS 4959: *WD Land and Training Areas, Home Counties,* 1965. ?Sheet 173.
   9. GSGS 4974: *Salisbury Plain Tr[ainin]g Area.* Sheet [167], ?1965 [▮Ob].
      With an extrusion covering Ministry of Defence property near Westbury.
   10. [Great Britain Decca Charts], 1973. 65 sheets: 83-86, 90-93, 97-99, 103-105, 112, 113, 116, 121-126, 130-137, 139, 144-150, 157-162, 167-172, 174, 175, 179-190.

2. GSGS 4620A coloured edition, with layers, 1962. Sheet 158 Edition 3-GSGS [▮DGI, Wc].
   For the Staff College. With the grid numbered in red. See also ✢**19**.M.4.

3. GSGS 5172: United Kingdom skeleton maps, 1972. 3 sheets recorded: [141] *Brecon,* [171] *London SE,* [178] *Dorchester* [▮NLS].
   Green, blue and contour plates only. The National Grid is in blue on *Brecon.*

4. District maps [unless noted ▮Ob or PC].
   London.
   1. M725: Edition 2-GSGS, 1960.
      Printed by the Hydrographic Department, Admiralty. The First Edition was GSGS 4692 [✢**19**.M.5]. For Editions 3- and 4-GSGS see the next map.
   2. GSGS Misc.1863, overprinted *London District Boundaries,* 1960.

   M725: *Greater London* Special Map.
   1. Edition 3-GSGS, 1967 (issued 1970) (✢11.1).
   2. Edition 4-GSGS, 1971 (✢11.2) [▮NLS].

   GSGS Misc.1522: *Sennybridge Artillery Ranges,* Edition 2, 1958; Edition 3, 1963.
   GSGS Misc.1764: *Catterick Area,* 1957.
   GSGS 4954: *Otterburn / Redesdale All Arms Training Area,* 1965 (✢**18**.M.7).
   GSGS 4965: *Ten Tors Training Area,* ?1965.
   GSGS 4968: *London District Boundaries,* ?1965. Not found.
   GSGS 4976: *Sennybridge Artillery Ranges,* ?1965. Not found.
   GSGS 4987: *Dartmoor Training Areas,* ?1966.
   GSGS 4988: *Glentrool Training Area,* ?1966.
   GSGS 4989: *Cairngorms Area,* ?1966. Not found.
   GSGS 5025: *Stanford Training and Gun Areas,* 1967.
   GSGS 5034: *Glen Affric Training Areas,* 1968.
   GSGS 5065: *Catterick Training Area,* 1969.
   GSGS 5066: *Sennybridge Training Area,* 1969.
   GSGS 5068: *Glen Affric / Strathconon Training Areas,* 1969.
   GSGS 5076: *Catterick and Warcop Training Centres,* ?1969.
   GSGS 5169: *RA Range Hebrides,* 1972 [▮BL]. With an inset of St Kilda.

21. 1:50,000 Map of Great Britain

National Grid series. Published in 204 sheets. Standard sheet coverage 40 by 40 km. The grid is blue on coloured issues. Heading: *Ordnance Survey : 1:50 000 First / Second Series.*

There are insets of Ve Skerries on Sheet 3, Foula, Fair Isle on 4, Auskerry on 5, Stack Skerry, Sule Skerry on 6, Sula Sgeir, Rona on 8, Flannan Isles, Gasker on 13, St Kilda and Boreray, Deasker and Causamul, Haskeir Island on 18, Huskeiran on 22, Fladda-chùain on 23, Mingulay and Berneray on 31, Oigh-sgeir on 39, Isle of May on 59, Milleur Point on 82, Hilbre Islands on 108, Puffin Island on 114, Grassholm Island, The Smalls on 157, Lundy on 180, Isle of Portland on 194, Isles of Scilly, Wolf Rock and Bawden Rocks on 203.

A. First Series

Produced from 1953-72 revision. Publication of all sheets was never intended, merely an interim issue based on photographically enlarged one-inch *Seventh Series* [✢**20**] material prior to the appearance of the 1:50,000 *Second Series* [✢B]. 153 sheets, 5-7, 21, 26-30, 37, 38, 42, 45-63, 67-71, 74-78, 81-84, 89-92, 95-98, 102-114, 116-175, 178-204 were made. Reprints from 1980 may bear the additional designation *Landranger Series.*

A portion of the Borders Region of Scotland south-east of Burnmouth, including part of the East Coast Main Line and the A1 road, was inadvertently missing from the first issue. The area was added as an extrusion to first reprints of Sheets 67 and 75; it formed a permanent part of Sheet 67.

1. Coloured edition, 1974-76. 153 sheets as listed above.

2. *Outline Edition,* 1974-76. 153 sheets as listed above.

3. *Index of,* later *Index to Large Scale National Plans,* 1978- . 100 sheets recorded: 28-30, 57-59, 63, 67, 70, 71, 74-78, 81-84, 89-92, 96-98, 102, 104, 108, 110, 114, 116, 117, 121, 123, 125, 126, 129, 130, 134-142, 144-150, 153-166, 168, 169, 171-175, 178-187, 190-198, 200-204.
   See also *Second Series* [✢B.3]. Further Scottish sheets are probable.

4. Coloured edition, with hill shading, 1980. Sheet 90 was experimentally printed [▮PC].

5. *The Heart of Hardy's Wessex,* 1980. Sheet 196 only [▮PC].
   The Thomas Hardy detail, overprinted in magenta, was printed by Cook, Hammond & Kell and published by Wessex Heritage Tours. With a preface by B. Drewitt.

Geological Survey of Great Britain: for 1:50,000 scale maps see ✢**3**.G.5, G.6, **13**.G.7, G.8.

Military issues

6. M726 coloured edition, 1974-76. 153 sheets as listed above, issued in numbered GSGS editions which continue sequentially on *Second Series* issues [✢B.11].

   The following dependent issues are recorded. It cannot at this stage be determined which sheets were issued in *First Series* and which in *Second.* See *Second Series* [✢B.11] for summary information.
   1. GSGS 5215: *Power Line and Obstruction Overprint.*
   2. GSGS 5235: *RAF Topographic Decca Chart.*
   3. GSGS 5256: *Topographic Dectrac Chart.*

B. Second Series

Produced from 1967-86 revision. Initially designated *Second Series.* Since 1980 maps have carried the additional series title *Landranger Series,* later *Landranger.* Rockall was added as an inset on Sheet 18 in 1984.

1. Coloured edition. All sheets.
   1. Second Series, 1974-80. 91 sheets: 1-4, 8-27, 31-36, 39-44, 64-66, 72, 73, 79, 80, 85-88, 93, 94, 99-101, 104-113, 115, 117-119, 127-129, 131, 132, 139, 141, 150-154, 159, 163, 166, 167, 170, 175-177, 187, 188, 196, 198, 199.
   2. Also designated *Landranger Series,* 1980-88. All sheets.

2. *Outline Edition,* 1974-88. All sheets.

3. *Index of,* later *Index to Large Scale National Plans,* 1978- . 91 sheets recorded: 9, 10, 26, 27, 38, 45, 53, 54, 64-66, 72, 73, 79, 80, 85-88, 93, 94, 99-101, 103, 105-107, 109, 111-113, 115-122, 124, 127-133, 137, 140-144, 150-155, 159, 162-165, 167-171, 174, 176-178, 180, 181, 183-185, 188, 189, 192-195, 197-199, 201-203.
   See also *First Series* [✣A.3]. Further Scottish sheets are probable.

4. Coloured edition, with layers, 1981. Sheet 42 was experimentally printed.

5. Coloured edition, with hill shading, 1995. 3 sheets: 90, 124, 160.
   Sheet 124 was published, the others made available to Consultative Committees.

6. Tourist Map. Coloured on a yellow base, with photographs obstructing mapping.
   The Broads, 1984.

7. One-inch Tourist Maps [Touring Maps] compiled from 1:50,000 *Second Series* mapping.
   1. Coloured with layers and hill shading.
      Dartmoor, 1985 (✣**20**.12.1).
      Lake District, 1988 (✣**20**.12.1). Other editions, 1994, 1998.
      North York Moors, 1982 (✣**20**.12.1). Another edition, 1994.
      Peak District, 1986 (✣**20**.12.1).
      Yorkshire Dales, 1992. Another edition, 1998.
   2. Coloured with hill shading. With contours.
      New Forest, 1985 (✣**20**.12.2).
   3. Coloured on a yellow base.
      Cotswold, 1983. Another edition, renamed *The Cotswolds,* 1997.
      Reprinted with major changes in 1992 in order to extend mapping to include the Chipping Norton area. Around Highworth it was reduced.

Geological Survey of Great Britain: for 1:50,000 maps scale see ✣**3**.G.5, G.6, ✣**13**.G.7, G.8.

8. Maps at scale 1:100,000.
   Lewis and Harris. In two sheets, *(North)* and *(South).*
   The north sheet has insets of Sula Sgeir and Rona, Flannan Isles.
   Uist and Barra. In two sheets, *(North)* and *(South).*
   1. *Solid Geology,* 1981. All 4 sheets.
   2. *Structure* edition, 1983. All 4 sheets.

Soil Survey of England and Wales

9. Coloured edition, 1984-89. 5 sheets: 81, 106, 108, 131, 150.

Soil Survey of Scotland

10. *Land Capability for Agriculture,* 1983. 31 sheets: 12, 21, 26-30, 37, 38, 45, 53, 54, 57-59, 63-67, 70-74, 76, 78, 82-85.

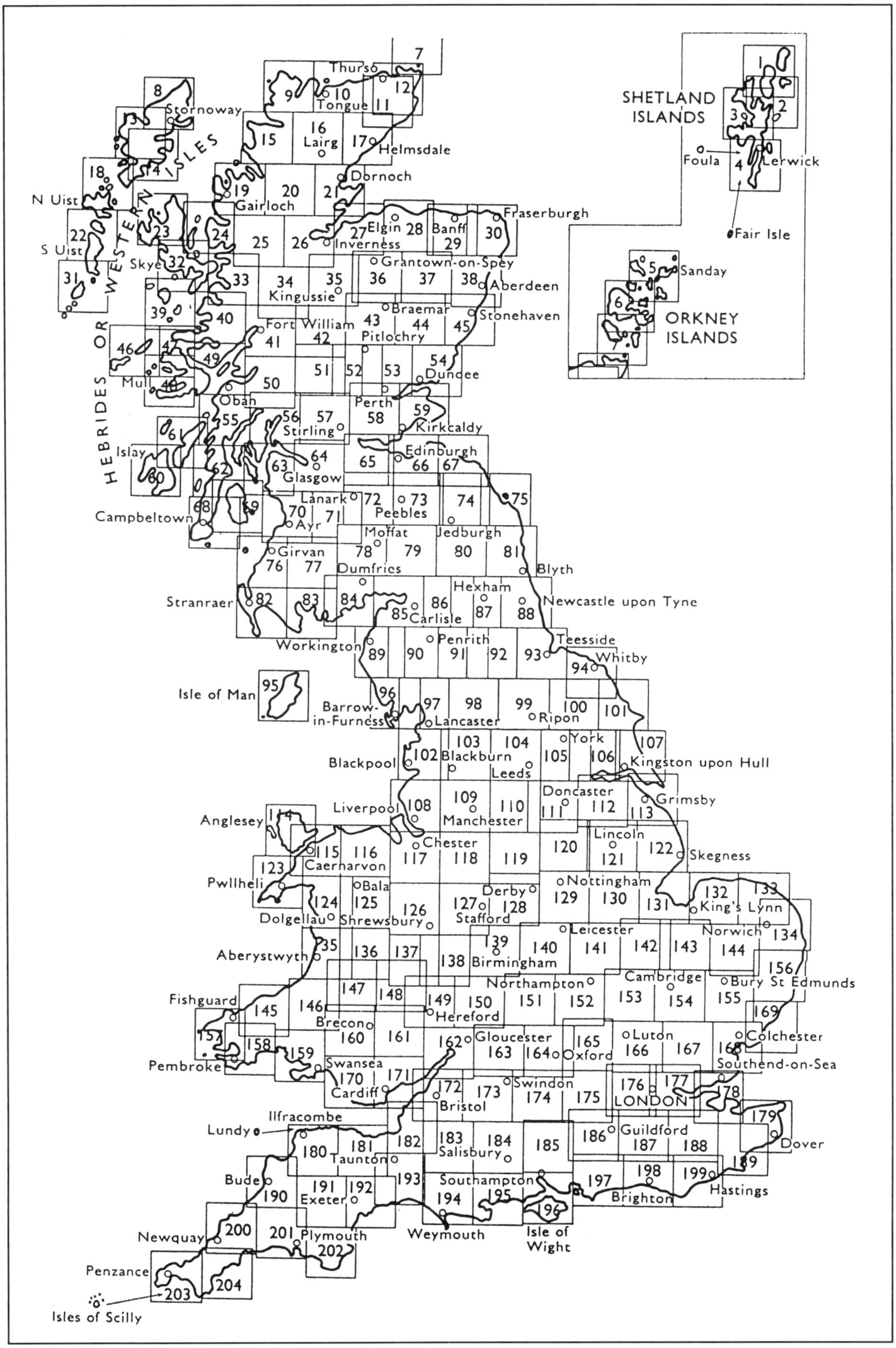

21. 1:50,000 Map of Great Britain

Military issues

11. M726 coloured edition, 1974-88. All sheets.
Issued in numbered GSGS editions in sequence from those in ✣A.6.

The following dependent issues are recorded:

1. GSGS 5215: *Power Line and Obstruction Overprint,* ?1976- . All sheets [▮BL, Wn].
Issue may have started in 1974, but no sheet dated before 1976 has yet been recorded. Overprinted in blue. 34 sheets, 9-12, 15-17, 19-21, 24-26, 33, 34, 40, 41, 71, 72, 73, 76, 78-81, 84-87, 135, 136, 146, 147, 160, are recorded with an additional overprint in magenta for official use only showing the *Limit of 80ft/25m Obstruction Cover Boundary.* These principally cover three areas in Northern Scotland, Northern England, and Wales. An independent legend sheet GSGS 5407 was issued in 1984.
2. GSGS 5215A: *RAF Topographic Decca Chart,* 1983- . 17 sheets.
The use of the GSGS number 5215 suggests that the Decca information is additional to the power line and obstruction overprint.
3. GSGS 5235: *RAF Topographic Decca Chart,* 1975- . 17 sheets.
Various chains.
4. GSGS 5256: *Topographic Dectrac Chart,* 1976- . 13 sheets.
Various chains.
5. GSGS 5295: *United Kingdom Training Areas,* 1980. Sheet [95] *Isle of Man.*
Some fifteen training area maps at scale 1:50,000 are recorded with this GSGS number, but copies of most of them have yet to be located. Furthermore many are special area maps and omitted here on that account.
6. GSGS 5670: *Global Positioning System Training Maps,* 1991. 4 sheets: 80, 86, 173, 174.
With National Grid in blue, overprinted with Universal Transverse Mercator Grid at 1 km intervals in purple constructed on WGS 84 Datum, also with graticule ticks at 1' and intersections at 5' intervals.
7. GSGS 5822: *Great Britain (UTM Grid) 1:50 000,* 1998. Sheet 9.
The National Grid is replaced by Universal Transverse Mercator Grid at 1 km intervals in black. In the top margin is the information that the UTM Grid was constructed on WGS 84 Datum, the geographicals are on OSGB 36 Datum.

Symbols **:** a **bold** number prefixed with ✚ is a cross reference to another section of the book; a number prefixed with ✣ is a cross reference within the current section; a reference number in ( ) at a district map identifies the next, or previous, such map listed with the same sheet lines; the ▮ symbol accompanies a source reference for maps rarely encountered (library sigla are listed on page 241); ❍ warns that there are noted exceptions to the information given in headings; ↑ identifies what is referred to here as War Office marginalia (for a description see page xxii); ❋ refers to the exceptional use of the heading *Ordnance Survey of Great Britain.*

22. One-inch Map of Ireland : First Edition

Surveyed for the six-inch county maps, 1829-42, with some revision to 1858 in the north. Further revision from second edition six-inch maps was incorporated as it became available [see ✣2, 3]. Reduced by pantograph, later by photography, from the six-inch county maps, and constructed on Bonne's Projection on the origin of 53°30'N,8°W. Laid out in 59 full sheets covering 36 by 24 miles, but published in quarters of these sheets covering 18 by 12 miles, in order to increase the pace of production. The original intention of regrouping the quarter sheets into full sheets was never realised, and in October 1858 the 205 small sheets covering land areas were renumbered in the range 1 to 205, the system generally used here. The comparative numbers may be found in the table on page 237. The same sheet layout was used, with variations, for three outline and the coloured editions [**✣22**, **23**, **24**, **25**]. Heading: *Ordnance Survey of Ireland.* The words "First Edition" do not appear.

Sheets 62, 83, 113, 171 have extrusions.

1. Outline edition. All sheets.
   Sheets were published without printed publication dates, in 1856-62 from the dates added in manuscript on the earliest recorded copies. Some 93 sheets initially carried quarter-sheet numbers (see page 237). Prototypes of the four quarters of full Sheet 36 were unused and passed to the Geological Survey of Ireland [✣G.1.1, G.1.2]. A record set includes 63 sheets with the heading *Survey of Ireland,* with space either for *Ordnance* or *Geological* [▮OSI].
   1. Without contours, 1856-62. 203 sheets: 3-205.
   2. With contours. 2 sheets: 1 (1858), 2 (1856).
   3. With contours added after first publication. 14 sheets ?only: 4-6, 9-12, 15, 16, 22-24, 111, 112.

2. Outline edition, revised 1889-90. 2 sheets: 71, 121.
   Revised from second edition six-inch sheets. Reissued with republication dates [✣3].

3. Outline edition, with republication dates. 30 sheets.
   Revised 1888-95 from second edition six-inch sheets.
   1. Without contours, republished 1888-97. 29 sheets: 56, 57, 67-71, 79-82, 89-92, 99-102, 109-111, 119-121, 128-130, 138.
      Sheets 71 [▮RGS], 121 [▮OSI] were earlier issued with revision dates [✣2].
   2. With contours, republished 1895. Sheet 112.

4. Hachured edition, without contours. 204 sheets.
   1. Black hachures (outline and hills engraved in the same plate), 1855-95. 200 sheets: 1-49, 51-135, 137-144, 147-155, 157-205.
      Sheets 1 (1SW), 2 (1SE), 3 (2NW), 9 (2SW) were initially published with quarter-sheet numbers. Sheet 17 was reissued with new hachures in 1869.
   2. Black or brown hachures (outline and hills engraved on separate plates, printed by zincography), 1895. 4 sheets: 136, 145, 146, 156.
      Sheets 136, 146, 156 without hachures are recorded [▮OSI, unpublished].

- For the coloured edition with hachures see **✣24**.A.5.

5. *Dublin (Large Sheet).* District map with hachures, without contours.
   The same title is used in respect of two different sets of sheet lines:
   1. *Sheets 101. 102. 111. & 112. (United by Electrotype),* [no date] ?1862-70 [▮Dtc].
      Undated. Authorised in 1862 and issued while Sir Henry James held the rank of Colonel. The sheet lines are those of the original full sheet 31.
   2. *Sheets 111. 112. 120. & 121. (United by Electrotype),* [no date] ?1891 [▮BL, Ob].
      Undated (BL accession date 1891). James's map was remade twelve miles to the south when Sir Charles Wilson was Director General. The sheet lines were reused in 1940 for Sheet 32 in the combined sheet series [**✣29**].

G. Geological Survey of Ireland

Three base map types were used: the quarters of a prototype full Sheet 36 that the Ordnance Survey discarded and offered to the Geological Survey, the outline edition and the hachured edition. *Geological Survey of Ireland* and *Ordnance Survey of Ireland* headings appear in tandem (the latter is lacking on Sheet 36). It is probable that as first issued Sheets 119-121, 128-130, 137-139, 147-149, 156-159, 165-170, 176-181, 183, 186-197, 200-205 (ie sheets dated if not published in 1858 or earlier) might have carried quarter-sheet numbers. See the list on page 237.

The Survey's original intention was to publish sheets showing solid geology without drift, and the quarters of "full" Sheets 36, 41, 47, 53 were first engraved in that style. However the decision was taken in 1856 to add the chief drift deposits, and the sheets printed earlier were scrapped. Thereafter most one-inch standard editions show drift in addition to solid geology. The words "With Glacial Drift" actually appeared in the 1901 Geological Survey catalogue, but they were removed again in 1902. A purpose made Drift Series began in 1902, coincident with the introduction of colour printing.

1. Solid edition. Hand coloured. All sheets.
   1. On experimental outline originals, without drift, 1853. 4 sheets: 36NW, 36NE, 36SW, 36SE. Not found.

      Exhibited to the Geological Society of Dublin in December 1853, and, with the solid geology fully engraved, at the British Association for the Advancement of Science meeting at Liverpool in September 1854.
   2. On experimental outline originals, showing drift, 1855 (published 1856). 4 sheets: 120 (36NW), 121 (36NE), 129 (36SW), 130 (36SE).
   3. On standard outline originals, 1856-77. 139 sheets: 21, 29, 36-38, 47-50, 61, 72, 74-119, 122-128, 131-205.

      Ten sheets, with quarter-sheet numbers 41NW, 41NE, 41SW, 41SE, 47NW, 47NE, 47SW, 47SE, 53NW, 53NE, were initially engraved without drift geology, but any stock was probably destroyed before issue.
   4. On hachured originals, 1874-90. 65 sheets: 1-36, 39-46, 51-60, 62-71, 73.

      This total includes new editions of Sheets 21, 29, 36 [✣G.1.3]. The new edition of Sheet 36 was published in 1876. Sheets 21 and 29 may have been transferred to the hachured base at the same time, but they are as yet unrecorded before their 1883 editions with revised geology.
   5. Published in new dated editions. 3 sheets: 8 (1907); 34, 58 (1913).
   6. *Re-edited* publications (ie changes in colouring or nomenclature), 1913-14. 39 sheets: 14, 24, 31-33, 44-46, 161, 171-178, 182-189, 191-201, 203-205.
   7. Revised editions. 121 sheets recorded: 24, 29, 31, 32, 36-38, 46-50, 57-61, 67-72, 78-82, 88, 90-92, 101, 102, 111, 112, 114, 115, 117, 118, 120-149, 151, 152, 154-159, 161-170, 172-201, 203-205.

      Many of these sheets were revised more than once. This list excludes sheets which were revised but which are already listed in the above categories.
   8. *Reprinted for the Government of Northern Ireland,* 1965-69. 4 sheets recorded: 20, 24, 27, 60.

2. *Drift Series,* 1902. Sheet 112 *Dublin* only. Colour printed in Dublin.

   Sheet 120 *Naas* was proved in 1935, but not published [▮GSI].

3. District maps. *Drift Series.* Colour printed in Southampton.

   Belfast District, 1904.
   Cork District, 1905.
   Limerick District, 1906.
   Londonderry District, 1908.

4. *Killarney and Kenmare District.* District map, colour printed in Southampton.
   1. *Solid Geology,* 1922.
   2. *Drift Geology,* 1922.

5. All sheets were available uncoloured. Those still available are printed by photolithography with Government of Ireland copyright.

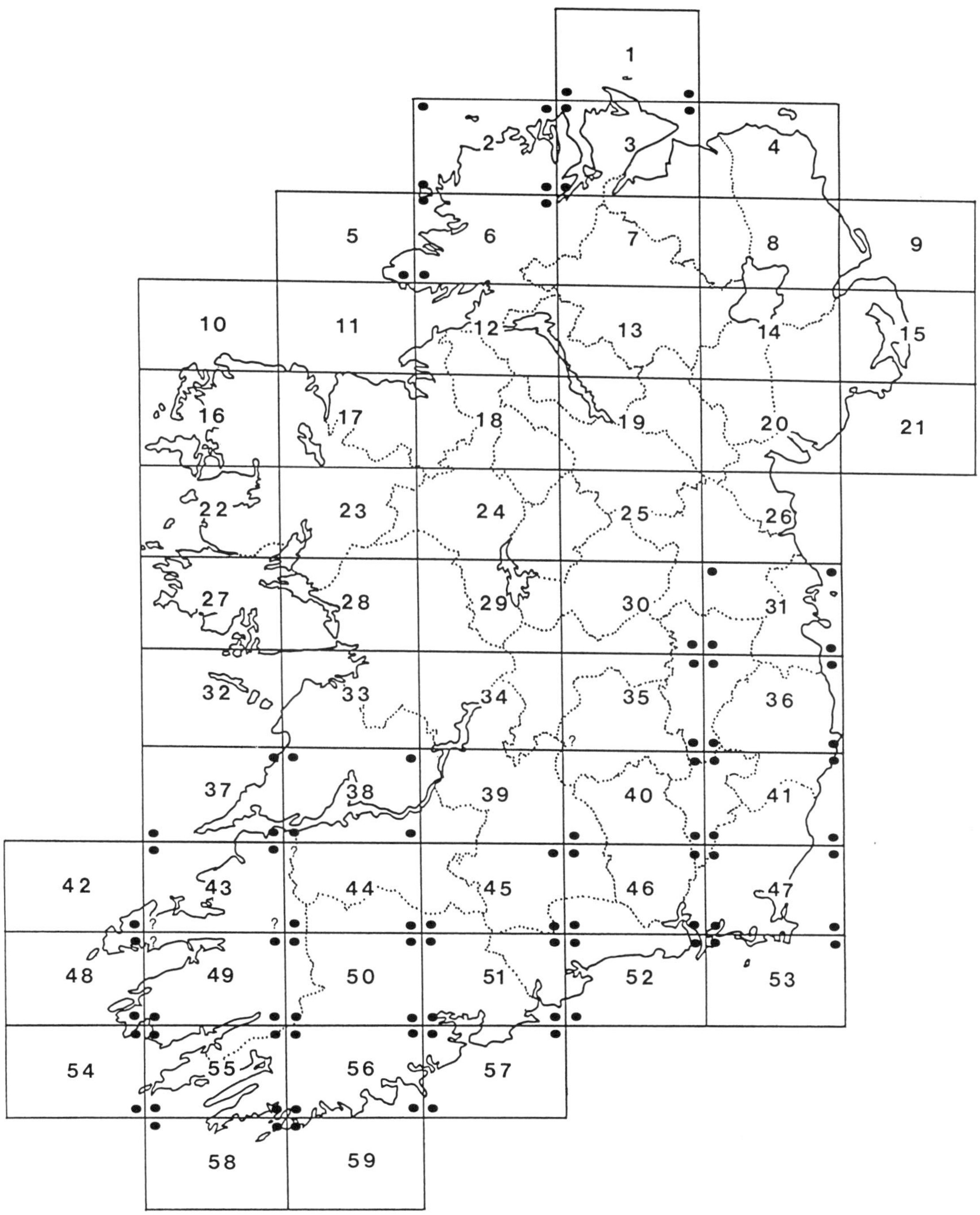

Sheets marked • were issued with quarter-sheet numbers
For the 205 small-sheet layout see diagram 23

22. One-inch Map of Ireland : First Edition, with the original numbering in full sheets

Geological Survey of Northern Ireland

After partition in 1922, Geological Survey of Ireland maps remained available in the north, some being *reprinted for the Government of Northern Ireland* [✣G.1.8, **✣69**.5]. The Geological Survey of Northern Ireland was set up in 1947 and began production in 1961 using one-inch *Popular Edition* or *Third Series* [**✣31**, **32**] mapping, still on the 205-sheet layout, with Irish National Grid. Publication was incomplete when the 1:50,000 scale was adopted. The sheet list offered here ignores the base mapping used.

One-inch mapping

6. Solid edition, 1961-68. 5 sheets: 7, 8, 29, 35, 36.

7. Drift edition, 1961-68. 5 sheets: 7, 8, 29, 35, 36.

8. All published sheets were available uncoloured.

1:50,000 mapping

It is planned to complete coverage of Northern Ireland in a further 37 sheets in 30: 11, 12/6pt, 13, 14, 17-21, 24-28, 32/31, 33, 34, 37/38pt, 44/56/43, 45-49, 57/58pt, 59/58pt, 60, 61, 70, 71/72. Sheets 11 and 21 have solid and drift editions on the same sheet of paper.

9. Solid edition, 1978- . Publication continues.

10. Drift edition, 1978- . Publication continues.

11. All sheets will be available uncoloured.

12. District map. Solid edition.
    Mourne Mountains, 1978.

23. One-inch Map of Ireland : Second Edition

Published [as ✣**22**] in 205 sheets. Produced from the first national revision of 1898-1901. Heading: *Ordnance Survey of Ireland*. The words "Second Edition" do not appear.

Sheets 62, 83, 113, 171 have extrusions.

A. Ordnance Survey issues

1. Outline edition, without contours, 1899-1902. All sheets.

2. Outline edition, reissued with contours, 1899-1902 (published 1908-19). 204 sheets: 1-126, 128-205.
   Sheets where there was no *Third Edition* equivalent [✣**25**.1, **25**.2] and which after 1922 covered the Irish Free State were kept in print by the Ordnance Survey of Ireland. Various production methods were used - engraving, litho- or zincography, then finally photolithography, with Government of Ireland copyright.

3. Hachured edition in brown, without contours, 1899-1900 (printed 1903). 3 sheets recorded: 136, 145, 146 [▮OSI].
   Used in the making of an Ordnance Survey of Ireland office record set of hill sheets. Published copies have not been recorded.

4. Hachured edition in brown, with contours, 1899-1902 (published 1909-11). 49 sheets recorded: 2, 6-8, 12-14, 18-21, 28, 142, 149-152, 159-166, 170-177, 183-188, 190-192, 194-196, 200-202, 205.
   Of the 37 sheets listed in OSPR 9/09, nine, 182, 190-192, 197-99, 203, 204, were apparently not published. However, Sheets 190-192 were at least printed [▮OSI]. The others have not been found.

5. Outline edition, with county, rural and urban district boundaries, 1900-03. By zincography. 203 sheets in 202: 1/2, 3-49, 51-196, 198-205.
   Sheet 198 has 197 as an unattributed extrusion. On reprint it is numbered Sheet 198/197. Sheets 71 and 72 were combined on reprint. These adjustments altered the total of sheets to 204 in 201. Reissues updated as far as 1939 are recorded, some on *Third Edition* base maps [✣**25**.4). Original issues are without contours. Contoured base maps are sometimes used for later printings.

6. *1" provisional edition for military purposes only.* None recorded.
   In outline with contours in red. An alpha-numeric system is added to the graduated border. Complete coverage of Ireland may have been required in this series, in which case Second Edition sheets must have existed where *Third Edition* coverage was lacking [see ✣**25**.5].

- For the coloured edition with hachures see ✣**24**.A.1, A.2.

7. District maps. Outline with coloured main roads. Without contours. With a simple border graduated at 10' intervals.
   Belfast, 1902.
   Cork, 1902 (altered on reprint to 1904).
   A *Cork District Manoeuvre Map,* 1901 may have been related (not found).
   Dublin and Vicinity, 1901 [▮PC].
   Prepared for the use of Officers. No civilian use of this map is recorded. The border is graduated at 5' intervals.
   Killarney, 1902 (altered on reprint to 1906).
   Wicklow (✣B.1).
   1. Published 1902, printed 1903 in Dublin.
   2. Published in Southampton, 1906.

B. Ordnance Survey of Ireland issues, from 1922

See also ✣A.2, A.5.

1. *Wicklow* district map (✣A.7, B.2).
    1. Outline edition, with contours and coloured main roads, 1938 [▮Dtc].
    2. *Nature's Gift to Greater Dublin : Water, Light, Power - and a 5.000 acre Mountain Lake!* 1936 [▮Dtf].

        An outline map without contours, overprinted in blue at the Sign of the Three Candles Ltd. Published in May 1936 by the Dublin and Wicklow Mountains Planning Movement.

With an alpha-numeric squaring system

2. District maps. Coloured with layers.

    Dublin District, 1950. Other editions, 1954, 1960.

    Wicklow District, 1948 (✣B.1).

    The mapped detail shifted by about a millimetre in relation to the 1938 map.

    Wicklow District, 1949. With altered sheet lines. Other editions, 1950, 1954.

With Irish National Grid

3. District maps.
    1. Maps not on Irish National Grid sheet lines: coloured with layers.

        Cork District, 1957. With altered sheet lines.

        Killarney District. With altered sheet lines.
        1. With magenta grid, 1956.
        2. With black grid, 1960.
    2. Maps on Irish National Grid sheet lines: coloured with layers.

        Cork District, 1967. With updated reprints.

        Dublin District, 1966. With updated reprints.

        Killarney District, 1968. With updated reprints.

        Wicklow District, 1966. With updated reprints.
    3. Map at scale 1:50,000 on Irish National Grid sheet lines: coloured.

        Wicklow Way, 1981.

M. Military issue

1. District map. Coloured edition (roads, water, woods, contours).

    Curragh Area, 1938 [▮Dtc].

    A full sheet map (36 by 24 inches) covering the area of Sheets 119, 120, 128, 129, overprinted in red with a two-inch numeric squaring system unique to the map (00 to 18 west to east, 00 to 12 south to north). With a neat line border.

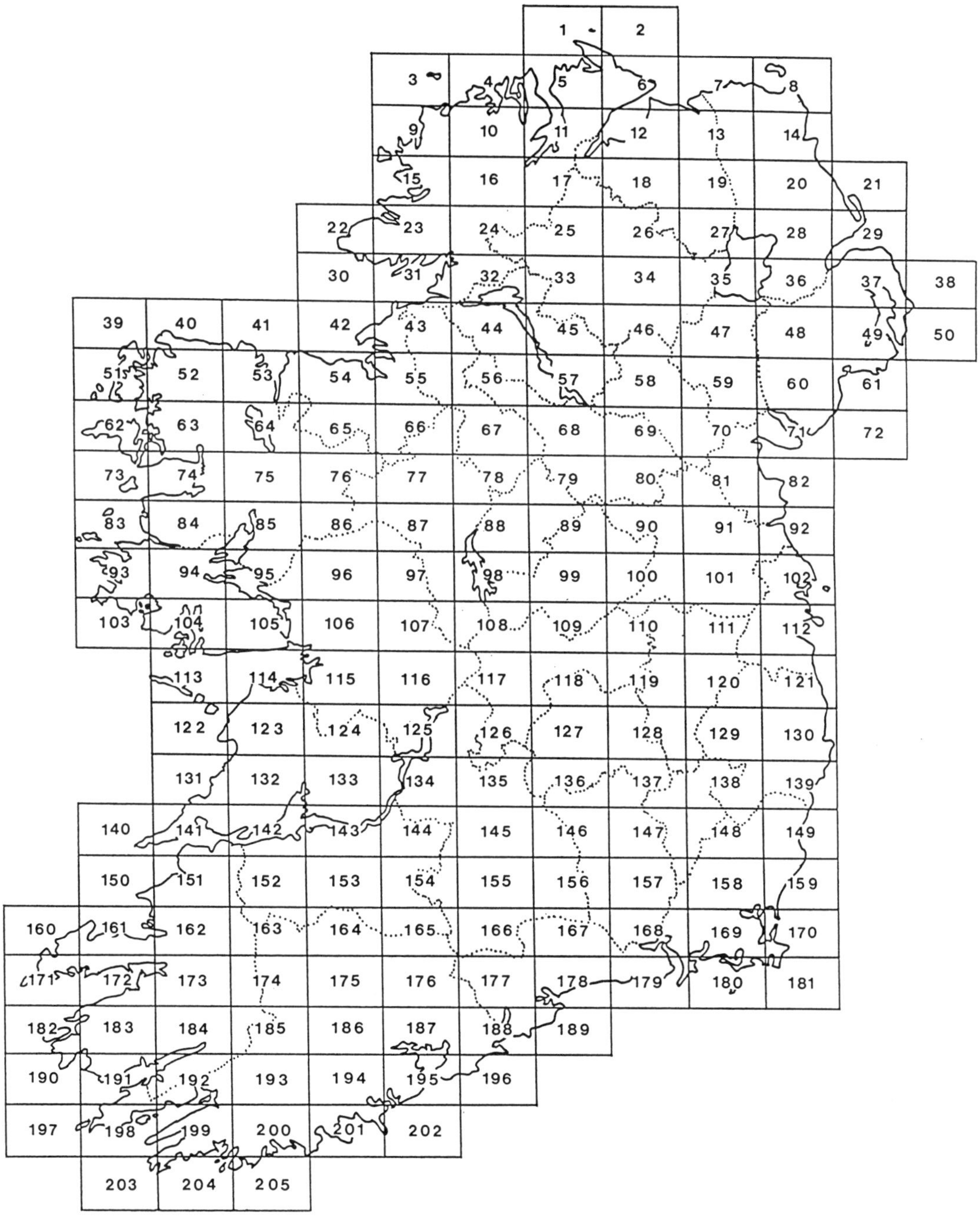

23. One-inch Map of Ireland : Second Edition

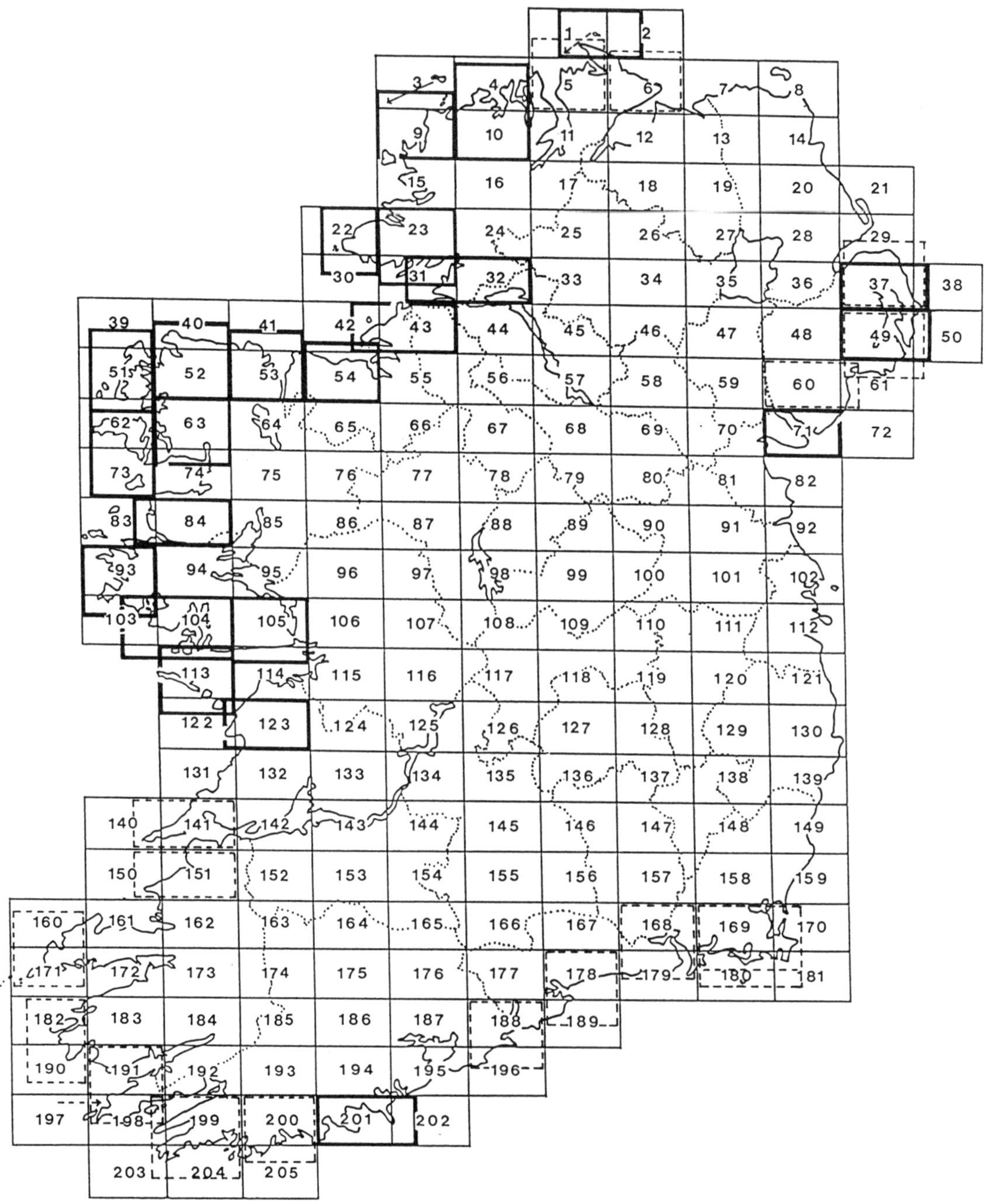

Sheets combined on publication are shown in bold
Sheet combinations rearranged on reissue are indicated by pecked lines

24. One-inch Map of Ireland, in colour

24. One-inch Map of Ireland, in colour

Laid out [as ✥**22**] in 205 sheets, reduced on publication to 187 as a consequence of sheet combinations. Further sheets were combined when reissued. Initially with a graduated border, from 1902 with an alpha-numeric border, the width of which was reduced from a half-inch to a quarter-inch in 1905 (see page xxiii). All sheets were produced from the first national revision of 1898-1901; on reissue some sheets were produced from the second national revision of 1908-14 [see ✥A.3]. All editions are coloured, with hachures but without contours, unless noted otherwise. Heading: *Ordnance Survey of Ireland.*

Sheets combined on publication: 1/2, 3 [inset]/9/15pt, 4/10, 22/30, 23/31pt, 32/31pt, 37/38, 40/52, 41/53, 43/31pt/42pt, 49/50, 54/42pt, 62pt/39/51, 62pt/73, 71/72, 74pt/63, 83pt/84, 93/103pt, 104/103pt/113pt, 105/114pt, 113/122pt, 122/123, 201/202.

Sheets 15, 74, 83, 114 were also published independently.

A. Ordnance Survey issues

1. Coloured edition, with hachures. With a graduated border, 1902. 16 sheets: 99-102, 109-112, 118-121, 127-130.

   Printed from transfers to stone. Issues of Sheets 101 [▮Mg, OSI], 119 [▮BFq], 129 [▮Dtf] dated 1901 are recorded, perhaps made for military purposes. Without alpha-numeric system, though 1919 reprints of Sheets 115, 120, 155 have graduated borders to which alpha-numeric systems were added [see ✥A.2.2, A.2.3]. For Sheet 36 in similar style see ✥A.3.2. The sixteen 1902 sheets were all remade in ✥A.2 style.

2. Coloured edition, with hachures. With an alpha-numeric border. All 205 sheets in 187 as described above.

   This total was later reduced to 205 sheets in 170, as described in ✥A.2.4, A.2.5. All sheets in this section were produced from the first national revision; for those produced from the second national revision see ✥A.3.

   1. With a half-inch border, *Printed at the Ordnance Survey Office, Southampton,* 1902-05. 65 sheets in 60: 1/2, 5-8, 11-14, 17-21, 25-29, 33-36, 37/38, 45-48, 49/50, 57-61, 65-70, 71/72, 76-82, 86-92, 186, 187, 194, 195, 201/202. Sheet 47 was reprinted in 1934 [▮NYp].
   2. With a half-inch border, *Printed from transfers to stone,* 1902-05. 109 sheets in 104 recorded: 40/52, 62pt/39/51, 62pt/73, 74, 74pt/63, 83, 83pt/84, 93/103pt, 94-99, 104/103pt/113pt, 105/114pt, 106-108, 112, 113/122pt, 114-119, 121, 122/123, 124-128, 130-185, 188-193, 196-200, 203-205.

      Eight sheets, 99, 112, 118, 119, 121, 127, 128, 130, first listed in ✥A.1 were remade and published in new editions here.
   3. With a quarter-inch border, 1905-07. 79 sheets in 72 recorded: 3/9/15pt, 4/10, 15, 16, 22/30, 23/31pt, 24, 32/31pt, 33, 34, 41/53, 43/31pt/42pt, 44, 54/42pt, 55, 56, 64, 75, 79, 85, 89, 90, 100-102, 109-112, 120, 121, 129-134, 136, 138, 139, 142-149, 152-154, 157-159, 161, 162, 164, 166, 167, 172-174, 183-187, 192-195, 201/202.

      Reissues carrying the new quarter-inch border (see page xxiii) may be identified from previous listing in ✥A.2.1, A.2.2. They usually carry new publication dates. A further eight sheets, 100-102, 109-111, 120, 129, first listed in ✥A.1 were remade and published in new editions here.
   4. Sheets first listed in ✥A.2.1, A.2.2 combined on reissue, 1906-08: 60/61pt, 140/141, 150/151, 160/171, 168/179, 169/170/180/181, 178/189, 182/190, 188/196, 191/197 [inset]/198pt, 199/203/204/198pt, 200/205.
   5. Sheet combinations first listed in ✥A.2.1, A.2.4 rearranged on reissue, 1906-08: 1/5, 2/6, 37/38/29pt, 49/50/61pt, 169/170/180/181.

      Sheets 1/5 and 2/6 superseded 1/2, 5, 6. Sheet 1/5 has an inset of Inishtrahull. Sheet 169/170/180/181 [✥A.2.4] was reduced by two miles in the south in 1908. Sheet 29 continued to be published separately.

3. Coloured edition, with hachures.
   Sheets in this section were produced from the second national revision, 1911-12. The appropriate *Third Edition* headings are lacking. The 1914 publication dates present on sheets in ✣A.3.2, A.3.3 are those of the outline originals.
   1. With a quarter-inch alpha-numeric border, 1913. Sheet 129 [▮Dtc].
   2. With a graduated border, 1914 (published 1919). Sheet 36 [▮Dtc].
      The graduated border contains an alpha-numeric system. All the borders of this type so far recorded first appear on 1919 printings [see ✣A.1].
   3. With an alpha-numeric squaring system, 1914 (published 1932). Sheet 60/61pt.
      Copy ▮OSNI. With contours in brown. The publication date offered is that of the earliest known printing.

4. Coloured edition, with contours in brown.
   Without hachures. Printed at Crabwood, presumably for the Ordnance Survey of Northern Ireland as a temporary expedient before the issue of *Popular Edition* Sheets 6 and 9 in 1948-49 [**✣31**.B].
   1. *Provisional Edition,* 1945. Sheet 35 recorded [▮RGS].
   2. Without edition heading, 1945. Sheet 47 recorded [▮RGS].

5. Coloured edition, with hachures, 1890 (issued c.1897). Sheet 129 recorded [▮Dtc].
   Made in advance of the first national revision. The black plate derives from **✣22**.2.1. The map was apparently a prototype for ✣A.1. With an alpha-numeric border, and route mileages to the nearest furlong.

6. Outline edition, with brown hachures, 1905. 2 sheets recorded: 118, 119 [▮Dtf].
   By ?lithography. With a simple border, and legend redesigned as for the sheets with a quarter-inch border in ✣A.2.3. The purpose of this issue has yet to be established.

7. District maps. Coloured with hachures.
   1. With a half-inch border. Without contours.
      The Curragh District, 1903 (?✣B.2).
      Dublin District.
         With an inset of Lambay Island.
         1. *Manoeuvre Map, 1904,* 1904.
            This is a manoeuvre map with no overprint.
         2. Published for civilian use, 1904. Reprinted five times to 1918.

   2. ?With a half-inch border. With contours.
      Manoeuvre Map, 1904 : Dublin District, 1904 (?**✣26**.4). Not found.
         Described in Nicholson (1988) as being with contours, but without military overprint. Other details including source are unconfirmed. The "slightly different sheet lines" to those of the other *Dublin District* [✣A.7.1] noted by Nicholson was probably a two-mile extension north lettered "X" above the "A" row of the alpha-numeric system, which may be the explanation of this curious feature of the 1918 map [**✣26**.4].

   3. With a simple border. Without contours.
      Maryborough - Carlow, 1905 [▮RGS].
         This map was not listed in Ordnance Survey catalogues, and was presumably made for military purposes.

   4. With a quarter-inch border. With contours in red.
      Belfast District, 1912.
         Sheet lines are identical to those of Sheet 17 in the proposed *Third Edition* : large sheet series, a sheet which in the event was not published [see **✣26**]. The specification approaches more closely than any other Irish map that of the *Third Edition (Large Sheet Series)* of England and Wales [**✣8**].

B. Ordnance Survey of Ireland issues, from 1922

Reprints, often revised, as required of sheets in ✣A.2 covering the Irish Free State.

1. Coloured edition, with hachures. 85 sheets in 65 recorded.
   Sheets lacking the original date of revision are in ✣B.1.1, unless second printings are recorded which carry second national revision dates.
   1. With first national revision dates or lacking date of original revision, 1938- . 49 sheets in 41 recorded: 2/6, 4/10, 11, 43/31pt/42pt, 55, 56, 58, 64, 67-69, 71/72, 73/62pt, 75, 80, 81, 92, 93/103pt, 94, 98, 99, 104/103pt/113pt, 105/114pt, 110-112, 113/122pt, 114, 116, 117, 121, 125, 130, 134, 136, 155, 161, 173, 175, 186, 192.
      Sheet 121 is the only sheet so far recorded that was reprinted before the Second World War, in 1938.
   2. Sheets headed *Third Edition,* 1945- . 4 sheets in 3 recorded: 174, 187, 200/205.
      The 1899 revision date on Sheet 200/205 is incompatible with *Third Edition* status.
   3. With second national revision dates, without *Third Edition* heading, 1946- . 33 sheets in 22 recorded: 1/5, 70, 101, 131, 140/141, 142, 143, 147, 148, 150/151, 153, 160/171, 162, 164, 166, 168/179, 169/170/180/181, 173, 184, 185, 191/197/198pt, 201/202.
   4. With revised road classification. 7 sheets in 5 recorded: 4/10, 94, 142, 143, 201/202.
      Classified roads are in red.

2. District map.
   The Curragh District, 1926 (?✣A.7.1). Documented but not found.

Symbols : a **bold** number prefixed with ✚ is a cross reference to another section of the book; a number prefixed with ✣ is a cross reference within the current section; a reference number in ( ) at a district map identifies the next, or previous, such map listed with the same sheet lines; the ▮ symbol accompanies a source reference for maps rarely encountered (library sigla are listed on page 241); ❍ warns that there are noted exceptions to the information given in headings; ↑ identifies what is referred to here as War Office marginalia (for a description see page xxii); ❁ refers to the exceptional use of the heading *Ordnance Survey of Great Britain.*

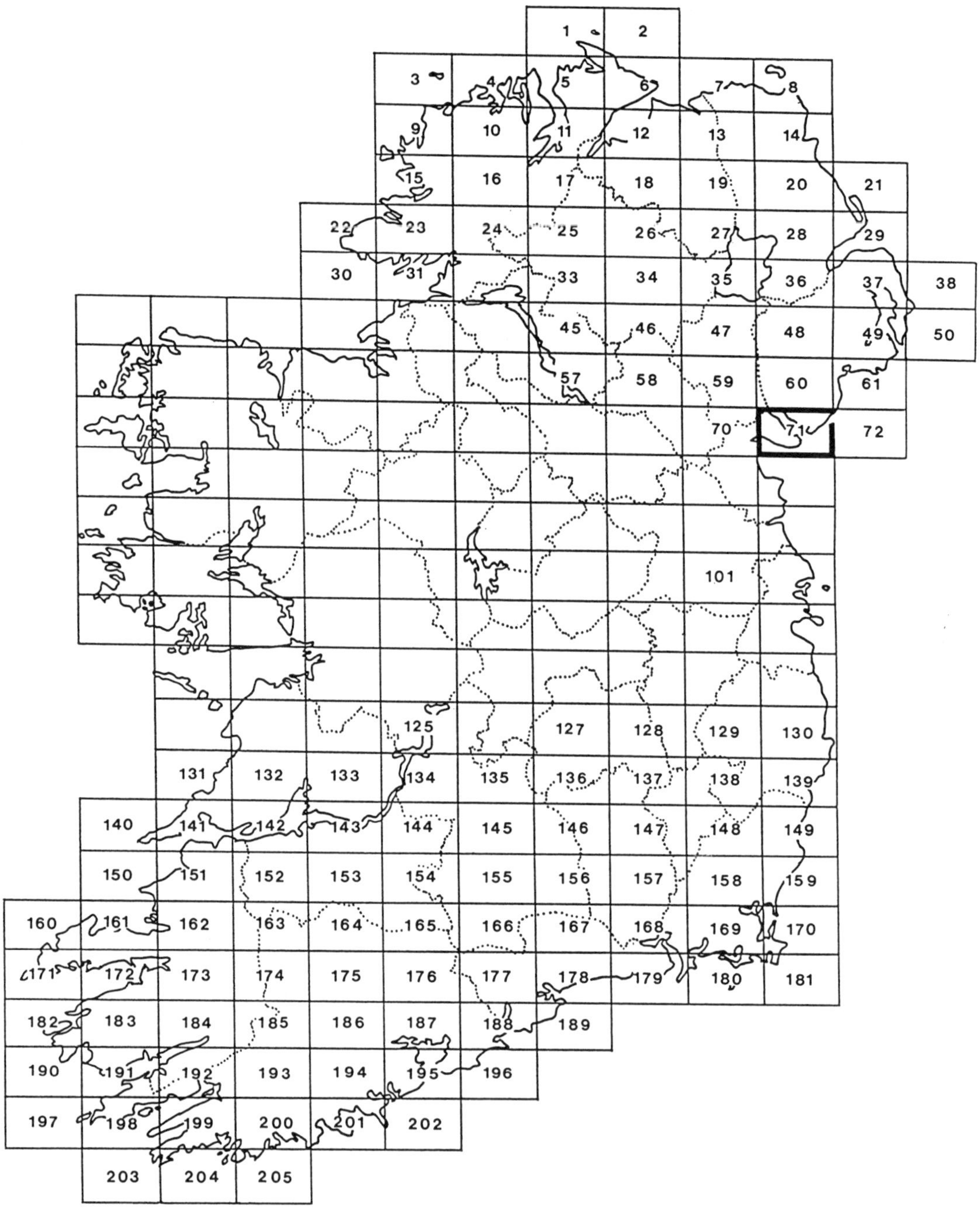

Sheets combined on publication are shown in bold

25. One-inch Third Edition Map of Ireland

25. One-inch Third Edition Map of Ireland

Laid out [as ✣**22**] in 205 sheets, to be reduced to 204 by the combination of Sheets 71 and 72. Produced from the second national revision of 1908-14 (abandoned). The edition was discontinued after the issue of 132 sheets in 131, 1-31, 33-38, 45-50, 57-61, 70, 71/72, 101, 125, 127-205. Heading, where present: *Ordnance Survey of Ireland,* usually followed by *(Third Edition).* Sheet 171 has an extrusion.

1. Outline edition, with contours, 1909-17 (published 1910-17). By engraving. 129 sheets in 128 recorded: 1-31, 34, 35, 37, 38, 46-50, 57-61, 70, 71/72, 101, 125, 127-205.
   Engraved issues of Sheets 33, 36, 45 are not recorded [see ✣2.1], though 36 is listed in OSPR 3/15, 33 and 45 in OSPR 5/15. Sheet 101 was printed [▮OSI] though probably not published. Two copper plates survive, dated 1916 and 1917 [▮Dna].

2. Outline edition, with contours. By litho- or zincography.
   1. Issues so far unrecorded as engraved maps. 4 sheets: 33, 36, 45, 1914-15 (publication date unknown) [▮Dtf]; 101, 1917 (published by 1927).
      See ✣1. Sheet 101 is first recorded on 1927 indexes produced by the Ordnance Survey of Ireland but so far no pre-war issue of this sheet has been recorded. After 1922 the sheets in ✣1 covering both Northern Ireland and the Irish Free State were kept in print. Various production methods were used - engraving, litho- or zincography, then finally, in Ireland, photolithography. The last known printing of a Northern Ireland sheet is Sheet 47, reprinted in 1942 in Crabwood [▮Dtf].
   2. Northern Ireland issues *printed in Southampton, 1924.* 19 sheets recorded: 6-8, 11-14, 17, 18, 20, 21, 24-27, 34, 35, 46, 47.

3. Hachured edition in brown, with contours, 1909-12 (published 1910-12). 50 sheets: 2, 156-176, 178-205.

4. Outline edition, with county, rural and urban district boundaries. 11 sheets recorded: 9, 12, 17, 25, 31, 48, 57, 153, 182, 188, 205 [▮Dtf].
   See ✣**23**.A.5. These are reissues updated as far as 1939 on *Third Edition* base maps.

5. *1" provisional edition for military purposes only,* 1915. ?All sheets. 4 sheets recorded: 49 [▮PC]; 129, 166 [▮Dtf]; 187 [▮Dtc].
   In outline with contours in red. An alpha-numeric system is added to the graduated border. If complete coverage of Ireland was achieved, Second Edition sheets must have existed where *Third Edition* coverage was lacking [✣**23**.A.6].

- For coloured editions see ✣**24**.A.3.

M. British military issues overprinted with War Office Irish Grid in purple

1. Outline edition, with contours. 2 sheets recorded: 7, 19 [▮BFq, both defective].
   The extent of coverage, date and GSGS number, if any, are all uncertain.

- For the use of Sheets 8 and 47 in GSGS 3917 see ✣**27**.

2. District maps.
   ?*Bantry Bay,* 1925. Not found and not confirmed.
      A 1925 publication date survives on GSGS 3943 *Bantry Bay* [see next].
   GSGS 3943: *Bantry Bay,* 1934. Outline edition [▮DGI].
      The eastern sheet line corresponds with that of Sheet 199; the others were plotted on metric grid lines. For the other sheet in GSGS 3943 see ✣**26**.M.2.
   ?*Londonderry,* 1924. Not found and not confirmed.
      A 1924 publication date survives on *Londonderry* in GSGS 3917 [see ✣**27**.1].

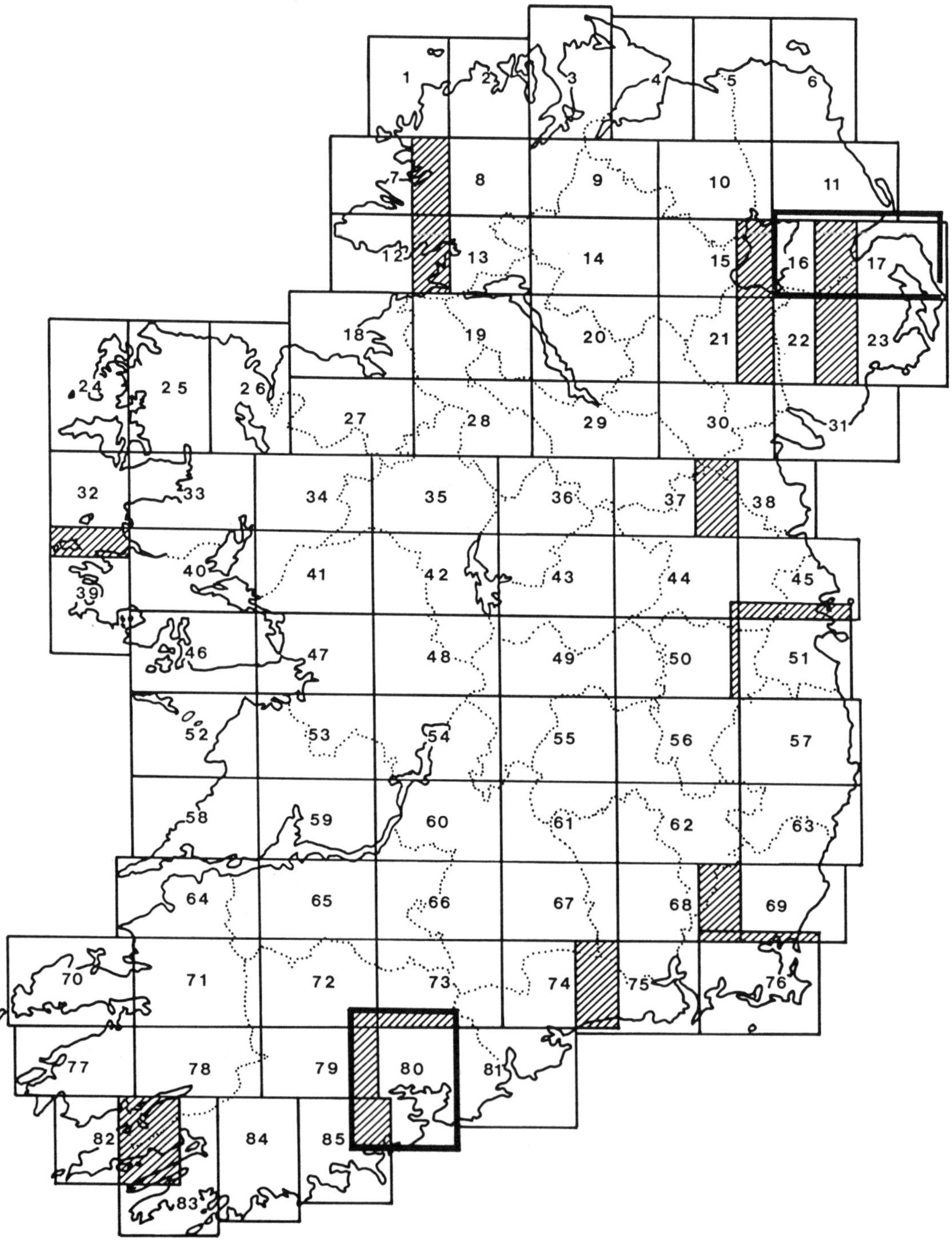

26. One-inch Third Edition Map of Ireland : large sheet series

26. One-inch Third Edition Map of Ireland : large sheet series

Constructed on Bonne's Projection on the origin of 53°30'N,8°W. Proposed in 1906 in 88 sheets, by 1920 laid out in 85, as shown here. This number would have been reduced by sheet combinations. Standard sheet coverage was to be 27 by 18 miles, four sheets covering the area of one half-inch sheet [✢**39**] or nine one-inch small sheets [✢**25**]. None were issued with these dimensions. Sheet 17 would have had the same sheet lines as *Belfast District,* 1912 [✢**24**.A.7.4]. Publication was discontinued after the issue of three sheets in two, 16/17 *Belfast,* 80 *Cork.* Ordnance Survey indexes show *Dublin District* as identical with Sheet 51, which is erroneous since *Dublin District* extends some two miles more to the north but one mile less to the south than the limits of Sheet 51. Produced from the second national revision of 1908-14 (abandoned). For the map border see page xviii. Heading: *Ordnance Survey of Ireland,* originally followed by *(Third Edition).* The words "large sheet series" do not appear.

With an alpha-numeric border

1. Coloured edition, with layers, hachures and contours, 1918. Sheet 80 *Cork.*
   A squaring system was added to some copies of the map [see ✢3]. Kept in print by the Ordnance Survey of Ireland without sheet number, probably until 1957.

2. District map. Coloured with layers, hachures, contours and hill shading.
   Killarney District, 1913.
   Kept in print by the Ordnance Survey of Ireland, probably until 1956.

With an alpha-numeric squaring system

3. Coloured edition, with layers, hachures and contours, 1918 (published 1918-19). 3 sheets in 2: 16/17 *Belfast,* 80 *Cork* [▮Dtc].
   See ✢1. Sheet 16/17 was reprinted for the Ordnance Survey of Northern Ireland in 1927 and 1931; it was revised as Sheet 7 in the *Popular Edition* in 1937 [✢**30**].

4. District map. Coloured with layers, hachures and contours.
   Dublin District, 1918 (?✢**24**.A.7.2).
   The 1898 revision date is unchanged from that on the known *Dublin District* map in ✢**24**.A.7.1. The *Third Edition* heading may reflect the product of the second national revision of 1914 in the Sheet 101 area. With an inset of Lambay Island. Maintained in print by the Ordnance Survey of Ireland until 1950.

M. British military issues overprinted with War Office Irish Grid in purple

1. Military edition. ?3 sheets in 2: ?16/17 *Belfast* (?1927), 80 *Cork* (1925). Not found.
   Sheet 80 was gridded in 1924. The existence of Sheet 16/17 is suggested by the survival of a 1927 magnetic variation date as part of the military overprint in ✢**27**.1.

2. GSGS 3943 outline edition (black plate only), 1934. Sheet 80 *Cork* [▮Ob].
   For the other sheet in GSGS 3943 see ✢**25**.M.2.

- For the use of Sheet [16/17] *Belfast* (1931) in GSGS 3917 see ✢**27**.1.

Irish military issues overprinted with 5000 yard grid in red

3. Coloured edition, with layers, hachures and contours, 1940. Sheet [80] *Cork* [▮Dtc].

- No district maps are recorded, though *Dublin District* at least is possible.

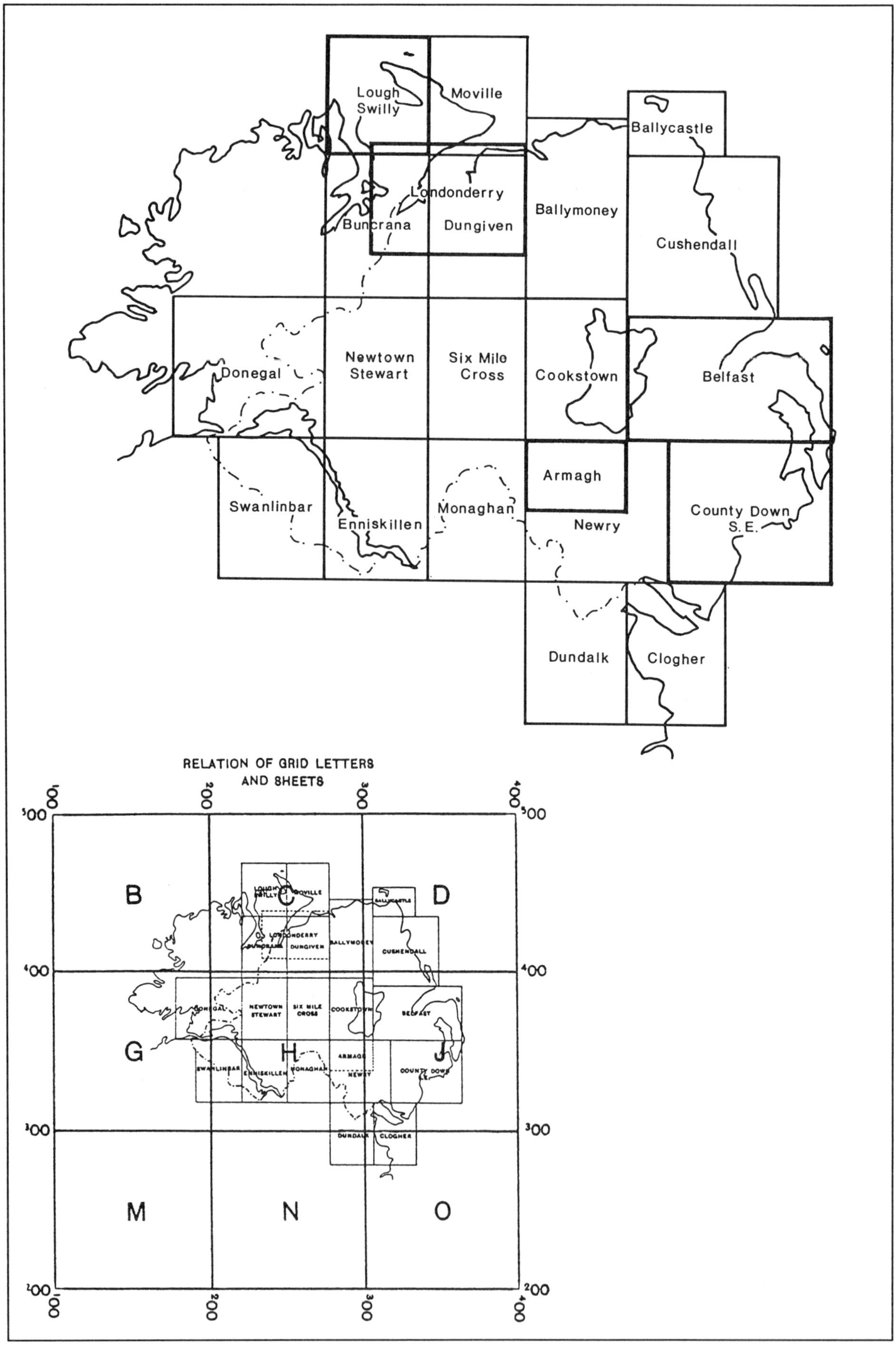

27. One-inch Military Map of Ireland

27. One-inch Military Map of Ireland

Constructed on Bonne's Projection on the origin of 53°30'N,8°W. The 1932-34 map comprised 21 multiform sheets, all but one derived from the 205-sheet map of Ireland [see **✚25**]. The exception is *Belfast* (Sheet 16/17 in the *Third Edition* : large sheet series [**✚26**]), and is the sheet which constitutes the nucleus of the sheet layout. The five coloured sheets were issued first, effectively as district maps. Coverage of Northern Ireland was completed by sixteen outline sheets in conjunction with three of the coloured sheets, leaving two of them, *Armagh* and *Londonderry,* presumably redundant. Except for *Londonderry* and *Belfast,* sheet lines which did not correspond with those of the one-inch 205-sheet series were plotted on metric grid lines. Only *Belfast* has a map border beyond the neat line. With War Office Irish Grid overprinted in purple. *Third Edition* [**✚25**] material was used where possible.

1. GSGS 3917 coloured sheets.
   1. With coloured water, roads, and contours, 1931-32 (issued 1932). 5 sheets: *Armagh, Belfast, County Down SE, Londonderry, Lough Swilly* [▮Ob].

      Sheet numbers are lacking on these sheets. *Londonderry,* a unique sheet on independent sheet lines covering twenty-eight miles by nineteen, carries the publication information *Printed at the Ordnance Survey Office, Southampton in 1924,* which may imply an earlier issue [**✚25**.M.2]. *Belfast* has a 1927 magnetic variation diagram as part of the military overprint, which may be evidence of a military issue that year [**✚26**.M.1]. *Lough Swilly* has the sheet lines of Sheet 1/5 in **✚24**.A.2.5, though extended north in order to place Inishtrahull in its correct geographical location. *Londonderry* and *Armagh* [47] were wholly duplicated by outline coverage. The contour plates had been made for the 1915 military map [**✚25**.5].
   2. With coloured water and roads, 1931 (issued 1939). *Belfast* [▮DGI].

      Contours are no longer coloured, though they remain on the black plate.

2. GSGS 3917 outline sheets, 1934. 41 sheets in 16: 2/6 *Moville,* 8 *Ballycastle,* 11/17 *Buncrana,* 12/18 *Dungiven,* 13/19/7pt *Ballymoney,* 14/20/21/28pt/29pt *Cushendall,* 24/32/23pt/31pt *Donegal,* 25/33 *Newtown Stewart,* 26/34 *Six Mile Cross,* 27/35 *Cookstown,* 44/56/43pt *Swanlinbar,* 45/57 *Enniskillen,* 46/58 *Monaghan,* 47/59/48pt/60pt *Newry,* 70/81 *Dundalk,* 71/72/82 *Clogher* [▮Ob].

   The sheet numbers relate to those of the one-inch 205-sheet map of Ireland. Sheet 2/6 *Moville* has the sheet lines of Sheet 2/6 in **✚24**.A.2.5, though extended north in order to pair with *Lough Swilly* [✢1.1].

There is evidence in OSR 1940-41 that the series was revived for wartime use when coverage of the entire island was apparently required by the War Office. The report notes in the section *War Work* : *Revision of existing maps,* under GSGS 3917, "small sheet series 160 sheets" (ie about the number required to cover the Irish Free State) and, more mystifyingly, "'2nd Edition' 24 sheets". There is further evidence in GS[GS] OR 5189 *Index to Ireland* dated 1940 which shows the half-inch series GSGS 4127 [**✚39**.M.2] and the one-inch GSGS 3917. This classifies as GSGS 3917 the complete 205-sheet one-inch layout of Ireland. However no such mapping has been located, though it is possible that the two (unfortunately defective) sheets recorded in **✚25**.M.1 are somehow related. The same section in OSR 1940-41 has an additional entry for the 76 sheets of GSGS 4136 [**✚28**], all of which were issued in 1940, the first five sheets in July, so it is possible that there was a change of policy which caused work on GSGS 3917 to be abandoned.

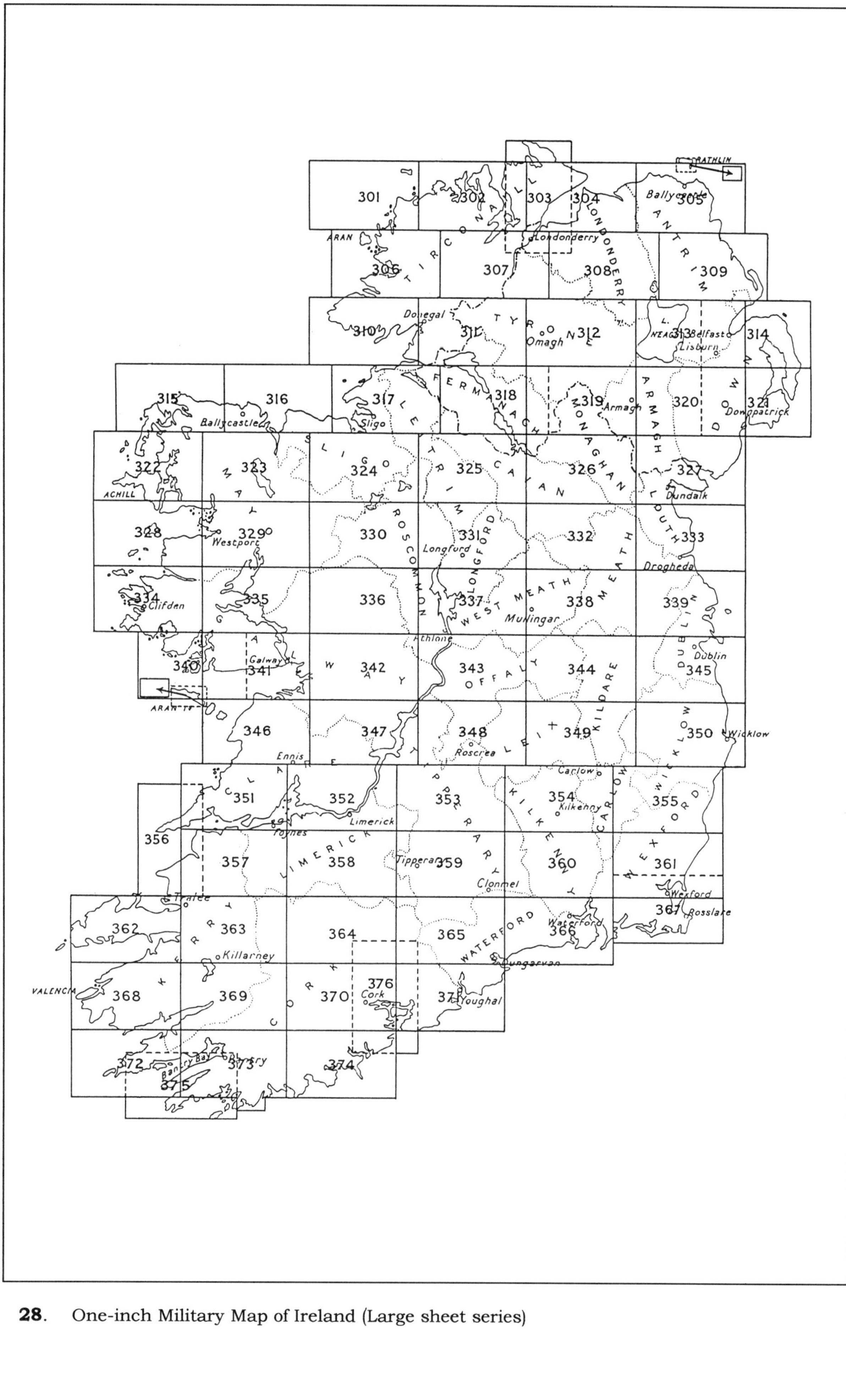

28. One-inch Military Map of Ireland (Large sheet series)

28. One-inch Military Map of Ireland (Large sheet series)

Issued in 76 sheets on War Office Irish Grid sheet lines. The sheets are numbered in the range 301 to 376, presumably in order to avoid confusion with the numbering of the 205-sheet map of Ireland [see **✣25**]. Standard sheet coverage 50 by 30 km. Some sheet lines are common with those of the quarter-inch map GSGS 4338 [**✣71**]. Created where possible from *Third Edition* [**✣25**] source material. With War Office Irish Grid in black, numbered in red.

There are insets of Rathlin Island on Sheet 305, Inishmore on 340. Sheet 376 was presumably produced to provide coverage of Cork Harbour on a single sheet. Sheets 350 and 355 between them fail to cover Ardnore Point. The Blasket Islands are not covered in this series.

1. GSGS 4136: [First Edition], outline with contours in black, 1940. All sheets.

2. GSGS 4136: Second Edition, with contours in black. All sheets.
   Several sheets lack Second Edition publication information. A *Diagram of grid reference letters* was added.
   1. With classified roads in red, woods in green, 1941. All sheets.
      Eight sheets, 309, 313, 317, 320, 321, 325-327 are recorded with road classification revised to 10 July 1941, two, 312, 376, to 1 November 1941.
   2. With classified roads in red, and layers, 1941. 51 sheets: 303-305, 307-309, 311-314, 317-321, 324-327, 330-333, 336-339, 342-345, 347-350, 352-355, 358-361, 364-367, 370, 371, 374, 376.
   3. With classified roads in red, woods in green, and layers, 1941. 51 sheets: 303-305, 307-309, 311-314, 317-321, 324-327, 330-333, 336-339, 342-345, 347-350, 352-355, 358-361, 364-367, 370, 371, 374, 376.

3. GSGS 4136: Third Edition. All sheets.
   Several sheets lack Third Edition publication information. The contours present on the black plate are overprinted in orange, with additional values above 1000 feet interpolated. Road classification information as at 1 January 1942 is shown.
   1. With coloured roads, woods, inland water and contours, 1942. All sheets.
      24 sheets, 301-316, 318-321, 324-327, are recorded as reprinted in 1952-54; ten sheets, 322, 323, 328, 329, 333, 339, 345, 350, 351, 355, are recorded as reprinted in 1959.
   2. Coloured as ✣3.1, with layers, 1942. 51 sheets: 303-305, 307-309, 311-314, 317-321, 324-327, 330-333, 336-339, 342-345, 347-350, 352-355, 358-361, 364-367, 370, 371, 374, 376.
      Sheets 313 and 314 were reprinted in 1962.
   3. With bogs overprinted in purple, 1942-43. All sheets.
      Northern Ireland was overprinted in 1942 when United States armoured forces were stationed there. Coverage of the Irish Free State was completed in 1943. Border sheets may be reprinted to incorporate the additional information.
   4. With training areas overprinted, 1943. 17 sheets: 304, 305, 307-309, 311-314, 317-321, 325-327.
      Two editions dating from 1943 were produced covering Northern Ireland only.

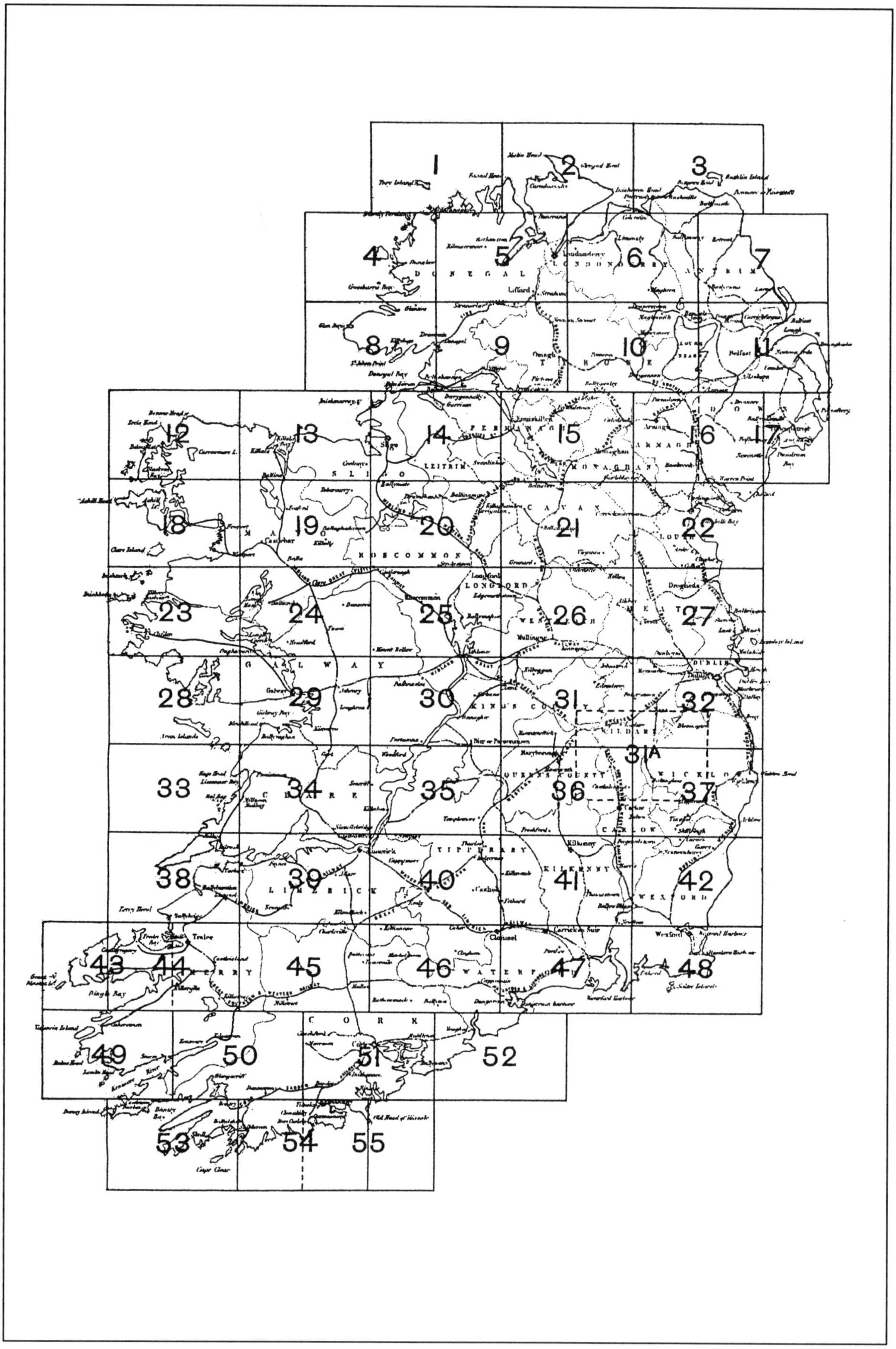

29. One-inch Military Map of Ireland : combined sheet series

29. One-inch Military Map of Ireland : combined sheet series

Constructed on Bonne's Projection on the origin of 53°30'N,8°W. Proposed in 54 and issued by the Ordnance Survey of Ireland in 55 sheets, each covering the area of four sheets of the 205-sheet map (presumably a mixture of *Third Edition* [✚**25**] and Second Edition [✚**23**]) in a system twelve miles south of the original 1855 full-sheet layout. District maps are recorded, sometimes numbered bearing an *A* suffix. Standard sheet coverage 36 by 24 miles. With Irish 5000 yard grid in red. With a neat line border. Sheet numbers and titles are overprinted in red. For Irish military use only. Identified as the *Combined One Inch Map* in the adjoining sheet diagrams on the military edition of the half-inch map [✚**39**.M.3].

1. Outline edition, with contours in black, 1940-41. All sheets.
   The fact that all sheets were indeed issued is supported by documents in file G2/X/0351 [▮Dm]. A March 1941 document headed *OS Map of Ireland 1" to 1 mile - Military Edition - Large Sheets incorporating 4 Sheets of Standard size* reveals that "The Ordnance Survey have now completed the above map which has all detail printed in Black and the 5000 yard grid in Red. The entire country is covered in 55 sheets." The eight sheets so far recorded are: 27 *Drogheda,* 29 *Galway,* 31 *Tullamore,* 32 *Dublin,* 36 *Tipperary,* 39 *Limerick,* 47 *Waterford,* 51 *Cork* [▮Dm]. Sheet 32 coincidentally has sheet lines identical with the later of the two versions of *Dublin (Large Sheet)* [✚**22**.5.2].

2. District maps recorded.
   1. Sheet 31A is a special map covering the Curragh district. Not found.
   2. Two untitled contiguous sheets covering the Shannon estuary and Limerick. They are coloured, including contours. The eastern sheet was reissued in 1942 with hachures. It was numbered Sheet 39A and entitled *Limerick Areas* [sic] [▮Dm].

Symbols **:** a **bold** number prefixed with ✚ is a cross reference to another section of the book; a number prefixed with ✣ is a cross reference within the current section; a reference number in ( ) at a district map identifies the next, or previous, such map listed with the same sheet lines; the ▮ symbol accompanies a source reference for maps rarely encountered (library sigla are listed on page 241); ❍ warns that there are noted exceptions to the information given in headings; ↑ identifies what is referred to here as War Office marginalia (for a description see page xxii); ❂ refers to the exceptional use of the heading *Ordnance Survey of Great Britain.*

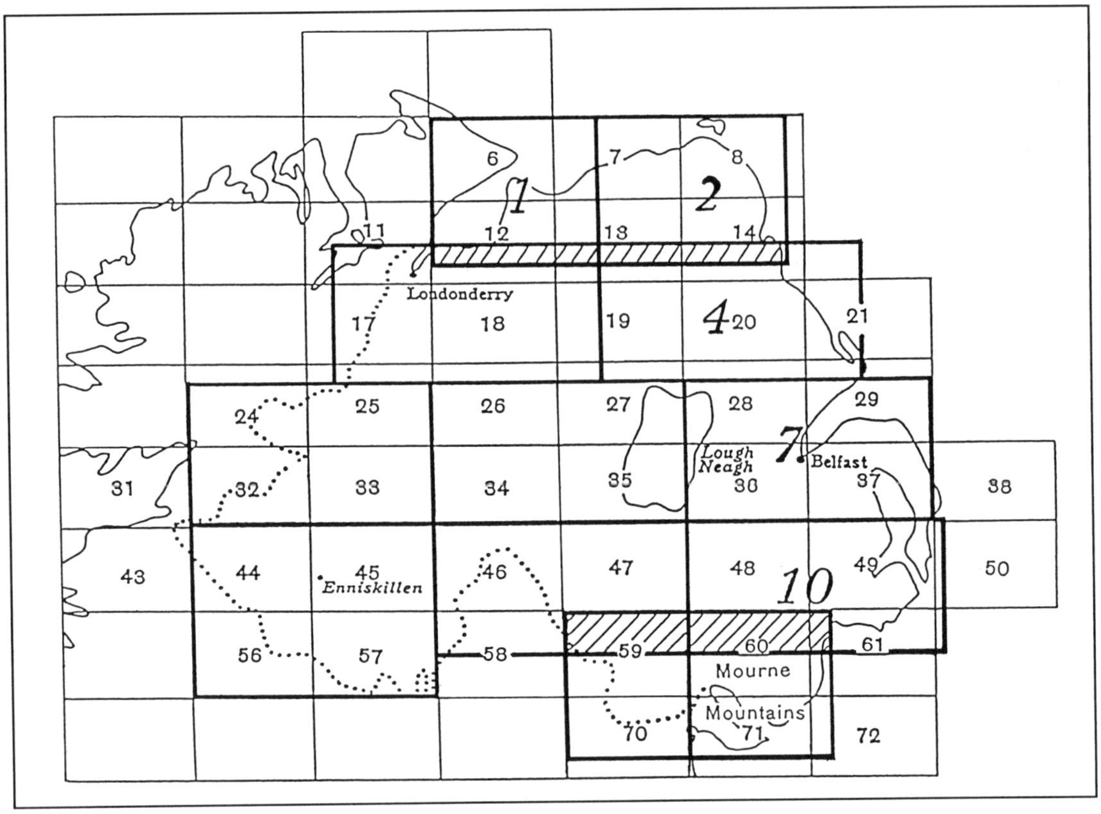

30. One-inch Popular Edition Map of Northern Ireland (1)

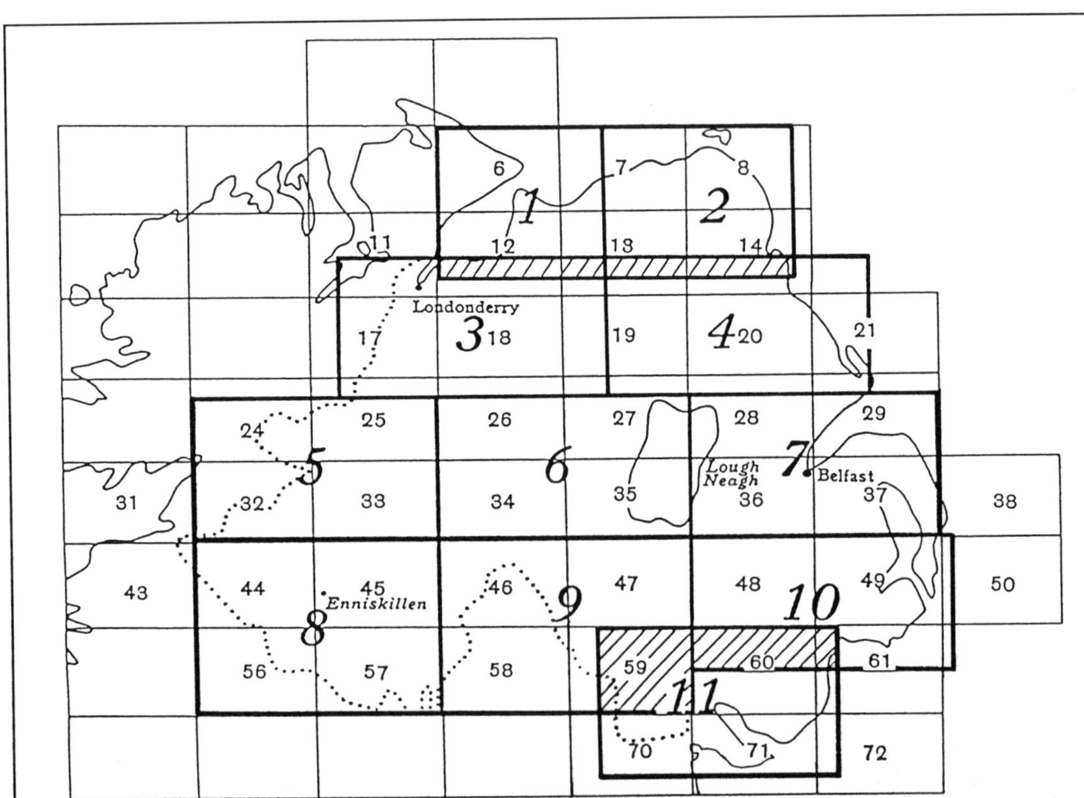

31. One-inch Popular Edition Map of Northern Ireland (2)

30. One-inch Popular Edition Map of Northern Ireland (1)

Constructed on Bonne's Projection on the origin of 53°30'N,8°W. Laid out in twelve sheets. As with **✣27** the one sheet (Sheet 7) already in existence was taken as the nucleus of the sheet layout. Four further numbered sheets, 1, 2, 4, 10, were published or in preparation when the decision was taken in about 1939 to adopt a revised layout in eleven sheets, wherein part of the original Sheet 11 and *The Mourne Mountains* district map (putatively Sheet 12) were combined as an enlarged Sheet 11. At the same time Sheet 9, apparently originally plotted to the same north-south sheet limits as Sheet 10, was enlarged to the same limits as Sheet 8. These developments are reflected in the adjoining sheet diagrams on Sheets 1, 2, 4. The war held up further progress: when it resumed the Irish National Grid was adopted for all further new and most reprinted sheets [**✣31**]. Produced from 1935-38 revision; *Third Edition* mapping was used [**✣25**]. For the map border see page xviii. Heading: *Ordnance Survey of Northern Ireland : One-inch Popular Edition.*

Sheet 7 has sheet lines identical to Sheet 16/17 in the *Third Edition* : large sheet series Map of Ireland [**✣26**]. Sheet 12 was to be the 1935 *Mourne Mountains* district map [✣4]. The various versions of the *Diagram shewing position of the Map in relation to sheets of the new Popular Edition* that appear in sheet margins of this and the next edition [**✣31**] should be used with caution. Sheet 9 suffers in that some diagrams continue to show it even in the 1950s as having the same height as Sheet 10 when on publication it has identical dimensions to Sheet 8. Sheet 10 is invariably depicted as having the same width as Sheet 7. The *Diagram shewing position of the Map in relation to the 1910 1" Series* is also sometimes erroneous.

With an alpha-numeric squaring system

1. Coloured edition, with layers, 1937. Sheet 7.
   Reprinted in 1944 and 1948, then again with Irish National Grid [**✣31**.4].

2. Outline edition, with water in blue, 1937. Sheet 7.
   Reprinted in 1944, then again with Irish National Grid [**✣31**.5].

3. *Land Utilisation Survey,* 1947. Sheet 7.
   Published by the Land Utilisation Survey of Northern Ireland. See also ✣7, **✣31**.3.

4. *The Mourne Mountains* district map.
   The intention to number the map Sheet 12 in the *Popular Edition* was never fulfilled.
   1. Coloured edition, with layers, 1935. Reprinted 1947.
   2. Outline edition, with water in blue, 1935 (published 1947) [▮OSNI].

With an alpha-numeric border

The adjoining sheet diagrams of Sheet 10 in ✣5, 6 show a twelve-sheet layout, otherwise an eleven-sheet layout is shown.

5. Coloured edition, with layers, 1938-39 (published 1939-40). 4 sheets: 1, 2, 4, 10.
   All sheets were reprinted during the war years. Post-war reprints of Sheets 2 and 10 were equipped with the Irish National Grid [**✣31**]; Sheets 1 and 4 (reprinted 1951 and 1950) were not.

6. Outline edition, with water in blue, 1938-39 (published 1939-40). 4 sheets: 1, 2, 4, 10.
   Sheets 2 and 4 were reprinted during the war years. Post-war reprints of Sheets 2 and 10 were equipped with the Irish National Grid [**✣31**].

7. *Land Utilisation Survey,* 1947-48. 4 sheets: 1, 2, 4, 10.
   Published by the Land Utilisation Survey of Northern Ireland. Irish Free State / Republic of Ireland areas are not coloured. See also ✣3, **✣31**.3.

31. One-inch Popular Edition Map of Northern Ireland (2)

Construction and origin of mapping are as in ✠**30**, though with the revised layout in eleven sheets wherein Sheet 9 as apparently originally plotted was enlarged, and a new Sheet 11 was created from part of the original Sheet 11 with Sheet 12. For the publication of Sheets 1, 2, 4, 7, 10 with alpha-numeric systems see ✠**30.** The Irish National Grid was adopted in 1948 for all further new and most reprinted sheets. First this appeared in the border only, then as a grid at 10 km intervals and finally at 1 km intervals. Produced from 1935-38 revision. For the map border see page xviii. Heading: *Ordnance Survey of Northern Ireland : One-inch Popular Edition* (by 1958 *One-inch Popular Map*).

Sheets 8 and 9 cover the same areas as Sheets 44, 45, 56, 57 and 46, 47, 58, 59 of the 205-sheet one-inch map of Ireland [✠**25**].

- Sheets 1, 2, 4 have adjoining sheet diagrams showing the eleven-sheet layout of this map, but for ease of reference they are listed in ✠**30** with the other sheets with alpha-numeric borders. They were in preparation at the same time, and published by 1940.

With Irish National Grid in the border only, measured at 1 km intervals

1. Coloured edition, with layers. 8 sheets.
   1. *Provisional Edition,* 1948-50. 6 sheets: 3, 5, 6, 8, 9, 11.
   2. Pre-war issues, reprinted ?1949. 2 sheets: 2, 10 [✠**30**.5].

2. Outline edition, with water in blue. 8 sheets.
   1. *Provisional Edition,* 1948-50. 6 sheets: 3, 5, 6, 8, 9, 11.
   2. Pre-war issues, reprinted ?1949. 2 sheets: 2, 10 [✠**30**.6].

3. *Land Utilisation Survey,* 1948-51. 6 sheets: 3, 5, 6, 8, 9, 11.
   Published by the Land Utilisation Survey of Northern Ireland. Irish Free State / Republic of Ireland areas are not coloured. See also ✠**30**.3, **30**.7.

With Irish National Grid at 10 km intervals

4. Coloured edition, with layers. 2 sheets.
   1. Produced from 1951 revision, 1953. Sheet 7.
   2. Pre-war issue, again reprinted c.1954. Sheet 2 [✠1].

5. Outline edition, with water in blue. 2 sheets.
   1. Produced from 1951 revision, 1953. Sheet 7.
   2. Pre-war issue, again reprinted c.1954. Sheet 2 [✠2].

6. *Belfast Regional Plan.*
   Outline maps in grey, with overprinted information.
   1. *Land Use (1960),* 1963. Sheet 7.
   2. *Recreation,* 1963. Sheet 7.
   3. *Development Limitations (Belfast Urban Area),* 1963. Sheet 7.

With Irish National Grid at 1 km intervals

Produced from 1953-55 revision.

7. Coloured edition, with layers, 1956-58. 2 sheets: 10, 11.

8. Outline edition, with water in blue, 1956-58. 2 sheets: 10, 11.

Geological Survey of Northern Ireland: for *Popular Edition* mapping see ✠**22**.G.6, G.7.

32. The One-inch Map (Third Series) of Northern Ireland

Irish National Grid series. Published in nine sheets. Standard sheet coverage 60 by 40 km. Mapping derives from *Popular Edition* material [✚**31**] and was produced from 1953-62 revision. Heading: *Ordnance Survey of Northern Ireland : The One-inch Map (Third Series).*

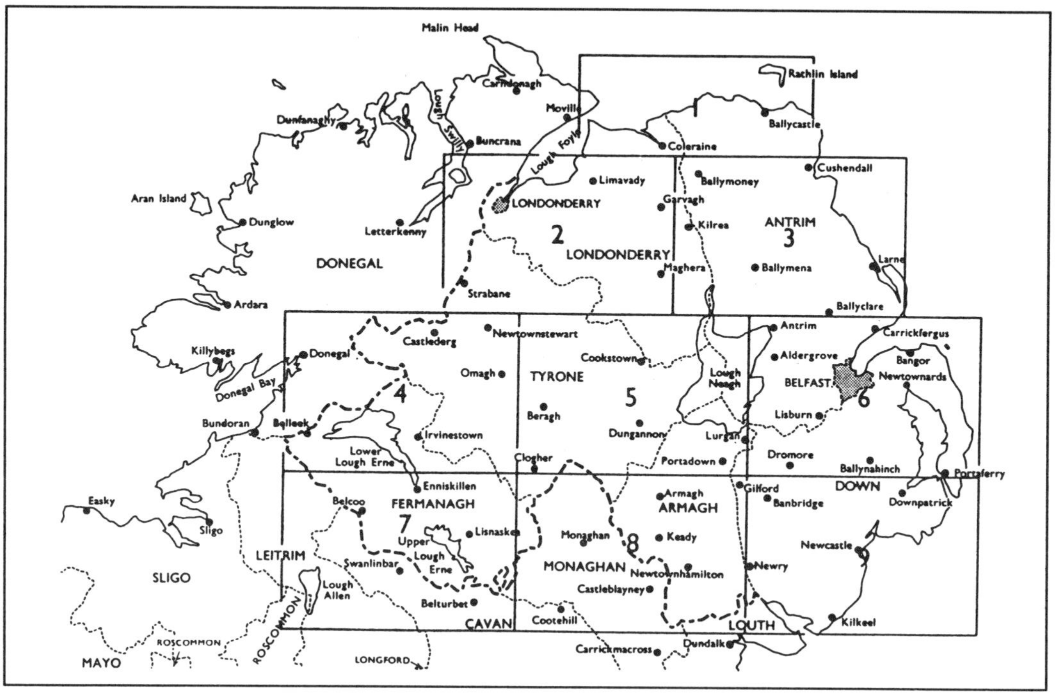

1. Coloured edition, with layers, 1960-64. All sheets.

2. Outline edition, 1960-64. All sheets.

Geological Survey of Northern Ireland: for *Third Series* mapping see ✚**22**.G.6, G.7, G.9, G.10.

M. Military issues overprinted with Irish National Grid co-ordinates ○

Grid values are overprinted in magenta, from ?1980 in red.

1. M723 coloured edition, with layers. All sheets.
   1. Edition 1-GSGS, 1965. All sheets.
   2. Edition 2-GSGS, 1967-69 (issued 1967-70). All sheets.
   3. Edition 3-GSGS, 1971-80. 5 sheets recorded: 1, 3, 6, 8, 9.
   4. Edition 4-GSGS, 1975-80. 3 sheets recorded: 1, 3, 6 [▮Wc].

   The following dependent issues are recorded:
   5. GSGS Misc.2057 coloured edition, with layers, 1965. 4 sheets: 1, 3, 5, 6 [▮Ob]. Without military overprint.
   6. GSGS 5102: *Royal Ulster Constabulary Divisional [& Subdivisional] Boundaries,* 1970. All sheets [▮NLS].
   7. GSGS 5102A. Not recorded.
   8. GSGS 5102B: *Bigram and Ward Boundaries,* 1978. All sheets [▮NLS]. These are in addition to the Royal Ulster Constabulary boundaries.
   9. GSGS 5135: *Topographic Decca Chart Northern Ireland,* 1969-71. All sheets.
   10. GSGS 5149: *Topographic Dectrac Chart Northern Ireland,* 1971. All sheets [▮Ob].
   11. GSGS 5249: *Helicopter Chart Northern Ireland,* ?1976. ?All sheets.
   12. GSGS 5383: *Topographic Decca Chart Northern Ireland,* 1982. All sheets.
   13. GSGS 5385: *Topographic Decca Chart Northern Ireland,* 1982. All sheets.

33. 1:50,000 Map of Ireland (1)

Irish National Grid series. Laid out in 89 sheets, of which nineteen were published by the Ordnance Surveys of Ireland and Northern Ireland before the decision in 1988-89 by Dublin to make adjustments to their sheet lines [see ✣34]. Standard sheet coverage 40 by 30 km. Newly drawn. The Irish National Grid is blue on coloured issues.

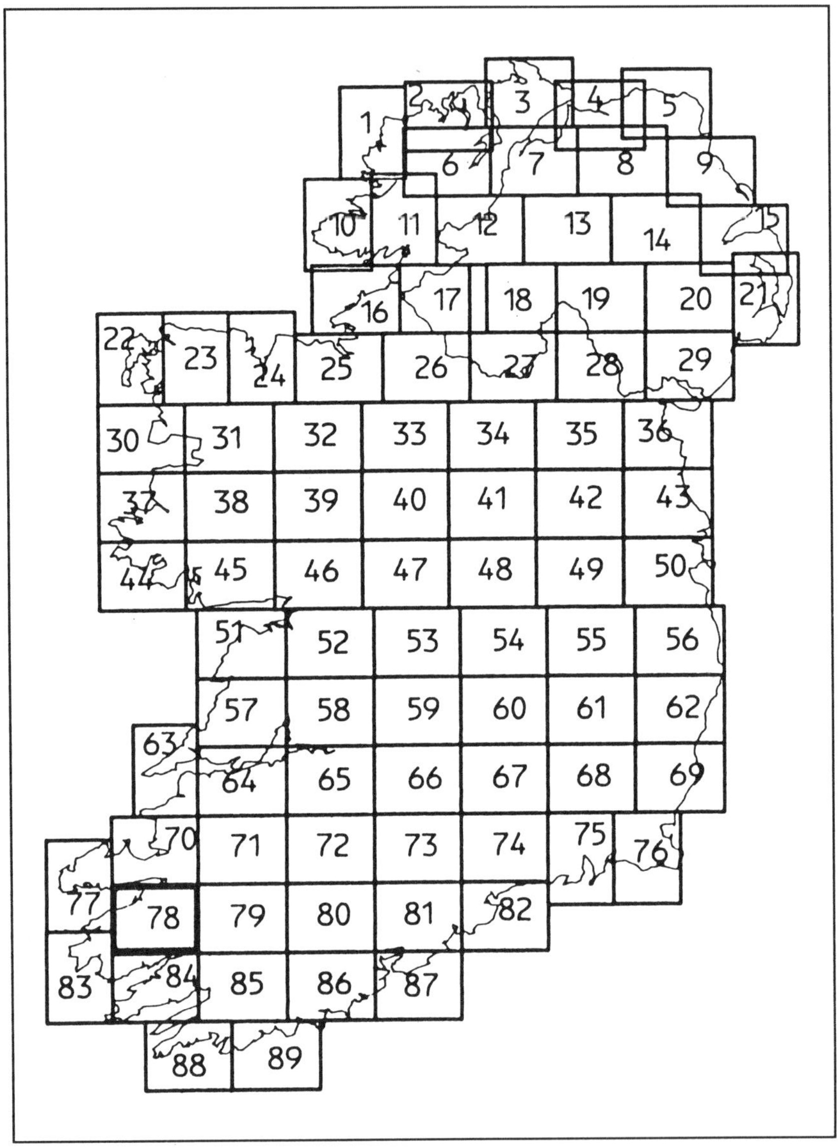

A. Ordnance Survey of Northern Ireland

- Eighteen *First Series* sheets, 4, 5, 7-9, 12-15, 17-21, 26-29, were published 1978-85. The changes in sheet lines that occurred in 1988-89 did not affect these sheets, and for ease of reference they are considered together with subsequent developments in ✣**34**.A.

B. Ordnance Survey of Ireland

1. 1st Series, Preliminary Edition, coloured, 1988. Sheet 78 only.
   Produced from digital data. See also ✣**34**.B.

34. 1:50,000 Map of Ireland (2)

Irish National Grid series, published jointly by the Ordnance Surveys of Ireland and Northern Ireland. With a layout revised in the south in 1988-89, still in 89 sheets until increased to 90 in 1993 by the addition of Sheet 36A. Standard sheet coverage 40 by 30 km. The Irish National Grid is blue on civilian coloured issues. See also **✛33**.

Early indexes show Sheet 36 plotted in landscape format, and some Ordnance Survey (Great Britain) indexes erroneously show Belfast's Sheet 36A in the identical location. Sheet 36 was published in portrait format with extended sheet lines in 1997. Some Ordnance Survey of Northern Ireland indexes show Sheets 34A and 35A plotted to the west of 36A, but their issue is now unlikely. Some Ordnance Survey of Ireland indexes show the 1:25,000 map *Oileáin Árann : The Aran Islands* as Sheet 51A, but it was issued unnumbered in 1993.

There are insets of Inishtrahull on Sheet 3, Stags of Broad Haven, Black Rock on 22, Inishshark, High Island on 37, Inishmore on 51, Tearaght Island on 70, Tuskar Rock on 77, Skellig Rocks on 83, Dursey Head on 84.

A. Ordnance Survey of Northern Ireland

1. Coloured edition, with layers. 19 sheets.
    1. First Series, 1978-85. 18 sheets: 4, 5, 7-9, 12-15, 17-21, 26-29.
    2. *Discoverer Series*, 1988-94. ?14 sheets: 4, 5, 7, 9, 13-15, 17-21, 29, 36A.

2. *Discoverer Series*, coloured, with layers, 1998- . Publication continues.
   Produced from digital data. It is anticipated that eighteen sheets, 4, 5, 7-9, 12-15, 17-21, 26-29, are to be published.

3. *Outline Edition*, 1978-85. 18 sheets: 4, 5, 7-9, 12-15, 17-21, 26-29.

4. *Soil Map*, 1993-95. 18 sheets in 17: 4, 5, 7-9, 12-15, 17-21, 26/28, 27, 29.
   Published for the Department of Agriculture, Northern Ireland.

Military issues

The new 1:50,000 map in Northern Ireland was far from complete in 1981 when the military version M728 was required. While preparation of the new map continued, Edition 1-GSGS issues of Sheets 7, 12, 18, 26, 29, and probably 13, 20, 21, 27, 28 were provisionally supplied by five-colour enlargements, without layers, of M723 material [**✛32**.M.1]. Detail was not enhanced at the joins, and contours remained measured in feet. The north-west corner of Sheet 12 was left blank. In order to hasten production of the new 1:50,000 map some sheets were printed initially without layers and in fewer colours, with roads and contours the same. Sheet 17 in Edition 1-GSGS appeared thus, as did Sheets 27 and 28 in Edition 2-GSGS and probably Sheets 12 and 26. New editions with layers followed when they were ready.

5. M728, Edition 1-GSGS, 1979-81. 19 sheets: 4, 5, 7-9, 12-15, 17-21, 26-29, 36A (1993).
   Each sheet is updated in sequentially numbered editions.

   The following dependent issues are recorded:
    1. GSGS 5309: *Border Crossing Points*, 1981. 9 sheets: 7, 12, 17-19, 26-29.
    2. GSGS 5309A: *Royal Ulster Constabulary Divisional & Subdivisional Boundaries*, 1981. 18 sheets recorded: 4, 5, 7-9, 12-15, 17-21, 26-29.
       Boundaries are shown in addition to the border crossing points. The title was later revised to *Northern Ireland RUC Divisional / Subdivisional Boundaries & Border Crossing Points*.
    3. GSGS 5309B: *Bigram and Ward Boundaries*, 1982- . 18 sheets: 4, 5, 7-9, 12-15, 17-21, 26-29.

B. Ordnance Survey of Ireland

Produced from digital data. Government of Ireland copyright dates are quoted.

1. 1st Series, Preliminary Edition, coloured. 8 sheets.
   For a ninth sheet, 78, see ✣**33**.B.1.
   1. Published in 1989. 2 sheets: 54, 56.
      A second issue of Sheet 54 had on its reverse a LandSat image covering an area mostly coincident with that of the conventional map.
   2. Published in 1992. 3 sheets: 6, 71, 79.
      These sheets mention the *Rambler Series* in their back cover notes.
   3. *The Rambler Series,* 1992. 3 sheets: 16, 25, 70.

2. *The Rambler Series,* First Edition, coloured, 1991. Sheet 78. See also ✣**33**.B.1.

3. *Discovery Series,* coloured edition, with layers. 71 sheets.
   1. Preliminary Edition, 1993. 9 sheets: 1-3, 10, 11, 30, 37, 38, 75.
      When reprinted these sheets are designated *First Edition* [✣B.3.2].
   2. First Edition, 1994-98 (published 1994-99). 71 sheets: 1-3, 6, 10, 11, 16, 22-25, 30-36, 37-89.
   3. 2nd Edition, 1994- . Publication continues.

Symbols **:** a **bold** number prefixed with ✣ is a cross reference to another section of the book; a number prefixed with ✣ is a cross reference within the current section; a reference number in ( ) at a district map identifies the next, or previous, such map listed with the same sheet lines; the ▮ symbol accompanies a source reference for maps rarely encountered (library sigla are listed on page 241); ❍ warns that there are noted exceptions to the information given in headings; ↑ identifies what is referred to here as War Office marginalia (for a description see page xxii); ❋ refers to the exceptional use of the heading *Ordnance Survey of Great Britain.*

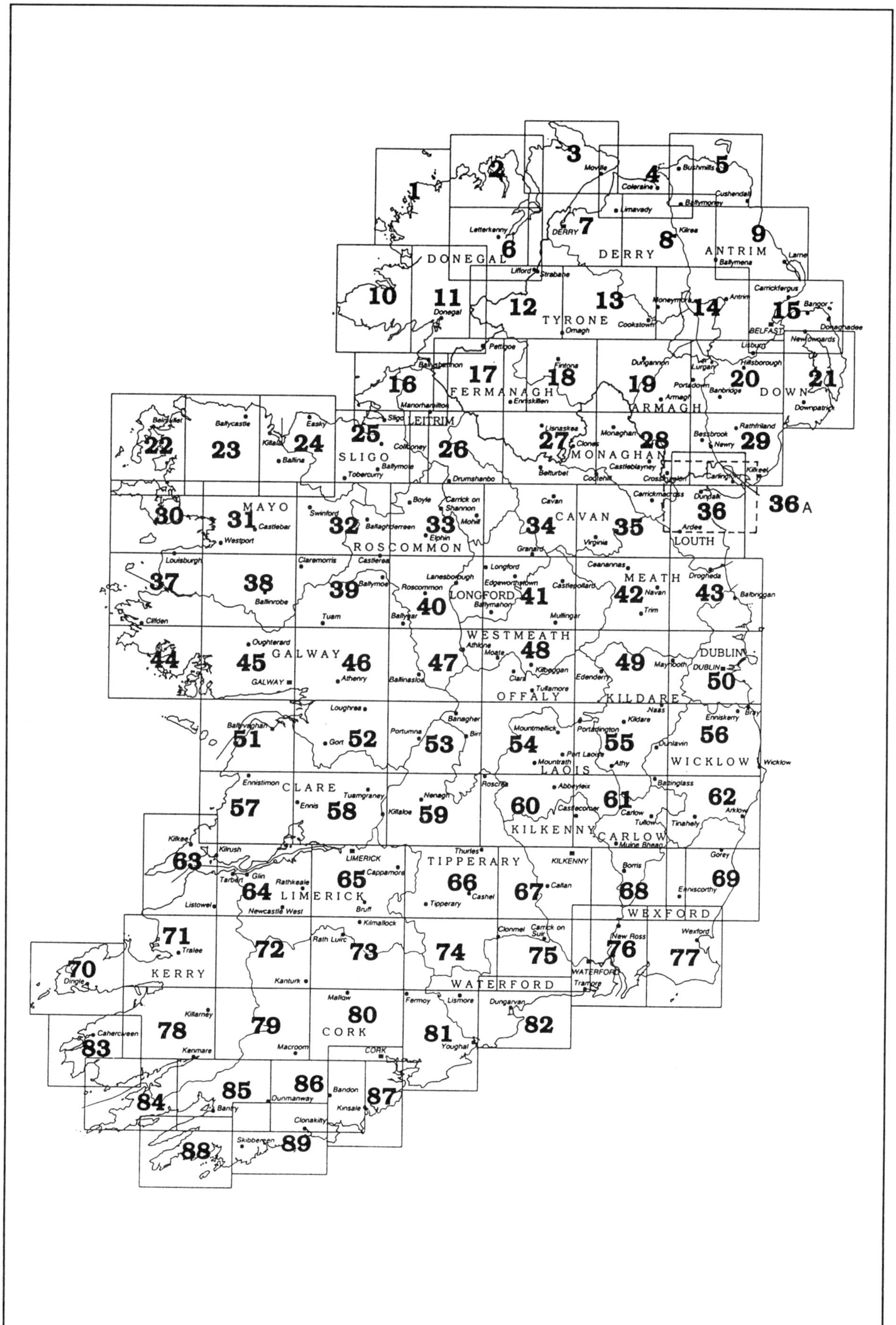

34. 1:50,000 Map of Ireland (2)

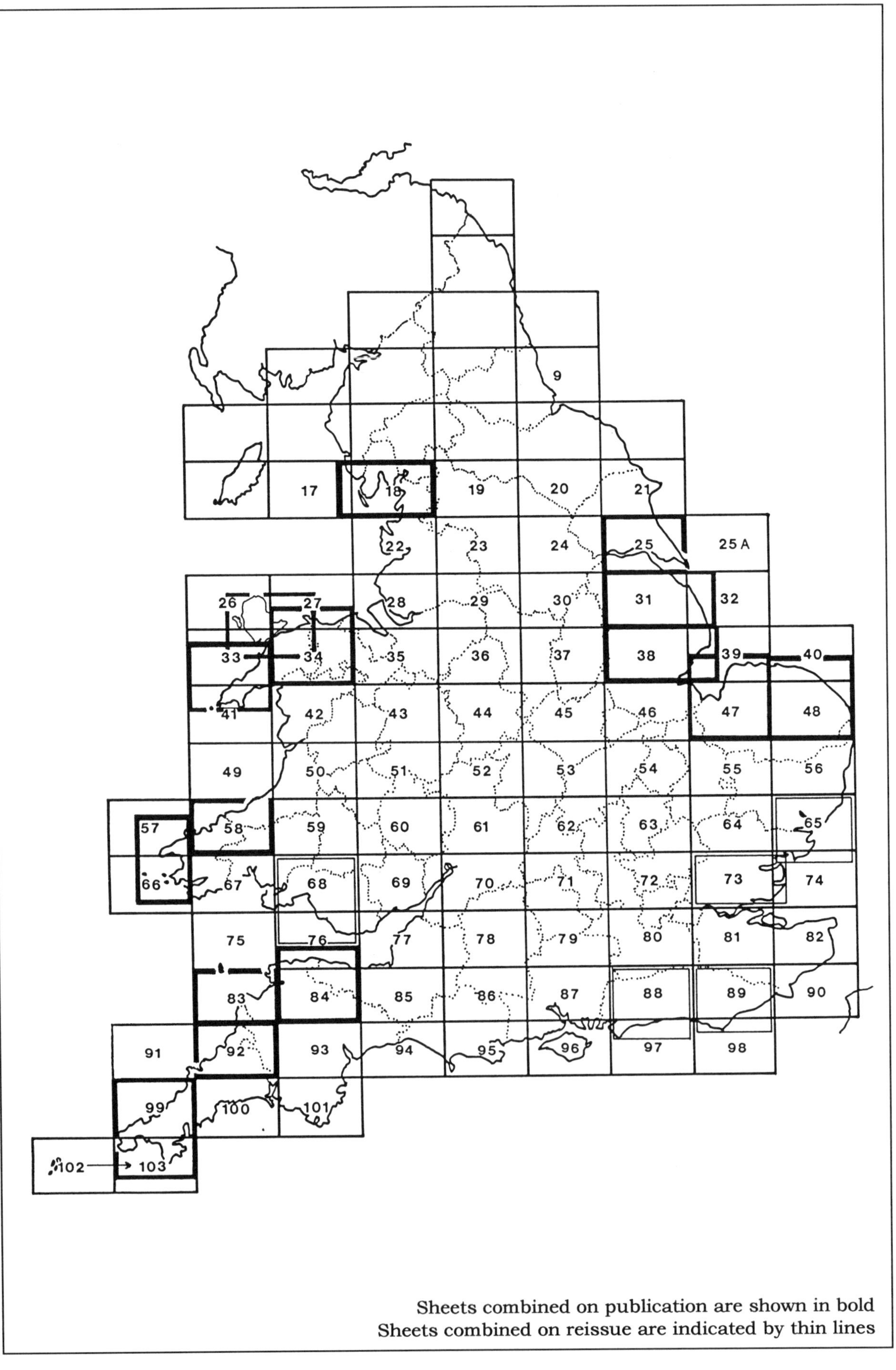

35. Half-inch Map of England and Wales : small sheet series

35. Half-inch Map of England and Wales : small sheet series

Constructed on Cassini's Projection on the origin of Delamere. Laid out in 104 sheets: 1-25, 25A, 26-103, to be reduced by sheet combinations. Publication was discontinued before completion. Standard sheet coverage 36 by 24 miles, the same as four one-inch *New Series* sheets. Reduced from the one-inch map. Without reference system. Heading: *Ordnance Survey of England* or *England and Wales.* The words "small sheet series" do not appear. With an outline of France on Sheet 90. As the series progressed the encasing of woods was removed, double lines superseded single for *other roads,* and hill shading was darkened. Paper size was reduced in 1905 (see page xxiii), and marginalia redesigned with the legend in two sections.

15 sheets in 11 were not published: 1-3, 4/5, 6/7, 8, 10/16, 11/12, 13-15.

1. Coloured edition. 6 sheets in 5.
    1. With original marginalia, 1903. 4 sheets: 56, 65, 74, 97.
       See ✣2.3, 2.4 for reissues of these sheets.
    2. With redesigned marginalia, 1905. Sheet 47/39pt.

2. Coloured edition, with hill shading. 88 sheets in 74.
    Produced from the first national revision, except Sheets 17/18, 72, 98, and most of the reissues listed in ✣2.3, 2.4, which claim second national revision derivation.
    1. With original marginalia, 1903-04. 45 sheets in 40: 9, 50-55, 61-64, 68-73, 75/83, 77-82, 84/76pt, 85-90, 91/92, 93-96, 98, 99/102/103, 100, 101.
       See also ✣2.3, 2.4. Sheet 102 is inset on 99/102/103.
    2. As ✣2.1, with beige base colour, 1904. 2 sheets: 9, 50 [▮Ob].
    3. With redesigned marginalia, 1904-07 (published 1905-07). 59 sheets in 48 recorded: 17/18, 19-24, 25/25A, 26/27pt/33pt/34pt, 27/34, 28-30, 31/32, 35-37, 38/39pt, 40/48, 41/33pt, 42-46, 49/58, 54-56, 57/66, 59, 60, 64, 67, 69, 71, 72, 77-81, 86, 87, 90, 91/92, 93, 101.
       The sheets listed in ✣1, 2.1 are reissues here. Others will no doubt emerge.
    4. Sheets combined on reissue, with redesigned marginalia, 1904-07 (published 1905-07): ?65/74pt, 68/76pt, 73/74pt, 88/97, 89/98.
       Component individual sheets were superseded. The Welsh part of Sheet 76 was only published combined with this reissue of 68. Sheet 65/74pt appears on indexes but has yet to be recorded.

3. District maps. Coloured with hill shading.
    Aldershot.
    1. With the Command and other boundaries overprinted, 1903.
    2. Without overprint, 1903. For civilian use.

    Aldershot District. With new sheet lines.
    1. With the Command and other boundaries overprinted, 1905.
    2. Without overprint, 1905. For civilian use.

    Birmingham District, 1907.
    East of England Manoeuvre Map, 1904, 1904.
    With the manoeuvre area boundary overprinted. In *Report on Army Manoeuvres 1904* [▮PRO (WO 279/8, 279/516)]. Also on sale.
    New Forest and Surrounding Country, 1904.
    With beige base colour.
    Oxford, 1904.
    Salisbury Plain.
    1. With the War Department boundary overprinted, 1903.
    2. Without overprint, 1903. For civilian use.

    Salisbury Plain. With new sheet lines.
    1. With the War Department boundary overprinted, 1906.
    2. Overprinted with War Office Cassini Grid (British System), c.1921 [▮DGI].

    South of England Manoeuvre Map, 1903. In four sheets: *North, East, South, West.*
    With the manoeuvre area boundary overprinted.

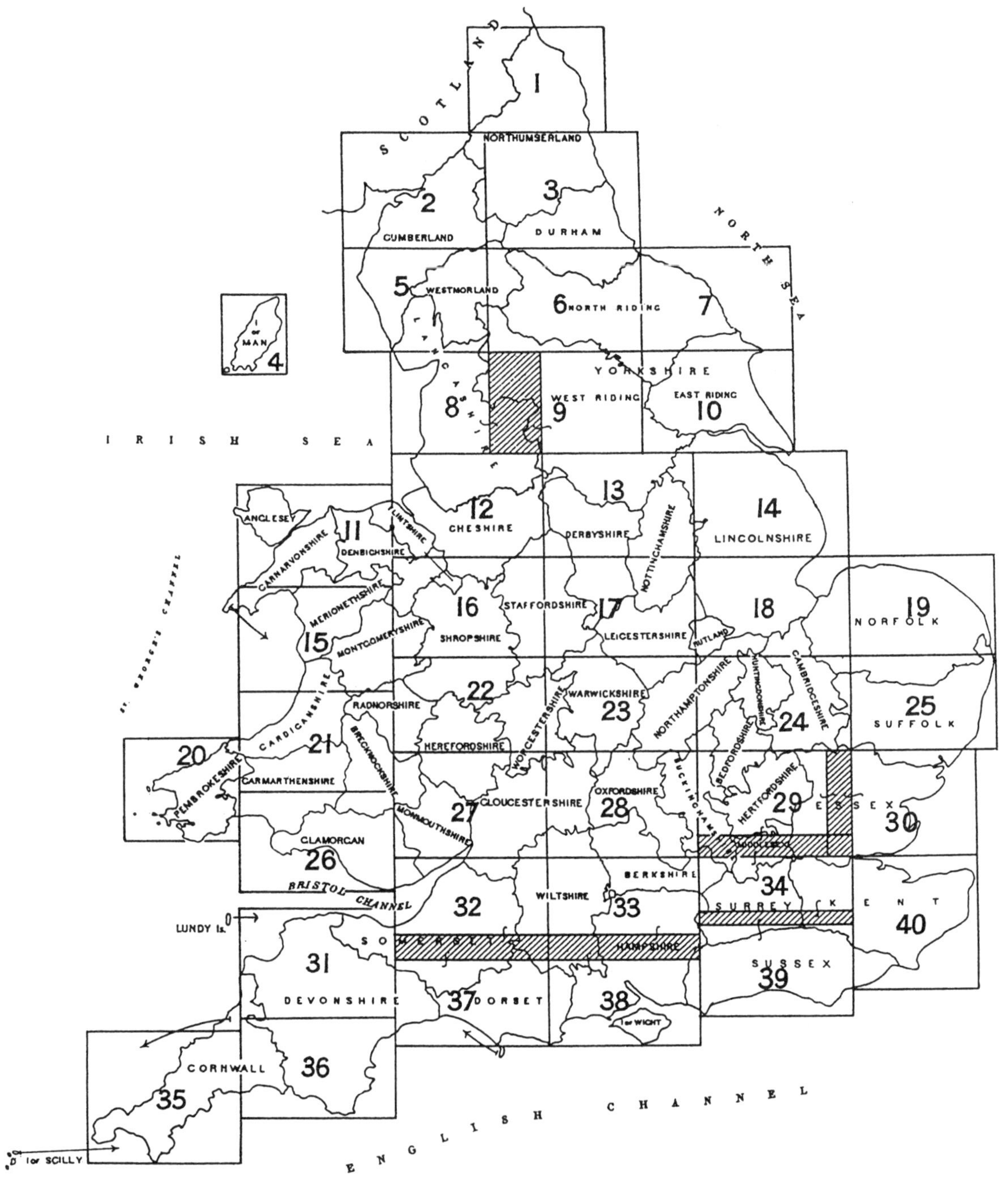

Sheet 20 was enlarged on reissue

36. Half-inch Map of England and Wales (Large Sheet Series)

36. Half-inch Map of England and Wales (Large Sheet Series)

Constructed on Cassini's Projection on the origin of Delamere, and published in 40 sheets. Standard sheet coverage 54 by 36 miles, the area covered by four one-inch *Third Edition* large sheets [**✚8**]. Four sheets cover the same area as nine half-inch small sheets [**✚35**]. Reduced from contemporary one-inch maps. Heading: *Ordnance Survey of England and Wales : (Large Sheet Series),* unless noted otherwise. The *Large Sheet Series* designation was cleared, presumably once all the small sheet maps had been superseded by 1908.

There are insets of the western tip of Holy Island on Sheet 11, Bardsey Island on 15, Lundy Island on 31, the Boscastle area, Isles of Scilly on 35, Portland on 37.

A. With no reference system

1. Coloured edition, with hill shading. All sheets.
   1. With woods in solid green, 1906-08. All sheets.
   2. With green tree symbols, 1906-10 (published 1908-13). 25 sheets recorded: 4, 11, 13-23, 26, 28-36, 38, 39.

2. Coloured edition, with layers and hill shading. 39 sheets.
   1. With woods in solid green, 1906-08 (published 1908). 16 sheets recorded: 3, 7, 9, 10, 12, 24, 25, 28-30, 32, 34, 37-40.
   2. With green tree symbols, 1906-09 (published 1908-09). 39 sheets: 1-3, 5-40.

3. *Country round Aldershot,* 1909. District map, coloured with layers.
   1. Overprinted in red for *Aldershot Divisional Inspections, 1909* [▮PC].
   2. Published 1910 without overprint. For civilian use. See also ✣B.10.

B. With an alpha-numeric squaring system ❍

Sheet 20 was extended more than six miles west to include coverage of The Smalls, and more than one mile south to bring St Gowan's Head within the neat line. After 1924 some sheets were published in new editions produced from the third national revision begun in 1912. These are characterised by titles lettered in the hatched Roman Capitals style of the one-inch *Popular Edition* [**✚10**], and irregularly by new publication or magnetic variation dates. The sheets recorded are 4, 9, 10, 12, 13, 16-40. The lower section of Sheet 6 was also revised probably for the 1927 British Association Leeds map [✣B.10], but the title lettering was apparently not altered in this case. No edition contains examples of them all.

1. Coloured edition, with hill shading. 39 sheets.
   1. Published 1909-14. 39 sheets: 1-3, 5-40.
   2. Produced from the third national revision, 1925-26. 6 sheets recorded: 19, 25, 32, 35, 36, 38.

2. Coloured edition, with layers. 39 sheets.
   1. Published 1910-14. 39 sheets: 1-3, 5-40.
      Sheets 11 and 15 were reprinted in 1945-46 for colour proving tests [▮CCS].
   2. Produced from the third national revision, 1924-32 (published 1925-39). 30 sheets recorded: 6, 9, 10, 12, 13, 16-40.
      Sheet 20 was reprinted in 1945-46 for colour proving tests [▮CCS].

3. Outline edition, 1914.
   The extent of this issue is unclear since it did not appear in publication reports and was apparently not sent to legal deposit libraries.
   1. Outline edition (black plate only). Sheet 22 recorded [▮Bg, Sg].
   2. Outline edition, with water in blue. Sheet 37 recorded [▮EXg].

4. *Training Map,* 1912-15 (issued 1914-15). 34 sheets recorded: 1, 3, 6-21, 23-25, 27-30, 32-40 [▮BL].
   Outline edition, with water in blue and contours in brown. The map title is on the reverse; it also appears on the map face of late printings. Some printings are recorded with roads also coloured, probably reflecting a phase when contours and roads shared a colour plate. Some printing was subcontracted: Sheet 27 is recorded in a printing by Percival Jones, and Sheet 34 by Moody Bros, both of Birmingham.

5. *Ministry of Transport Road Map.* 39 sheets.
   Road classification was constantly revised, and updated on later issues. A special set of six maps was made at the two-inch scale for the London area [**✢125**].
   1. With second class roads in green, 1923. 39 sheets: 1-3, 5-40.
   2. As ✢B.5.1, produced from the third national revision, 1924-29 (published 1926-29). 23 sheets recorded: 10, 12, 13, 19, 20, 23-40.
   3. With second class roads in purple, 1936. 14 sheets recorded: 6, 10, 12-14, 17, 19, 23-25, 30 32, 34.

6. *Outline Edition,* 1930-31. All sheets.
   All sheets have 1930 or 1931 print codes and, in spite of their printed publication dates, were not issued before then.
   1. "Published" 1912-15. 14 sheets: 1-3, 5, 7-9, 11, 14, 15, 17, 18, 21, 22.
   2. "Published" 1924-30. 26 sheets: 4, 6, 10, 12, 13, 16, 19, 20, 23-40.
      Produced from the third national revision. Sheet 4 is otherwise unrecorded with this revision, which renders its 1925 "publication" date a curiosity.

7. Outline edition, 1942. All sheets.
   Characterised by a 1942 print code, but no *Outline Edition* heading.
   1. With uncoloured water. 8 sheets: 7, 16, 22, 23, 26, 28-30.
   2. With water in blue. 20 sheets: 1, 2, 4-6, 8, 9, 14, 18-21, 27, 28, 32-34, 37-39.
      Sheet 28 appears to have been made, but may not have been issued.
   3. With water in blue, and an alpha-numeric border. 13 sheets: 3, 10-13, 15, 17, 24, 25, 31, 35, 36, 40.

8. *Outline Edition,* post-war printings. 33 sheets.
   1. With water in blue, 1945-55 (published 1946-55). 28 sheets: 3, 5, 6, 8-10, 12-14, 17-19, 23-25, 27-33, 35-40.
      A printing of Sheet 16 was destroyed before publication.
   2. With uncoloured water, 1948-62. 6 sheets: 7, 16, 22, 26, 30, 34.

9. Outline edition in grey, with water in blue, 1933. 2 sheets: 18, 24 [▮Cu].
   For the Fenland Research Committee.

10. District maps. Coloured with layers.
    British Association Topographical Map for the Bristol Meeting 1930, 1930.
    British Association Topographical Map for the Leeds Meeting 1927, 1927.
    Country round Aldershot, 1909 (published by 1915). Reprinted 1922.
    The sheet lines of the 1909 map [see ✢A.3] were rearranged in order to conform with the alpha-numeric squaring system of the series sheets.

C. With National Yard Grid at 10,000 yard intervals ❍

On National Yard Grid sheet lines. Extant half-inch mapping was used and transferred to the Transverse Mercator Projection (see page xiii), except in the case of *Greater London* [✢C.3], for which mapping on the Transverse Mercator Projection was newly drawn.

1. Special District (Relief) Maps.
   Birmingham District, 1933 (published 1934)❋. Also proved in 1945 [▮CCS].
   The Cotswolds, 1931 (published 1932)❋. Also proved in 1945 [▮BSg].
   - For *Greater London* see ✢C.3.

2. Special District Map. Coloured with layers.
The Peak District, 1936.

3. *Greater London* (✣M.1)❋.
The only half-inch map to be made based on revision for the one-inch *Fifth Edition* [**✚11**]. The drawing is also stylistically akin. Proof copies entitled *London Area,* with and without relief, are in PRO (OS 1/149).
1. Coloured editions with relief.
    1. Special District Map, 1935.
    2. Special District (Relief) Map, 1935.
    3. Special District (Relief) Map, 1935 (published 1945). Without grid.
2. Outline editions. Without grid.
    1. Outline edition, with woods in grey, 1935 (published 1942).
    2. Outline edition in grey, 1935 (issued 1942). Not found.
       For the Ministry of Town and Country Planning.
    3. *Outline Edition,* with water in blue, woods in grey, 1935 (published 1945).
    4. *Outline Edition,* with water in blue, 1935 (issued 1945). Not found.
       For the Ministry of Town and Country Planning.
3. *Population of Greater London,* 1935 (published 1936).
   The distribution of population, based on the 1931 Census, was compiled by A.C. O'Dell. An accompanying leaflet showing *Profiles* was also produced.
4. *London Area : showing the City of London and Metropolitan Boroughs, County, Parliamentary and Municipal Boroughs, Parliamentary County Divisions* (green), *Urban and Rural Districts, Civil Parishes* (red), *Metropolitan Police District* (purple), *London Passenger Transport Area* (blue), *and Catchment Area Boundaries,* 1936. Without grid.
5. *Highway Development Survey (Greater London),* 1937. Without grid.
   In Sir Charles Bressey and Sir Edwin Lutyens *Highway Development Survey 1937 (Greater London),* London, HMSO, 1938. For the Ministry of Transport.

M. Military district map with War Office Cassini Grid at 10 km intervals

1. *Greater London* (✣C.3, ?M.2).
Coloured issues, without the relief of the civilian editions. The grid was initially overprinted in purple.
1. *Military Edition,* preceding application of GSGS number, 1940 [▮Bg].
2. GSGS 4159: *Military Edition,* 1940 [▮PC].
3. GSGS 4159: *Military Edition,* with grid in black, 1946 [▮PC].

Military district maps with National Grid (Military System)

2. GSGS 4679, later M621: *Greater London* (?✣M.1). Not found.
The sheet lines and grid are not confirmed. The number was allocated in 1949.

3. *Greater London.*
A reduced area map on National Grid sheet lines, with the grid overprinted in purple at 1 km intervals.
1. GSGS Misc.1519 coloured edition, 1951 [▮Ob].
2. GSGS Misc.1519, overprinted *London District Boundary Map,* 1951 [▮Ob].

Other specially constructed maps were issued overprinted for specific military purposes, especially army manoeuvres before the First World War. See also GSGS 4167 1:100,000 Great Britain [**✚41**].

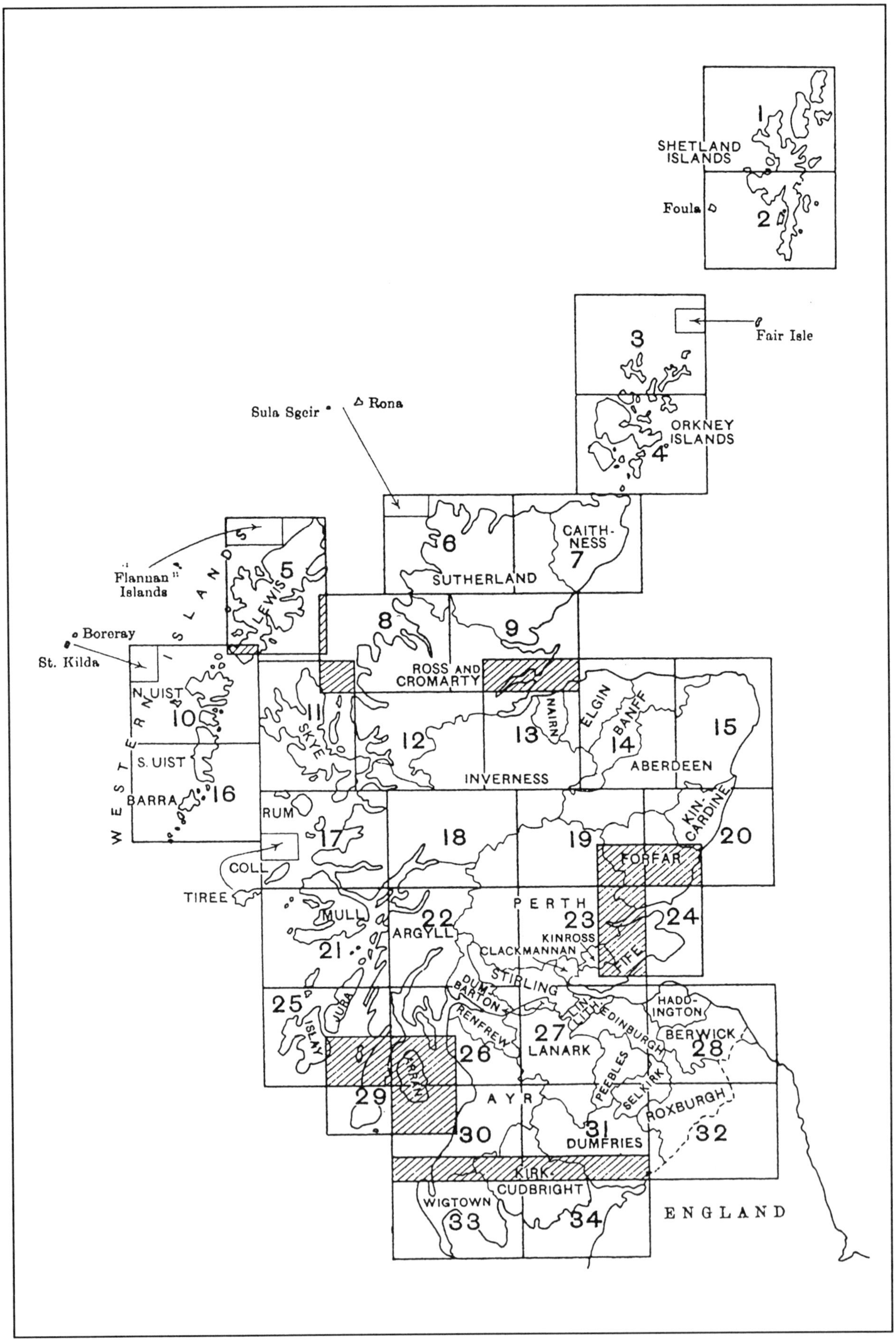

37. Half-inch Map of Scotland

37. Half-inch Map of Scotland

Constructed on Bonne's Projection on the origin of 57°30'N,4°W, and published in 34 sheets. Standard sheet coverage 48 by 36 miles, the area covered by four one-inch sheets [✚**15**]. Reduced from contemporary one-inch maps. Heading: *Ordnance Survey of Scotland,* unless noted otherwise.

There are insets of Fair Isle on Sheet 3, Flannan Isles, Gasker on 5, Sula Sgeir, Rona on 6, St Kilda and Boreray on 10, the southern and eastern tips of Skye on 11 from 17 and 12, Tiree on 17.

A. With no reference system

1. Coloured edition, with hill shading. All sheets.
    1. With green tree symbols, 1908-10. 27 sheets: 6-9, 11-15, 17-34.
    2. With black tree symbols, 1910. 7 sheets: 1-5, 10, 16.

2. Coloured edition, with layers, 1910-11. 18 sheets: 17-34.
    With green tree symbols.

3. District map. Coloured with hill shading.
    Loch Fyne and Loch Lomond District, 1908 [▮NLS].

B. With an alpha-numeric squaring system ❍

1. Coloured edition, with hill shading, 1910-15 (published 1912-after 1915). 29 sheets: 1, 6-9, 11-34.

2. Coloured edition, with layers, 1912-14. 29 sheets: 6-34.
    Dated exceptionally are Sheet 10 (1910, published 1939), Sheet 16 (1910, published 1919) [▮NLS].

3. *Training Map,* 1912-14 (issued 1914-15). 6 sheets recorded: 13, 23, 24, 26-28 [▮BL].
    Outline edition, with water in blue and contours in brown.

4. *Ministry of Transport Road Map.* All sheets.
    Road classification was constantly revised, and was updated on later issues.
    1. With second class roads in green, 1923. All sheets.
    2. With second class roads in purple, 1936. Sheet 27 recorded.

5. Outline edition, with water in blue, 1942. All sheets.
    1. With an alpha-numeric squaring system. 10 sheets: 7, 10, 11, 14, 17-21, 23.
        Sheet 20 was printed but apparently not issued in this form [▮RML].
    2. Without squaring system. 25 sheets: 1-6, 8, 9, 12, 13, 15, 16, 20, 22, 24-34.

6. Outline edition, with water and contours in black, printed 1945. Sheet 31 [▮RML].
    Three pulls were supplied for some undisclosed Ordnance Survey purpose, one of which, remarkably, survives. Without squaring system.

7. Special District (Relief) Map.
    Island of Skye, 1932❋. Another edition, 1937. Also proved in 1945 [▮BSg, CCS].

Other specially constructed maps were issued for specific military purposes, especially army manoeuvres before the First World War.

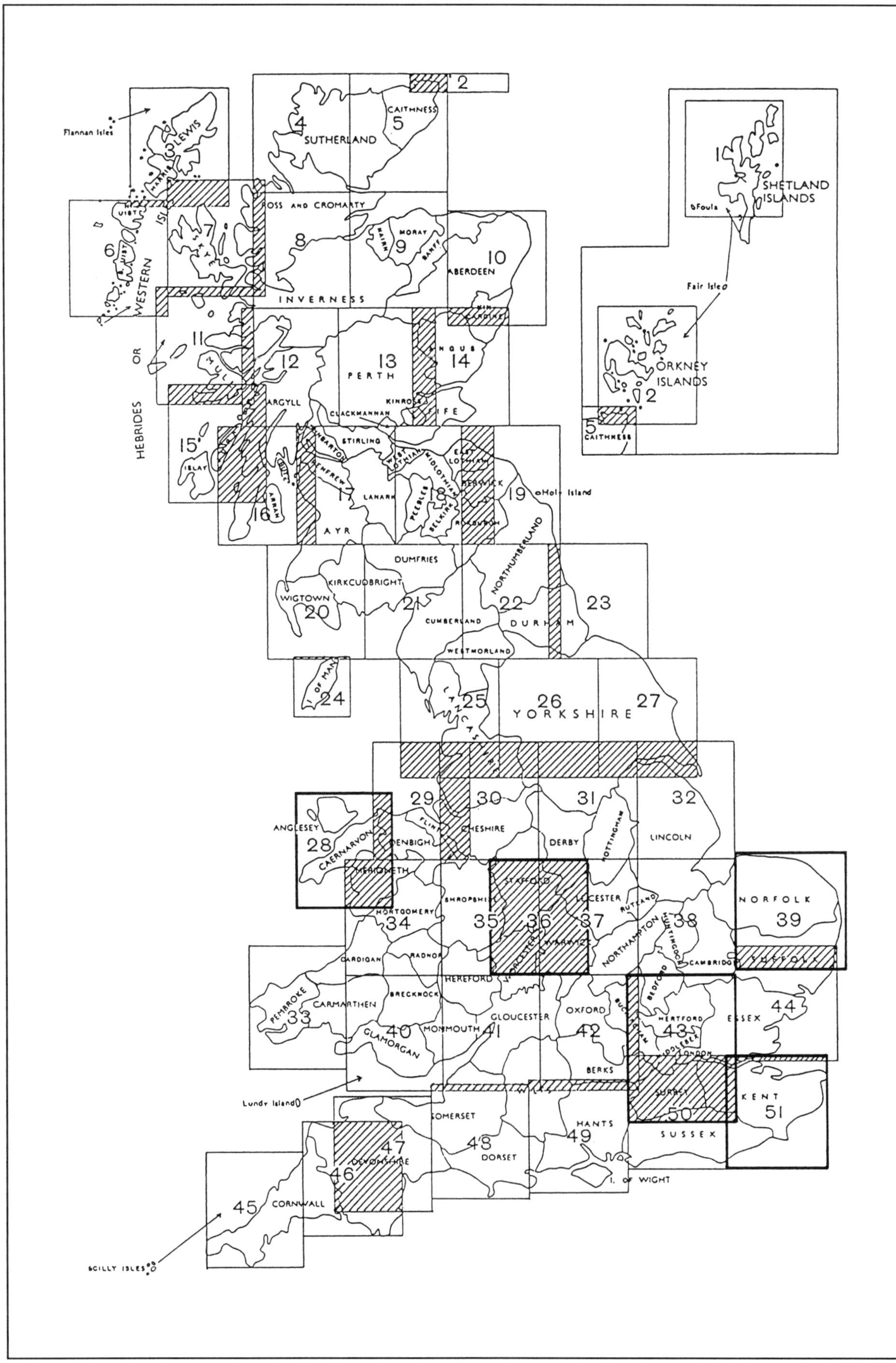

38. Half-inch Map of Great Britain

38. Half-inch Map of Great Britain

National Grid series. Laid out in 51 sheets of which five were published. Sheet 36 would in effect have been a district map, coverage of its area being divided completely between the neighbouring Sheets 35 and 37. *Greater London* was plotted as Sheet 43, but by the time of its publication, the series had been cancelled, so it was issued as a district map without sheet number. Standard sheet coverage 80 by 95 km. The National Grid appears at 10 km intervals. Heading: *Ordnance Survey of Great Britain.*

A. Provisional Edition

Produced from 1930-36 revision.

1. Coloured edition, with layers, 1956. Sheet 51 only.
   Proof copies were printed with the heading *Second Edition* [▮PRO (OS 1/441)].

2. *Outline* edition, with woods in grey, 1956 (published 1957). Sheet 51 only.

B. Second Series

Heading: *Half Inch Second Series.* Produced from 1947-57 revision. Newly drawn from one-inch *Seventh Series* [**✚20**] source material at a variety of scales.

1. Coloured edition, with layers, 1958-62. 4 sheets: 28, 36, 39, [43] *Greater London.*
   Proof copies of Sheet 37 *Leicester* were printed in 1961, some with experimental road depiction [▮RML, CCS]. Proof copies of *Greater London* carrying sheet number 43 were printed [▮PC].

2. *Outline* edition. 2 sheets: 36 (edition *A/,* 1958, published 1960), [43] *Greater London* (1962, published 1963).

3. Coloured edition, with layers, 1962 (printed 1970). Sheet [43] *Greater London* [▮PC].
   Headed *Sample copy - market research only.* Marginalia at the foot of the map is cleared. This is an experimental reprint to illustrate a scale approaching 1:100,000.

4. District Map. Coloured with layers and hill shading.
   Snowdonia National Park, 1966.
   Renamed *Snowdonia and Anglesey,* 1983; subtitled *Eryri a Môn,* 1986.

- For the *Greater London* district map see the references to Sheet [43] above.

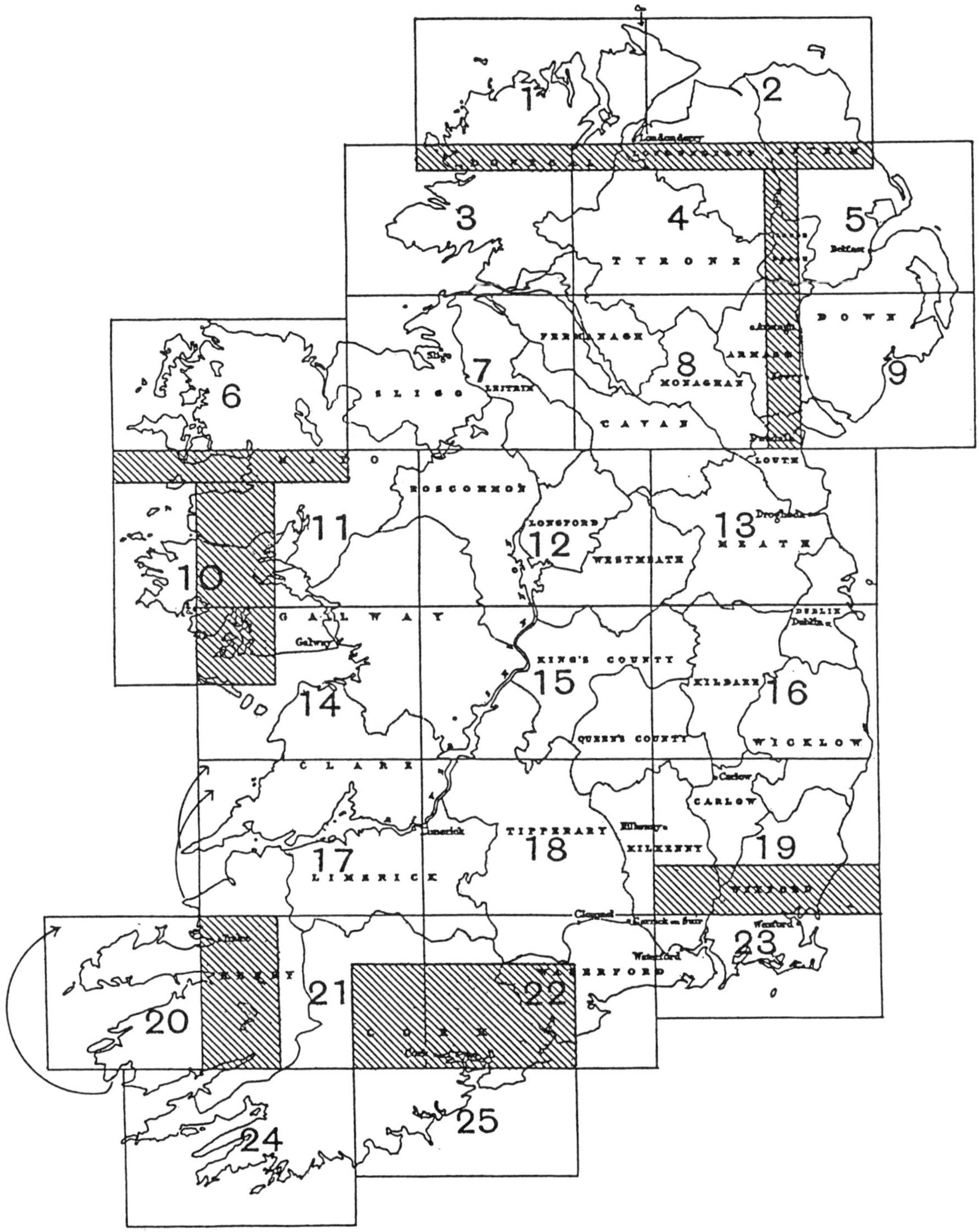

Sheet 25 was reduced on reissue

39. Half-inch Map of Ireland

39. Half-inch Map of Ireland

Constructed on Bonne's Projection on the origin of 53°30'N,8°W, and published in 25 sheets. Standard sheet coverage 54 by 36 miles, the area covered by nine one-inch sheets [✣**25**]. Reduced from the contemporary one-inch map. With an alpha-numeric squaring system, and with heading: *Ordnance Survey of Ireland,* unless noted otherwise in each case.

There are insets of Inishtrahull (later enlarged) on Sheet 1, Loop Head, Kerry Head on 17, Bolus Head on 20. Later issues of Sheet 24 have Dursey Head as an inset rather than an extrusion.

A. Ordnance Survey issues

1. Coloured edition, with hill shading, 1911-18 (published 1911-19). All sheets [▮BL].

2. Coloured edition, with layers, 1912-18 (published 1912-19). All sheets.

3. *Training Map.* 2 sheets recorded: 16 *Dublin and The Curragh* (1914) [▮PC], 21 [▮Dtf].
   Outline edition, with water in blue, contours in brown. These sheets were probably issued in 1914, though were not published in ✣A.1, A.2 until 1918 and 1916.

B. Ordnance Survey of Ireland issues, from 1922

It is unlikely that Dublin had any further responsibility for Sheet 5, its coverage being wholly within Northern Ireland. Sheets 2, 4, 5 were published in Belfast from 1929 and Sheet 9 at the latest from 1934 [✣C]; issues of Sheets 2, 4, 9 by Dublin before the introduction of the Irish National Grid [✣B.3] were rare. Sheet 25 as first issued [see ✣A] covered a vertical distance of 48 miles. As a consequence of a 1940 Irish military directive to avoid or reduce overlaps between sheets, twelve miles were removed from the overlap to the north, military issues being renumbered 25A [✣M.3]. The civilian map followed suit, but was not renumbered.

1. Coloured edition, with hill shading.
   1. With squaring system in black, 1932. Sheet 16 recorded [▮Dtc].
   2. With squaring system in red, 1945. Sheet 7 recorded [▮PC].
      The Ordnance Survey of Ireland catalogue of 1946 refers to the continuing availability of the map in this style, but the 1949 edition states that no further hill-shaded sheets will be reprinted.

2. Coloured edition, with layers. ?24 sheets (1-3, ?4, 6-25).
   1. With squaring system in black. 2 sheets recorded: 13 (1940) [▮Wc], 16 (1932) [▮Sg].
   2. With squaring system in red, 1945- . 22 sheets recorded: 1, 3, 6-25.
   3. With squaring system in black, c.1950-55. 4 sheets recorded: 2, 17, 20, 24 [▮Bg, Dtf].
      Sheet 2 (1950) claims a revision date of 1937 (presumably Belfast's. See ✣C).

With Irish National Grid at 10 km intervals

3. Coloured edition, with layers. 24 sheets.
   1. With grid in purple, 1955-56. 24 sheets: 1-4, 6-25.
   2. With grid in black, numbered in red, 1956- . 24 sheets: 1-4, 6-25.
      With updated reprints. Most sheets were renamed.

4. Outline edition, showing railway mileposts, 1980. Sheet 16 recorded [▮Dtf].
   The cover index shows all 25 sheets, but it is unclear how many were in this edition.

5. *Gravity Anomaly Map,* 1987-89. 8 sheets: 12, 13, 15-19, 23.
By T. Murphy, respectively in *Geophysical Bulletin* 46, 38, 43, 36, 45, 44, 40, 41 (Communications of the Dublin Institute for Advanced Studies, Series D).

Geological Survey of Ireland

6. *Bedrock Geological Map of the carboniferous of Central Ireland* (at scale 1:100,000), 1992. 6 sheets: 12, 13, 15, 16, 18, 19.
Colour printed sheets, with the heading *Bedrock Geology 1:100,000 Map Series.* Compiled by Chevron Mineral Corporation of Ireland and Ivernia West plc, and published on their behalf by the Geological Survey of Ireland. Printed by the Ordnance Survey of Ireland.

7. *Bedrock Geology* (at scale 1:100,000), 1992- . Publication continues.
Colour printed sheets, also with the heading *Bedrock Geology 1:100,000 Map Series.* Other than Sheet 6, the first to be issued, the maps are produced from digital data. Complete coverage of the Republic of Ireland is intended, in 24 sheets in 21: 1/2pt, 3/4pt, 6, 7, 8/9pt, 10-25. Completion of publication is intended by 2000. Northern Ireland areas are uncoloured. Each map is accompanied by a memoir.

C. Ordnance Survey of Northern Ireland issues, from 1929

1. Coloured edition, with layers. 4 sheets: 2, 4, 5, 1912 (published 1929) [▮Dtc]; 9, 1918 (published by 1934) [▮Cu]. Sheet 4 was reprinted in 1947.

2. Outline edition, with water in blue. Sheet 4, 1912 (published ?1947) [▮BFq].

Produced from 1936-38 revision. With heading: *Ordnance Survey of Northern Ireland.*

3. Coloured edition, with layers, 1938-39 (published 1939). 3 sheets: 2, 5, 9. Reprinted 1946-47.
See also ✣B.2.3.

4. Outline edition, with water in blue, 1938-39 (published ?1947). 3 sheets: 2, 5, 9 [▮BFq].

With Irish National Grid at 10 km intervals

5. Coloured edition, with layers.
   1. With grid in purple, 1958. Sheet 5 only.
   2. With grid in black, 1962. Sheet 5 only.

M. British military issues overprinted with War Office Irish Grid

Sheets 5 and 9 (not 2) use ✣C.3 base maps. Sheet 25 retains its original dimensions (see the note to ✣B). The grid at 10 km intervals is coloured blue, except where noted.

1. Coloured edition, with hill shading, 1940. ?All sheets.
This version was probably made for the Air Ministry.

2. Coloured edition. All sheets.
   1. Preceding application of GSGS number, 1940. ?All sheets.
   2. GSGS 4127: [First Edition], 1940. All sheets [▮BL].
   3. GSGS 4127: Second Edition, 1941. 4 sheets: 7-9, 12 [▮DGI, Ob].
   The grid is coloured green. Classified roads as at 1 January 1942 are in red. Printed by the 515th Corps Field Survey Company, Royal Engineers.

Irish military issues overprinted with 5000 yard grid in red

The sheet lines of Sheets 4, 5, 9, 25 were altered in 1940 to avoid or reduce overlaps. They were replaced by Sheets 4A (six miles less coverage in the north), 5A, 9A (each nine miles less coverage in the west), 25A (twelve miles less coverage in the north: see note to ✣B). Mapping on five sheets covering Northern Ireland, 2, 4A, 5A, 8, 9A, was redrawn. Most issues except the redrawn sheets are headed *Modified Edition.* Secret issues were also prepared on this base map, not listed here. The copies recorded are mostly in ▮Dm, Dtc, Dtf.

3. Outline edition, with water in blue, contours in brown, 1940. 26 sheets.
   1. With uncoloured woods. 21 sheets: 1, 3, 6, 7, 10-25, 25A.
      Documents dated 27 August 1940 in file G2/X/0351 [▮Dm] confirm that uniquely both Sheets 25 and 25A were issued. A ?prototype of Sheet 16 [▮Dtc] using the black plate of the 1932 edition [✣B.2.1] still has woods in green and the alpha-numeric squaring system as well as the 5000 yard grid.
   2. With woods in green. 5 sheets: 2, 4A, 5A, 8, 9A.

4. Coloured edition, with hill shading, 1942. ?All 25 sheets.
   The classification of roads, coloured red and blue, is listed.

5. Coloured edition, with layers, 1943. ?All 25 sheets.
   The classification of roads is listed. Later reprints may lack the layer colours. Sheet 16 (1951) is in this style [▮PC].

Symbols : a **bold** number prefixed with ✚ is a cross reference to another section of the book; a number prefixed with ✣ is a cross reference within the current section; a reference number in ( ) at a district map identifies the next, or previous, such map listed with the same sheet lines; the ▮ symbol accompanies a source reference for maps rarely encountered (library sigla are listed on page 241); ❍ warns that there are noted exceptions to the information given in headings; ↑ identifies what is referred to here as War Office marginalia (for a description see page xxii); ❁ refers to the exceptional use of the heading *Ordnance Survey of Great Britain.*

40. The Half-inch Map (Second Series) of Northern Ireland

Irish National Grid series. Published in four sheets. Standard sheet coverage 120 by 80 km. Topography was based on the one-inch *Third Series* [**✣32**]. Sheet 4 covers the same area as one-inch Sheets 5, 6, 8, 9. Newly drawn. With a coastal outline of Scotland. The Irish National Grid appears at 10 km intervals. Heading: *Ordnance Survey of Northern Ireland : The Half-inch Map (Second Series).*

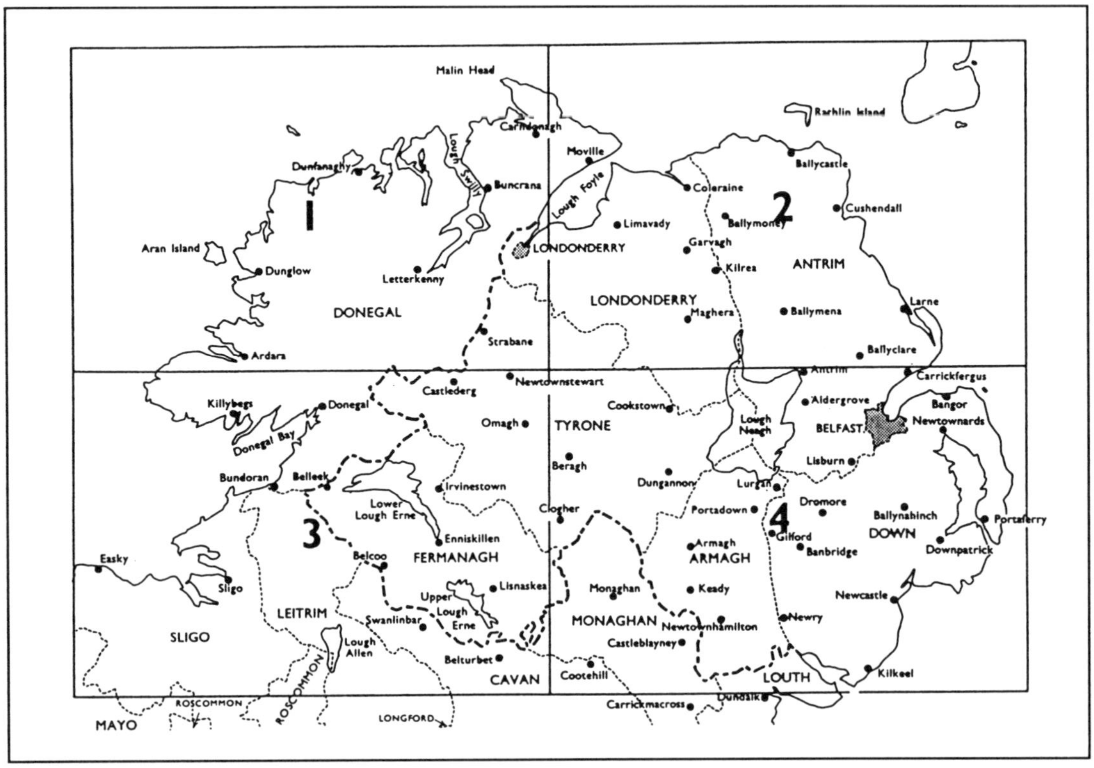

1. Coloured edition, with layers, 1968-70 (published 1968-71). All sheets.
2. Outline edition, with water in blue, 1967-69. All sheets.

41. 1:100,000 Map of Great Britain

Enlarged from the half-inch map of England and Wales [✢36]. Laid out on grid sheet lines in 21 rows lettered A to V (without I) and eight columns numbered 1 to 8 of sheets measuring 80 by 60 km. Prepared at the Ordnance Survey. The printing was mostly in separate west and east half sheets by Field Survey Companies, a few by the Survey Training Centre, Royal Engineers. With War Office Cassini Grid at 1 km intervals in black, numbered in blue. Some sheets have *Training Map* or *For Training* printed in black or red in the margins.

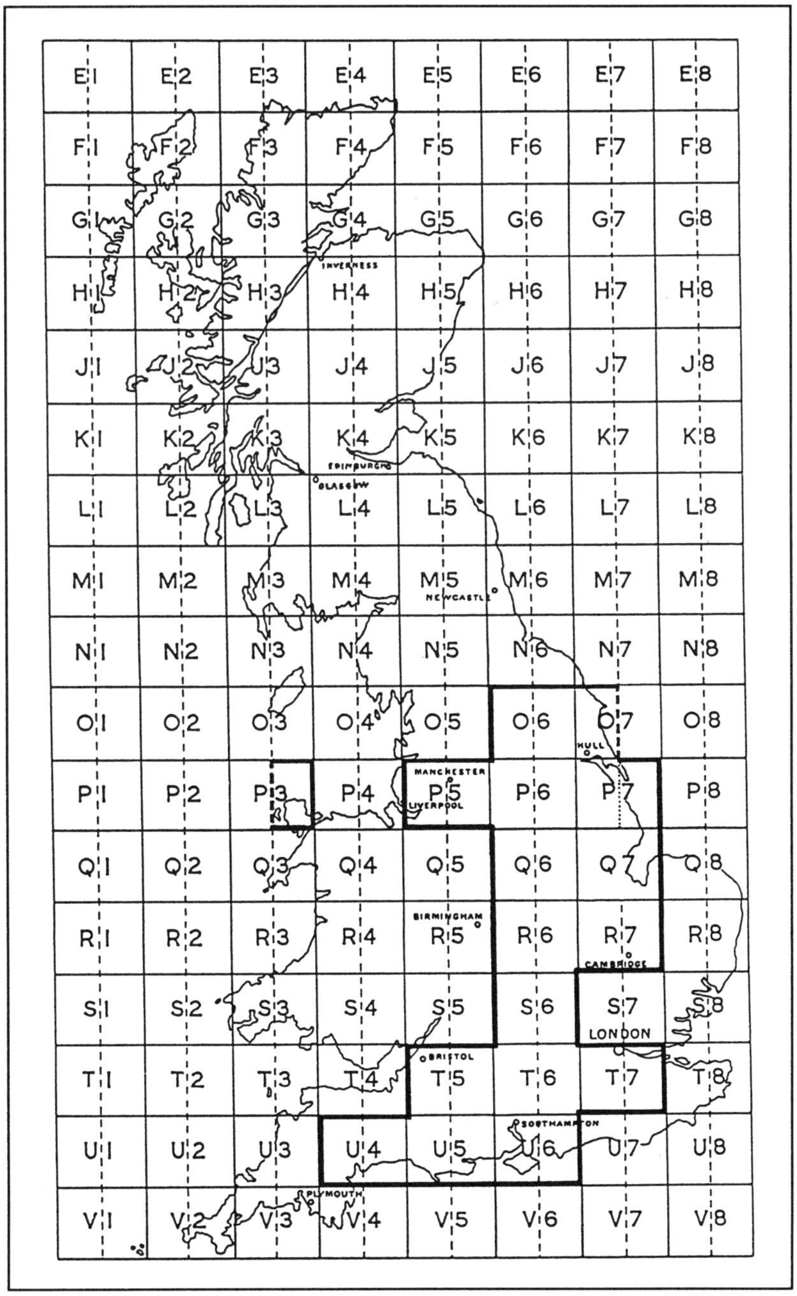

1. GSGS 4167: *Great Britain* or *Gt Britain,* First Edition, coloured.
   1. Full sheets, 1941. 2 sheets recorded: P7 [▮DGI], Q7 [▮RGS].
   2. Half sheets, 1941. 30 sheets recorded: O6W, O6E, O7W, P3E, P5W, P5E, P6W, P6E, P7W, P7E, Q6W, Q6E, R6W, R6E, R7W, R7E, S6W, S6E, T5W, T5E, T6W, T6E, T7W, T7E, U4W, U4E, U5W, U5E, U6W, U6E [▮RGS, BL, BSg, Ob].

      Cancelled copies of Sheet Q6W in outline with water in blue and woods in green [▮NLS], and Sheet R7W in black outline [▮PC] are recorded.

42. 1:100,000 Map of England and Wales

National Grid series. Published in 53 sheets. Standard sheet coverage 60 by 60 km. A *Policy and Practice for the Protection of Groundwater* map published by the National Rivers Authority, later the Environment Agency, under the aegis of the Soil Survey and Land Research Centre and the British Geological Survey. Ordnance Survey mapping at 1:100,000 is used.

There are insets of the Berwick area on Sheets 1 and 2, Lleyn Peninsula on 14, Bishops and Clerks, Grassholm Island, The Smalls on 34, Lundy Island on 41, the Isles of Scilly on 53. The Isle of Man is not included in this series. Scottish areas are not covered.

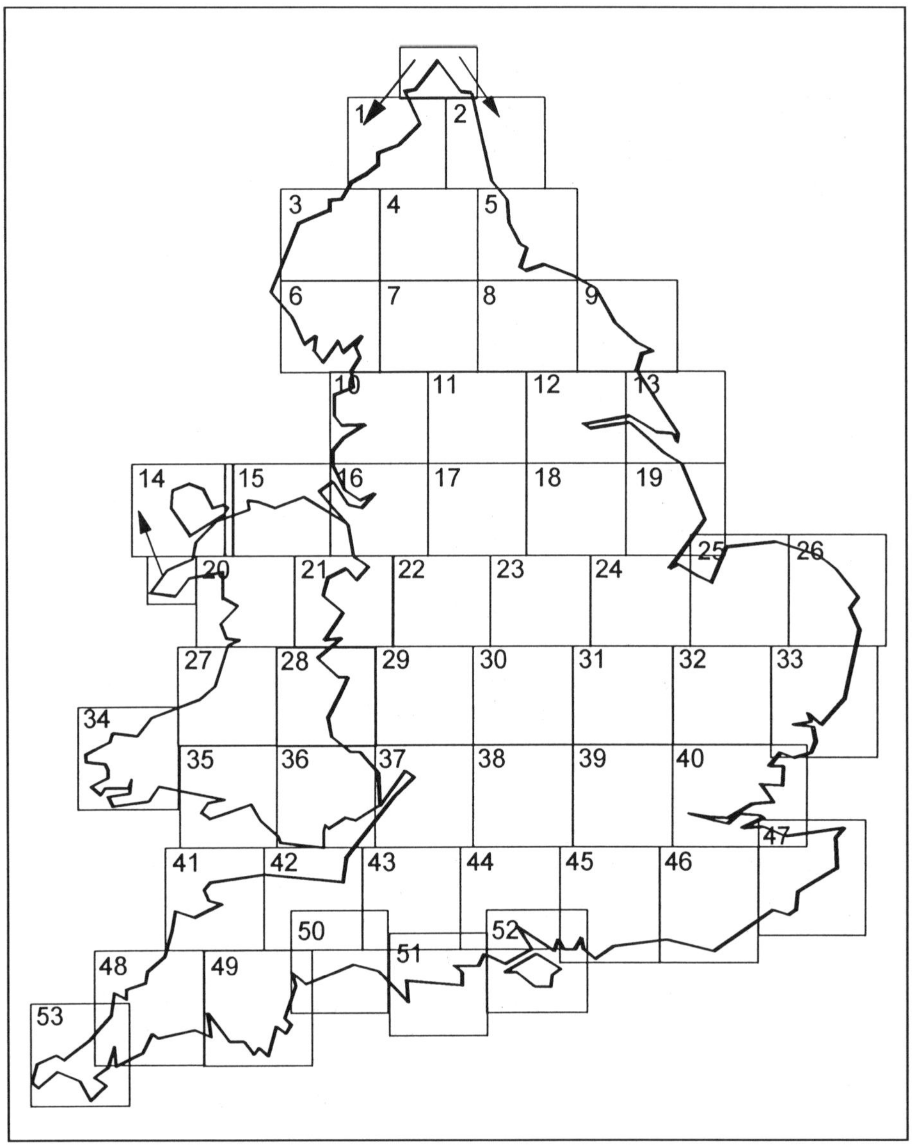

1. *Groundwater vulnerability*, 1994-98. All sheets.

43. 1:100,000 Map of Ireland

Irish National Grid series. Publication was proposed in ? sheets, Sheets 1-4 by the Ordnance Survey of Northern Ireland, 5-? by the Ordnance Survey of Ireland. Ordnance Survey of Ireland sheet layout has not (1999) been revealed. The standard sheet coverage of the Northern Ireland sheets is 110 by 75 km; the four sheets meet at grid reference H600850. The Irish National Grid is at 1 km intervals in blue. Newly drawn, and compiled from 1:50,000 mapping. Heading: *Ireland 1:100 000.*

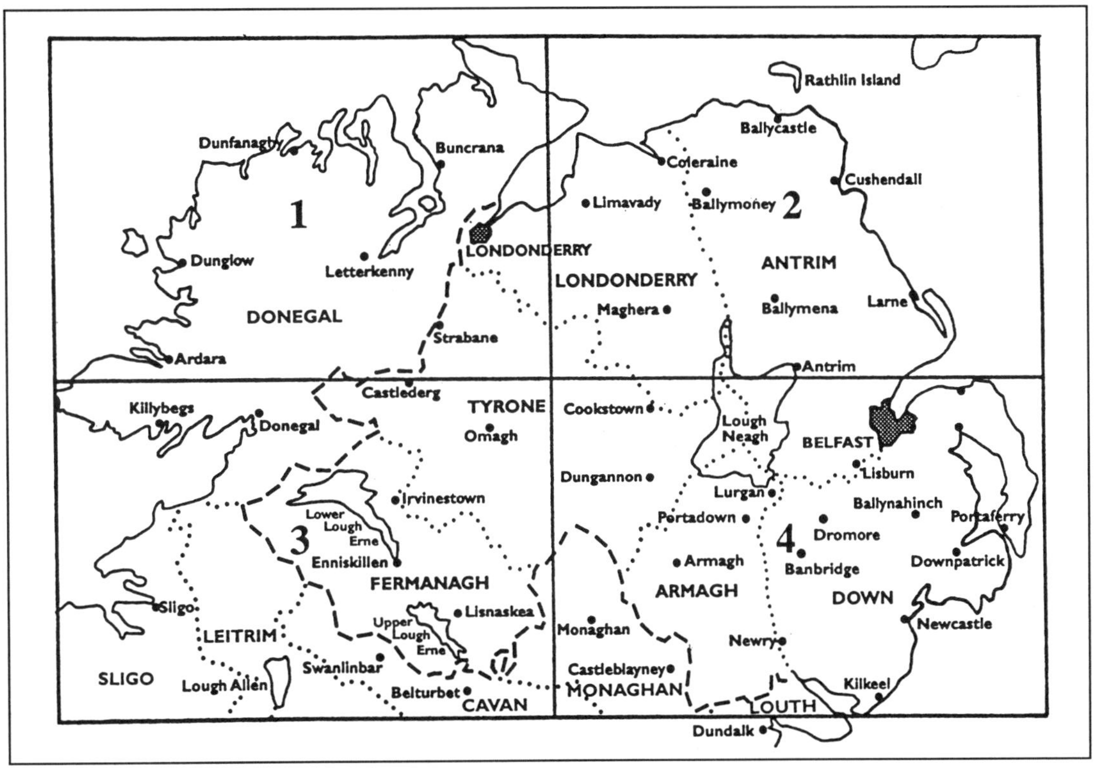

1. Coloured edition, with layers, 1993. Sheet 4 *South East Ulster* [▮PC].
   This sheet was printed though not published. Publication of this series is indefinitely delayed (1999).

44. 1:100,000 Map of France

New drawings were prepared at the Ordnance Survey from GSGS 4040A and 4040B, which were 1:50,000 enlargements of the 1:80,000 *Carte de l'Etat-Major* of France constructed on Bonne's Projection. The drawings were used for both the present 1:100,000 map, GSGS 4249, and the 1:50,000 map of France, GSGS 4250. Six 1:50,000 sheets were required to cover the same area as one 1:100,000 sheet. In the case of the Channel Islands, the various Ordnance Survey island maps provided source material. The 1:100,000 map was initiated in November 1941 and used during Operation Overlord. The whole of France but for a small area in the north-east was covered by this series. Three sheets in two cover the Channel Islands, initially numbered 5E/4Ept *Guernsey - Les Pieux,* 5F/5Ept *Jersey - Iles Chausey.*

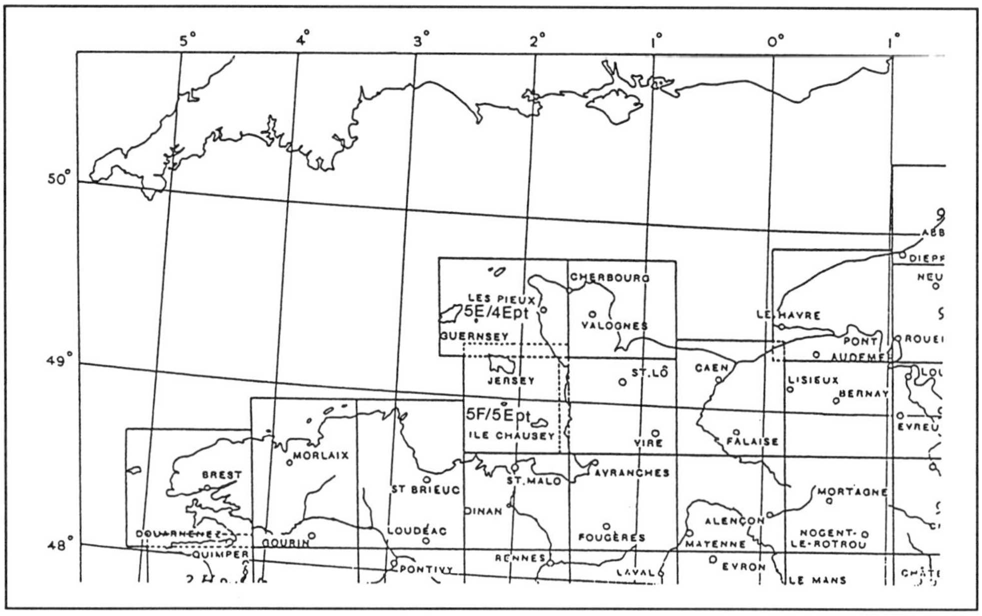

A. With Lambert Zone 1 Grid at 1 km intervals

1. GSGS 4249: First Edition, coloured with brown layers, 1942. 3 sheets in 2: 5E/4Ept, 5F/5Ept [■DGI, Wc].
   The grid is black, numbered in red. A coloured edition has yet to be recorded.

2. GSGS 4249: Second Edition.
   The grid is black, numbered in purple (✣A.2.1), red (✣A.2.2). Sheet numbers are simplified to 5E and 5F. Sheet 5E is renamed *Les Pieux - Guernsey.*
   1. Coloured edition, with purple layers, 1943 (issued 1943-44). 2 sheets: 5E, 5F.
   2. Coloured edition, 1943 (issued 1943-44). 2 sheets: 5E, 5F.
   3. GSGS 4249 (AMS M661): AMS 1, coloured edition, 1944. 2 sheets: 5E, 5F [■Wn].
   4. GSGS 4249 (AMS M661): AMS 2, coloured edition, 1944. 2 sheets: 5E [■Wn], 5F.

B. With Universal Transverse Mercator Grid at 1 km intervals

With the grid overprinted in purple, and mapping transferred to the Transverse Mercator Projection. Lambert Zone 1 Grid principal co-ordinates are retained.

1. AMS M661 (GSGS 4249): Third Edition-AMS.
   1. Coloured edition, with purple layers, 1952. 2 sheets: 5E, 5F [■RGS].
   2. Coloured edition, 1952. 2 sheets: 5E, 5F [■Wn].

45. 1:250,000 Maps of North West Europe and France

Initially two series, GSGS 2733 *North West Europe* and GSGS 2738 *France*, produced by both the War Office and the Ordnance Survey. They were constructed on different projections so their sheet lines lay at an angle to each other. But their sheets shared a common system of numbering. Sheets 1, 2, 4, 5 constituted GSGS 2733 covering Belgium, the remainder GSGS 2738, which extended across Northern France and into Germany. This map was produced by direct reduction of Le Service Géographique de l'Armée 1:200,000 map of France. Sheets 1A, covering Calais and south-east England, and 3 were first members of GSGS 2738, then GSGS 2733. The mapping of the English area bears no resemblance to the contemporary Ordnance Survey quarter-inch map. Sheets 7 and 8, later 3A/8 [see diagram 47], cover Jersey.

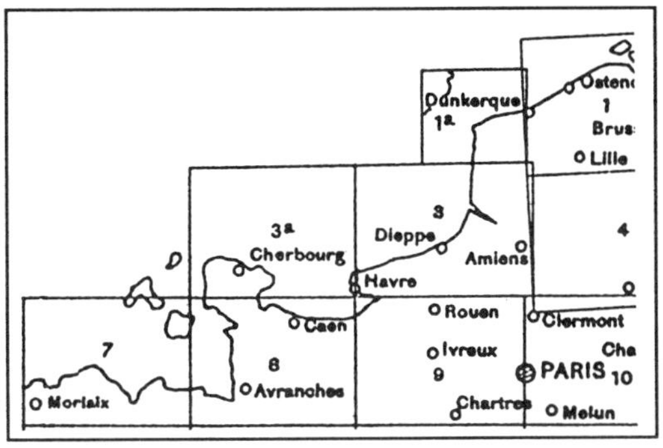

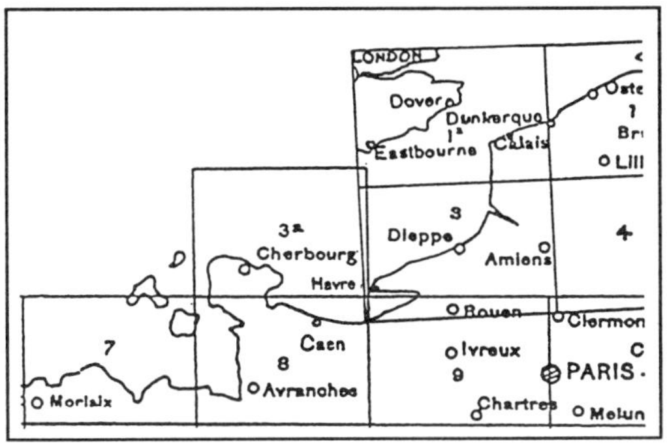

A. With an alpha-numeric squaring system

1. GSGS 2738: *France*, coloured edition, 1914. 3 sheets: 1A, 7, 8.
   Sheet 1A covers the Calais area and shows a coastal outline of England.

2. GSGS 2733: *North West Europe*, coloured edition, 1917. Sheet 1A.
   Sheet 1A, in its retitled, redrawn, enlarged and newly projected form (its appearance on some indexes notwithstanding) of 1917, includes coverage of south-east England.

3. GSGS 2738: *France*, coloured edition, 1914 (revised 1938). 2 sheets: 7, 8 [▮RGS].
   It is documented that sixteen sheets west and south of GSGS 4042 [✚47] were revived as part of the British "rearmament" series and were used by the British Expeditionary Force in 1939-40. The alpha-numeric system was retained for lack of a suitable military grid. This issue appears *de facto* to have been the second edition.

4. GSGS 2738: *France*, 3rd Edition, *Ground Air*, coloured with brown layers, 1942. Sheet 8.

B. With Lambert Zone 1 and Nord de Guerre Grids

Extended to cover all of France not included in GSGS 4042 [✚47] for use in Operation Overlord. Sheet 7 was named *St Brieuc*, Sheet 8 was combined with 3A and named *Cherbourg & Caen*. The grids are black, the Lambert numbered in red, the Nord de Guerre usually in blue.

1. GSGS 2738: *France*, coloured edition, with purple layers.
   1. GSGS 2738, 1943. 3 sheets in 2: 3A/8 (Fourth Edition), 7 (Third Edition).
   2. [AMS M561], 1943-44. 3 sheets in 2: 3A/8 (AMS 2), 7 (AMS 1) [▮Wn].

2. GSGS 2738: *France*, coloured edition.
   1. AMS M561 (GSGS 2738): AMS 3, 1943 (issued 1947). Sheet 3A/8 recorded [▮Wn].
      Overprinted over the other grids by the Universal Transverse Mercator Grid at 10 km intervals in blue. This is probably one of its earliest appearances.
   2. AMS M561 (GSGS 2738): AMS 4, 1943 (issued 1949). Sheet 3A/8 recorded [▮Wn].
      The Universal Transverse Mercator Grid is absent.

46. 1:250,000 Map of Europe (Air)

Constructed on the Lambert Conformal Conical Projection, and laid out on graticule sheet lines. Standard sheet coverage 1°10' in latitude by 2°15' in longitude, including overlaps with adjoining sheets, 10' to the north and 15' to the east. With a graticule at 10' intervals in black. Where present, intersections of the relevant military grids are in orange and air information overprinted in red (blue or magenta on Army Map Service issues). The War Office began compilation in 1938, where possible from GSGS 2738 [✚**45**] and GSGS 4042 [✚**47**]. The map was designed especially to meet the air navigational requirements of the Royal Air Force. Sheet M30/8 *Channel Islands* covers the whole Channel Island group and M31/4 *Boulogne* part of Kent and Sussex, for which quarter-inch *Fourth Edition* mapping [✚**56**] is used. This series does not cover Great Britain. A special set of six sheets covers Ireland [✚**70**]. Heading: *1:250,000 Europe (Air).* Aeronautical map training sheets in England [✚**54**.M.14] and Scotland [✚**59**.M.10] were produced to the specification of this series.

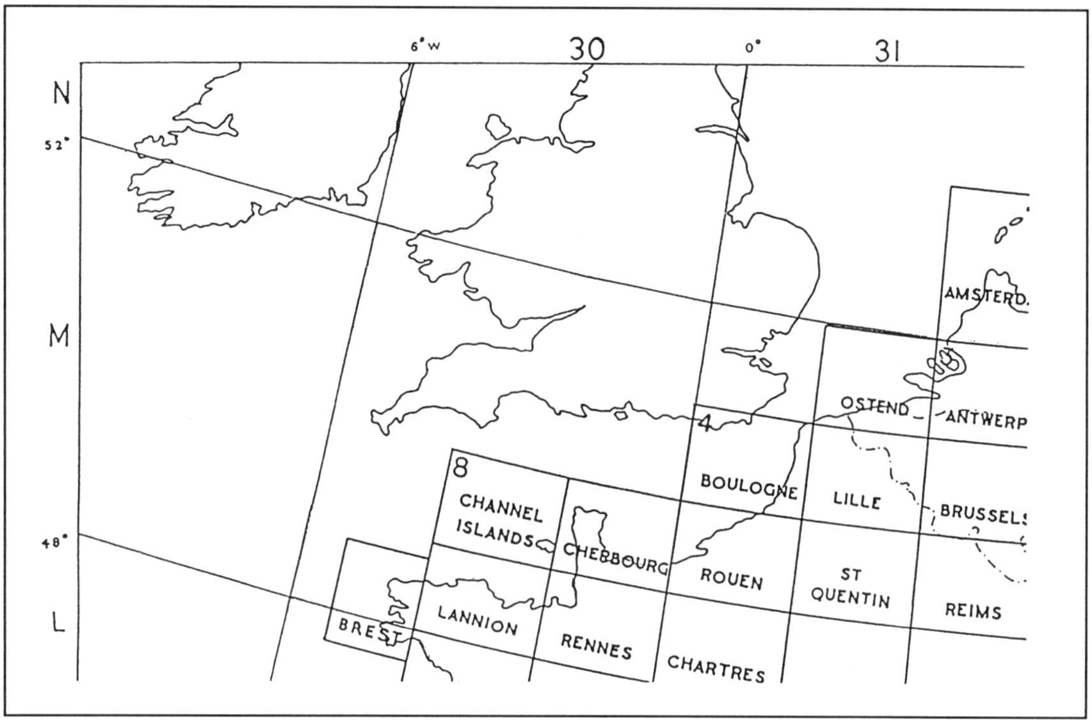

1. GSGS 3982: *Europe (Air),* coloured edition, with purple layers.
   1. GSGS 3982: 1st Edition, 1942 (issued 1942-43). 2 sheets: M30/8, M31/4.
   2. [AMS M502]: AMS 1, 1943. 2 sheets: M30/8, M31/4 [▌Wc, Wn].

2. GSGS 3982: *Europe (Air),* coloured edition, with purple layers and bathymetric layers.
   1. GSGS 3982: 2nd Edition, 1943. 2 sheets: M30/8, M31/4.
   2. [AMS M502]: AMS 2, 1943-44. 2 sheets: M30/8, M31/4 [▌Wc, Wn].

3. GSGS 3982: *Europe,* coloured edition, with purple layers and bathymetric layers. Without air information.
   1. GSGS 3982: 2nd Edition, 194x. Not found.
   2. [AMS M502]: AMS 2, 1944. Sheet M31/4 recorded [▌Wc].

4. GSGS 3982: *Europe,* coloured edition. Not found.
   Unlayered versions are listed in GSGS and AMS catalogues, but which sheets were made and in which editions is uncertain.

GSGS (Air) 5010, a "Salmon and Shrimp" series of coastal sheets, was extrapolated from GSGS 3982 for Coastal Command. It was so called because it offered marine contours, but skeleton detail inland. Sheets 8 and 9 cover the Channel Islands, Sheet 13 part of Kent [▌BL].

47. 1:250,000 Map of North West Europe

Laid out on Nord de Guerre Grid sheet lines. One of a series of GSGS maps initiated in 1936, known as the British "rearmament" series. Issued in nine sheets, later extended north into Holland. Standard sheet coverage 175 by 125 km, including 25 km overlaps with sheets adjoining east and north. Issues for field use displayed the Nord de Guerre Grid in black, numbered in blue. Sheet 1 *Folkestone - Boulogne* covers part of Kent and Sussex, for which England and Wales quarter-inch *Fourth Edition* mapping [**✣56**] is used.

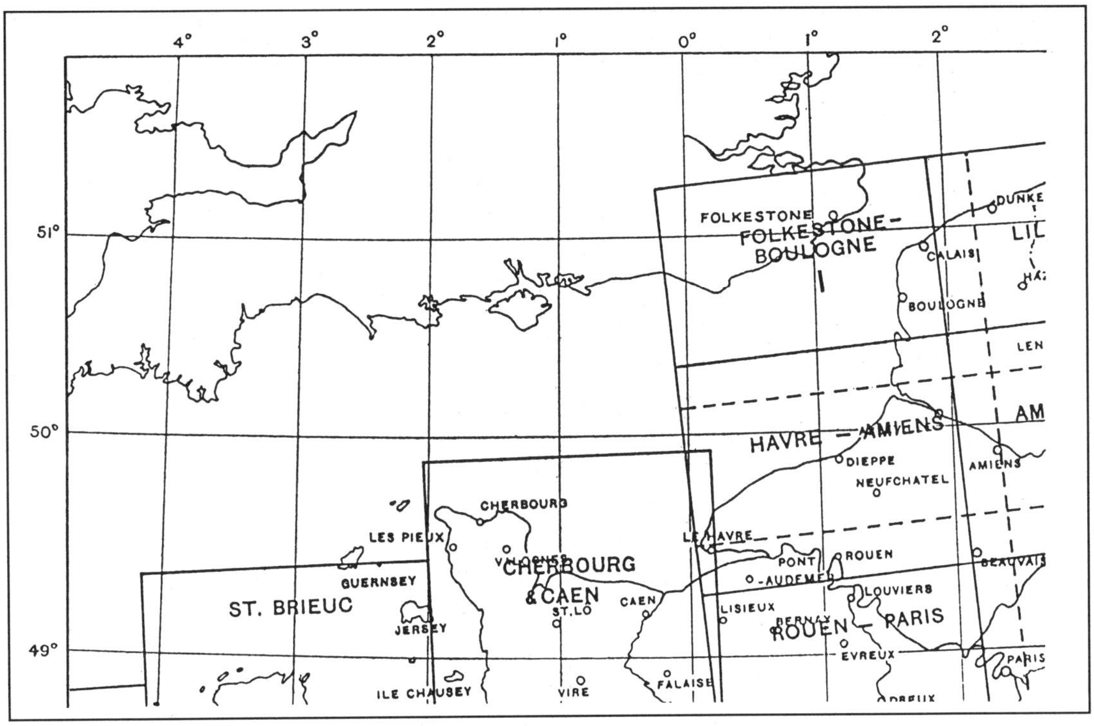

1. GSGS 4042: [First Edition], coloured, 1937. Sheet 1 [▮Wc].
   Reissued 1939 [▮Wc]. This was presumably the edition used by the British Expeditionary Force. The Nord de Guerre Grid is even displayed across England.

2. GSGS 4042: Second Edition.
   With War Office Cassini Grid, called *British Modified Grid,* over the British area, numbered in purple (red on ✣2.5). Used during Operation Overlord.
   1. GSGS 4042: *Ground/Air,* coloured with brown layers, 1942 (issued 1943). Sheet 1 [▮Wc].
   2. GSGS 4042: *Army/Air,* coloured with purple layers, 1943. Sheet 1.
   3. [AMS M503]: AMS 1, *Army/Air,* coloured with purple layers, 1944. Sheet 1 [▮Wn]. The War Office Cassini Grid is here called *English Grid.*
   4. [AMS M503]: AMS 2, *Army/Air,* coloured with purple layers, 1944. Sheet 1 [▮Wn].
   5. GSGS 4042: *Army/Air,* coloured, 1943. Sheet 1.

3. GSGS 4042: Third Edition, *Army/Air,* coloured with purple layers, 1950. Sheet 1 [▮RGS].
   With National Grid (Military System) over the English area, numbered in purple.

4. GSGS 4042: Third Edition, *Army/Air,* coloured with purple layers, 1950. Sheet 1 [▮DGI].
   For planning purposes only. As ✣3, with Nord de Guerre Grid data crossed through and replaced by the Universal Transverse Mercator Grid overprinted in orange.

5. GSGS 4042: Fourth Edition, coloured, 1953. Sheet 1 [▮DGI].
   With Universal Transverse Mercator and National Grids, both in black. The map was made for planning purposes only, and not for use in the field. Printed by the Survey Production Centre, Royal Engineers (British Army of the Rhine).

48. 1:250,000 Geological map of the United Kingdom and Continental Shelf

Constructed on the Transverse Mercator Projection on origins of 0°Lat and 15°W, 9°W, 3°W, 3°E according to UTM zone (see page 244). Laid out nominally in 119 sheets (some combined) on graticule sheet lines, each 1° of latitude by 2° of longitude. With British and Irish National and Universal Transverse Mercator Grids in various colours on land, and a graticule in black at 10' intervals and UTM intersections on sea. Sheets are named and indexed by their south-west corner co-ordinates. Published as the *UTM Series* by British Geological Survey.

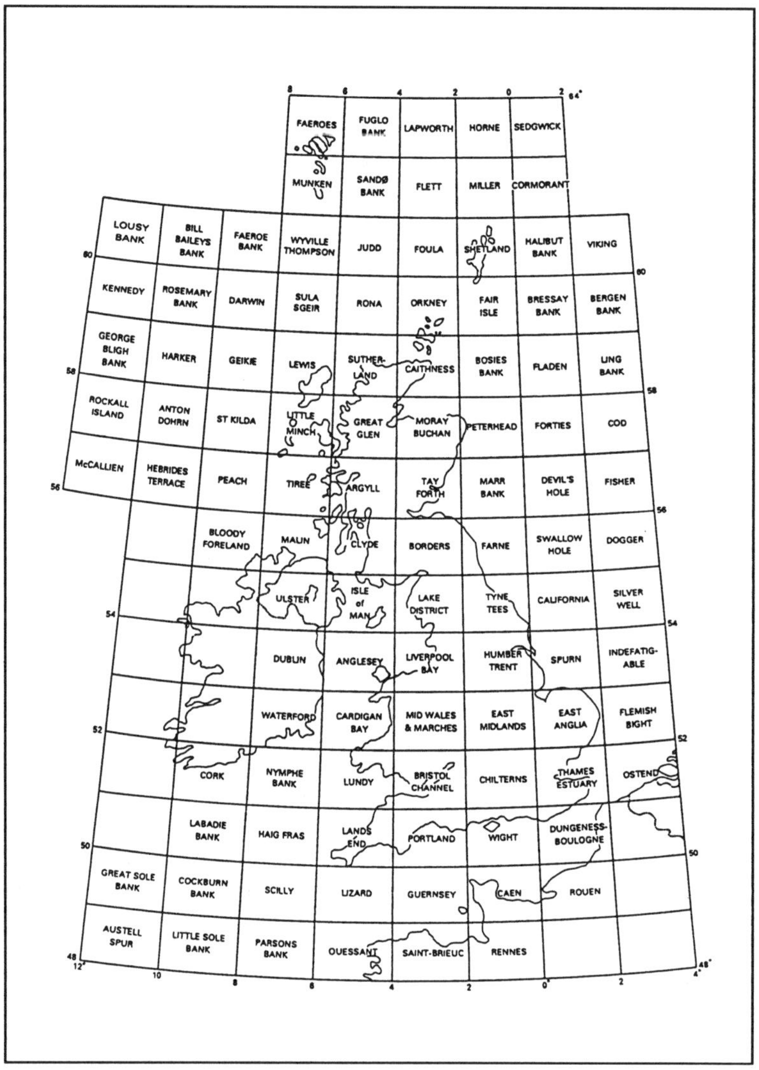

1. Geological editions.
   These three geological types are usually offered separately, though ✢1.3 may be combined either with ✢1.1 or ✢1.2.
   1. Solid edition, 1977- . Publication continues.
   2. Quaternary edition, 1984- . Publication continues.
      Information for offshore areas only is usually published.
   3. *Sea Bed Sediments*, 1982- . Publication continues.

2. Geophysical editions.
   1. *Aeromagnetic Anomaly*, 1977- . Publication continues.
   2. *Bouguer Gravity Anomaly*, 1975- . Publication continues.
   3. *Free-air Gravity Anomaly*, 1981- . Publication continues.
      Sheets covering the continental shelf edge only are published.

49. Quarter-inch Geological Survey of Great Britain : Index Map

Intended for publication nationwide, on sheet lines numbered south to north drawn up by the Ordnance Survey, but engraved by J.W. Lowry and published by the Geological Survey. Showing sheet lines and numbers of the one-inch *Old Series* map [+2]. An official index diagram showing intended sheet lines beyond Wales has not been located.

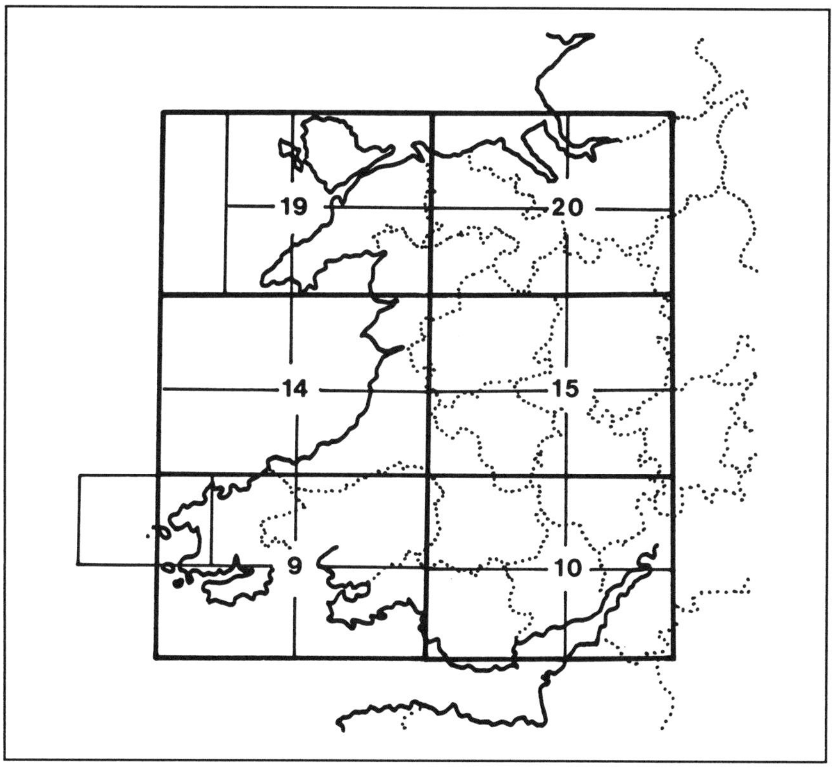

Diagram showing the six Welsh sheets set against the sheet lines of the one-inch Old Series

1. Hand coloured issues, 1858. 6 sheets: 9, 10, 14, 15, 19, 20 [BL].

2. Hand coloured issue, revised 1874. Sheet 10 documented.

3. All published sheets were available uncoloured.

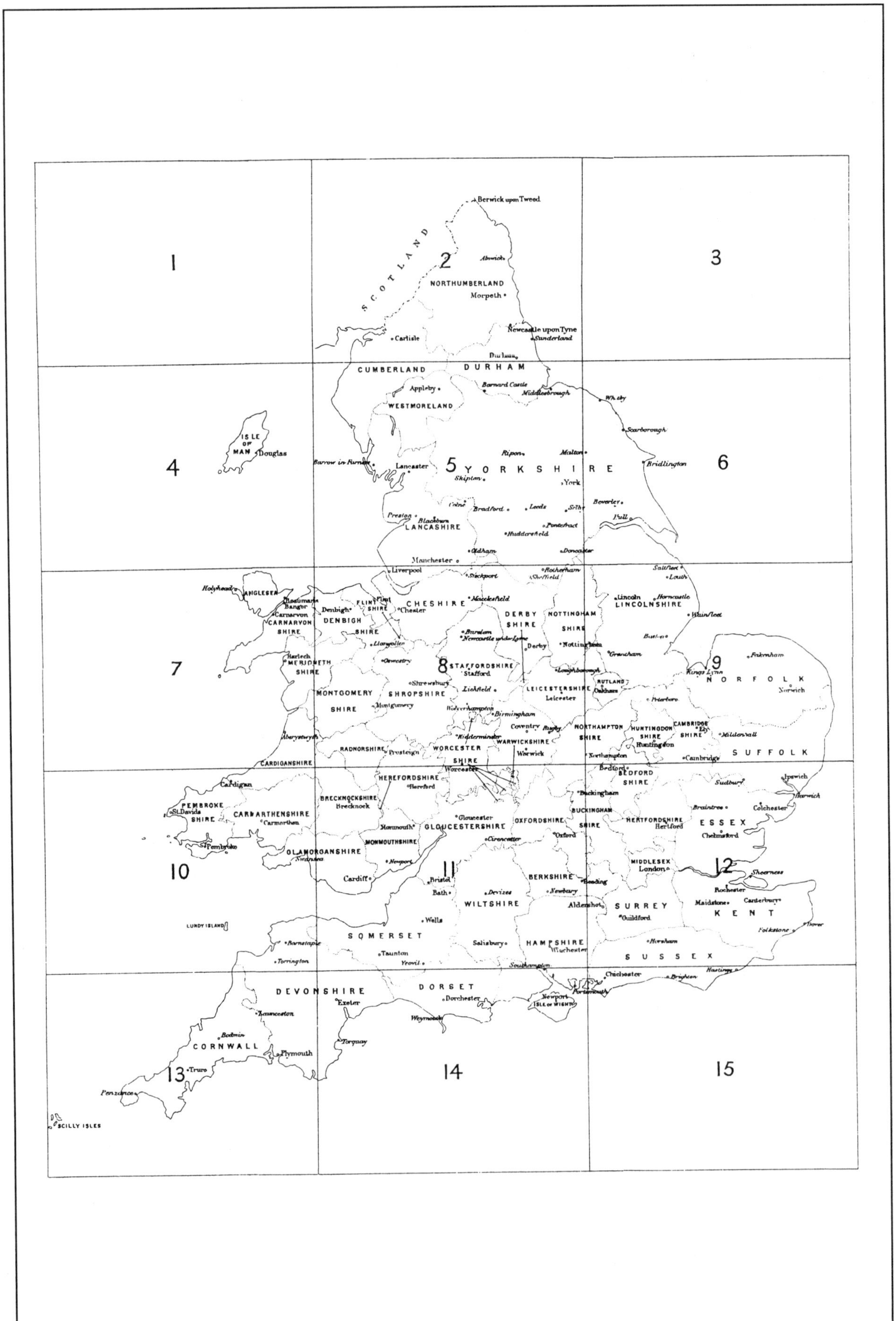

50. Quarter-inch General Map of England and Wales

50. Quarter-inch General Map of England and Wales

Constructed on Cassini's Projection on the origin of Delamere, and published in fifteen sheets. Standard sheet coverage 120 by 90 miles. Sheet 1 is a title sheet and Sheet 3 blank except as the *Index of Colours* of the Geological Survey issues. With a graticule at 20' intervals. Reduced from one-inch *Old Series* maps [**✢2**]. The full title is *A General Map of England and Wales Showing County Boundaries, Railways, Rivers, Canals, Roads, and Principal Parks.* Heading: *Ordnance Survey of England and Wales.*

The Scottish portion of Sheet 2 is blank. There is an extrusion for the Isles of Scilly on Sheet 13. French and Irish mapping is omitted.

1. Outline edition, 1891 (published 1891-92). By engraving. All sheets.

2. *Temporary Edition.* A heading added to reissues of ✢1. ?14 sheets: 2-15 [▮BL].

3. Outline edition, with hill shading. Not found.
   OSR 1892 is the earliest of several annual reports that refer to the preparation of this edition, but it is unlikely that any sheets were completed.

Geological Survey of England and Wales

With a new title Sheet 1: *Geological Map of England and Wales....1896* and in the top margin *Index Map.* Without the date these words form an additional heading to each sheet.

4. Hand coloured edition. All sheets.
   1. By engraving, 1889-96. 14 sheets: 1, 2, 4-15.
   2. By heliozincography, 1896. Sheet 3 *Index of Colours* only.

5. Colour printed edition, by lithography unless noted. All sheets.
   Some sheets retain the publication dates as in ✢4.
   1. Printed by the Ordnance Survey, by heliozincography, 1896-97. 2 sheets: 1, 3.
   2. Printed by Wyman, 1889-96 (published 1896-97). 13 sheets: 2, 4-15.
   3. Reprinted by Wyman, with revisions, 1901. 3 sheets recorded: 8, 11, 12.
   4. Reprinted by the Ordnance Survey, with revisions, 1906. Sheet 5 recorded [▮BL].

6. All sheets were available uncoloured.

7. District map.
   Geological Map of the Isle of Man, 1898.
   A section of Sheet 4 lithographed by Wyman. In G.W. Lamplugh *The Geology of the Isle of Man* (Memoirs of the Geological Survey, United Kingdom), London, HMSO, 1903.

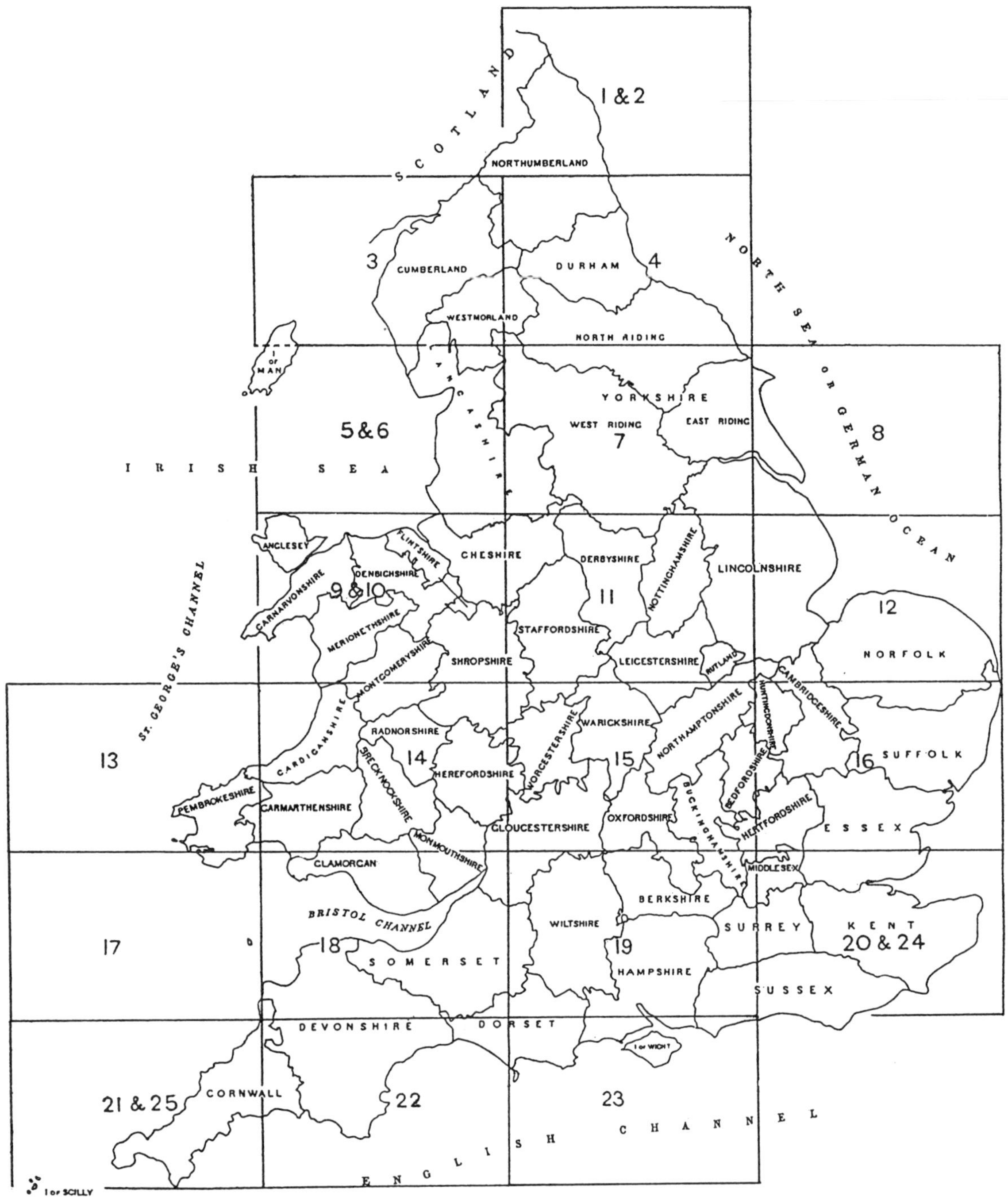

Sheets 19 and 23 in ✣2 were combined on reissue

51. Quarter-inch Map of England and Wales : First Edition

51. Quarter-inch Map of England and Wales : First Edition

Constructed on Cassini's Projection on the origin of Delamere and laid out in 25 sheets, reduced on publication to twenty by sheet combinations. Matrices of the *General Map* [**✣50**] were cut and pieced together in this new format before being electrotyped. Standard sheet coverage 90 by 60 miles, the area covered by 25 one-inch *New Series* sheets [**✣3**]. The same basic sheet layout is used for the *Second Edition* [**✣52**]. With a graticule at 20' intervals, except where noted. Produced from the first national revision of 1893-98. Heading: *Ordnance Survey of England and Wales.* The words "First Edition" do not appear.

The Scottish portion of Sheet 1/2 is blank; there is a coastal outline on Sheet 3. Sheet 20/24 has the same sheet lines as the county map of *Kent* [✣4.2]. Sheet 5/6 has an extrusion from 3 to complete the Isle of Man.

1. Outline edition, 1899-1901 (published 1900-01). By engraving. All 25 sheets in 20: 1/2, 3, 4, 5/6, 7, 8, 9/10, 11-19, 20/24, 21/25, 22, 23.

   The portion of South Wales on Sheet 17 is also covered by an unattributed extrusion on 13. An unattributed extrusion covering Lundy Island and the Devon coast was added to Sheet 18 on reissue. An outline of Ireland was added to Sheet 13 on reissue.

2. Coloured edition, with hill shading. 24 sheets in 19.
   1. First issues, 1902-03. 24 sheets in 19: 1/2, 3, 4, 5/6, 7, 8, 9/10, 11-16, 18, 19, 20/24, 21/25, 22, 23.

      The Sheet 17 land areas are covered by unattributed extrusions on 13 and 18. There is an outline of Ireland on Sheet 13.
   2. Sheets combined on reissue, 1903 (published ?1904). Sheet 19/23.

      The map assumed the printed publication information of Sheet 23 [✣2.1]; it was therefore published after 1903. It was reprinted in 1905.

3. *Aero Map,* probably after 1911. 4 sheets recorded: 11, 12, 15, 16 [▮RGS].

   Coloured editions, with hill shading. These sheets carry the publication information of their source maps in ✣2.1, in all cases 1906-07 reprints. But their date of issue was probably after 1911: see the information provided on Sheet 19/23 which is recorded in *Second Edition* [**✣52**.3]. Sheet 20/24, if no other, was probably also issued. With enhanced waterways in blue, roads in red, railways in black.

4. District maps.
   1. Coloured with hill shading.

      British Association [Map of Yorkshire] 1906, 1906 [▮PC].

      A map specially prepared for the York meeting of the association in 1906. The supplied part of the title is taken from the map cover.

      East Anglia.
      1. *Prepared specially for the British Association for the Advancement of Science. Cambridge Meeting, 1904,* 1904 [▮PC].
      2. Sales edition, lacking British Association references, 1904 [▮PC].

      Salisbury Plain, 1902 (✣4.3).

2. Outline with coloured main roads: county maps.
Anglesey, Carnarvonshire, Denbighshire, Flintshire and Merionethshire, 1901.
Bedfordshire, Cambridgeshire, Huntingdonshire, Northamptonshire and Rutland, 1901.
Brecknockshire, Herefordshire, Montgomeryshire, and Radnorshire, 1901.
Cardiganshire, Carmarthenshire and Pembrokeshire, 1901.
Cheshire. Shropshire. Staffordshire and Flintshire. (Det.), 1901.
Cornwall, 1901.
The Isles of Scilly are inset.
Cumberland and Westmorland, 1901.
Derbyshire, Nottinghamshire and Leicestershire, 1901.
Devonshire, 1901.
Essex, 1901.
Glamorgan and Monmouthshire, 1901.
Gloucestershire, Warwickshire and Worcestershire, 1901.
Hampshire and Wiltshire, 1901.
Isle of Man, 1901.
Kent, 1899 (published 1900).
With the sheet lines of Sheet 20/24.
Lancashire, 1901.
Lincolnshire, 1901.
Norfolk and Suffolk, 1901.
Northumberland and Durham, 1900.
Oxfordshire, Buckinghamshire, Berkshire, Hertfordshire, Middlesex and London, 1901.
Somerset and Dorset, 1901.
Surrey and Sussex, 1901.
Yorkshire (Eastern half), 1901.
Yorkshire (Western half), 1901.

3. Outline with coloured main roads.
Bath and Bristol, 1902.
Birmingham, 1902.
Leicester, 1902. Renamed *Leicestershire,* 1907.
London, 1902.
Manchester and Liverpool, 1902.
Northampton, 1902.
Salisbury Plain, 1901 (✢4.1).
Sheffield, 1902.

4. Outline.
Buxton, 1902 [▮Cu].
Not in legal deposit collections, and possibly a repayment service map.

5. Outline with manoeuvre area boundary in red.
East of England Manoeuvre Map, 1904, 1904.
Two different overprints have been recorded. In *Report on Army Manoeuvres 1904* [▮PRO (WO 279/8, 279/516)]. Also on sale.
South of England Manoeuvre Map, 1903.
Two different overprints have been recorded. In *Report on Combined Manoeuvres 1903* [▮PRO (WO 279/7, 279/516)]. Also on sale.

Geological Survey of England and Wales

All sheets use First Edition base mapping. Later editions use *Second Edition* [✢**52**] and *Fourth Edition (with National Grid)* [✢**56**.B] mapping. The National Grid was also applied to reprints of the earlier editions. The base map used is ignored here. The maps were colour printed. The endeavour has been to list new editions and those reprints which were revised, but to omit unrevised reprints or those "with minor amendments".

There are coastal outlines of Scotland on Sheet 3, of Ireland on Sheet 13/17pt.

A title sheet *Geological Survey : The Quarter Inch Geological Map of England and Wales prepared in 1906-1910 on the Ordnance Survey revised map of England and Wales* was published in 1913. An *Index to Colours and Symbols used on the Quarter-inch Map of England and Wales 1906-1910* was published in 1913, with another issue in 1927. This was provided with a border on its northern and eastern edges, and was designed to fill the north-eastern corner of a wall map of the whole of England and Wales. The title sheet would be located in the north-west corner. Some indexes display this layout.

5. Solid edition (or unspecified). All 25 sheets in 19.
   1. First issue, 1907-10. All 25 sheets in 19: 1/2, 3, 4, 5/6, 7, 8, 9/10, 11, 12, 13/17pt, 14-16, 18/17pt, 19, 20/24, 21/25, 22, 23.
   2. Revised editions, 1921-22 (published 1922). 2 sheets, 15, 19.
   3. Revised editions, 1928-40. 18 sheets in 14 recorded: 1/2, 7, 8, 9/10, 11 (twice), 12, 13/17pt, 14-16, 18/17pt (twice), 19 (twice), 20/24, 23.

      Sheet 21/25 was published in a new edition, not noted as revised, in 1926. Sheet 4 may also exist, with its post-war issue [✢5.4] labelled *3rd Edition.*
   4. Revised editions post-war. 4 sheets in 3 recorded: 1/2 (1951), 3 (1959), 4 (1952, as 3rd Edition).

      Sheet 21/25 was reprinted with revisions in 1969. For Sheet 22 see ✢6.

6. Drift edition. 6 sheets in 5.
   1. First issue, 1906-07. 5 sheets in 4: 8, 12, 16, 20/24.
   2. Revised editions, 1931-36. 5 sheets in 4: 8, 12, 16, 20/24.
   3. Revised edition post-war. Sheet 22, 1952 (published 1953).

      The map was completely redrawn, with revisions, in a Solid with Drift edition.

7. All sheets were available uncoloured.

8. *Gravity Survey Overlay,* 1954-68. 10 sheets in 7: 7/8, 11, 12, 15, 16, 19/23, 20/24.

   Sheet 7/8 thus became an additional combined sheet.

9. Geological Survey district maps.

   The Bristol District, 1955. Solid edition.

   With a graticule, but no National Grid.

   The Country around Cambridge, 1938.

   For the meeting of the British Association for the Advancement of Science at Cambridge in 1938. Reprinted c.1948.

The mapping was also used as a base for indexes to large-scale maps. Other specially constructed maps were issued for specific military purposes, especially army manoeuvres.

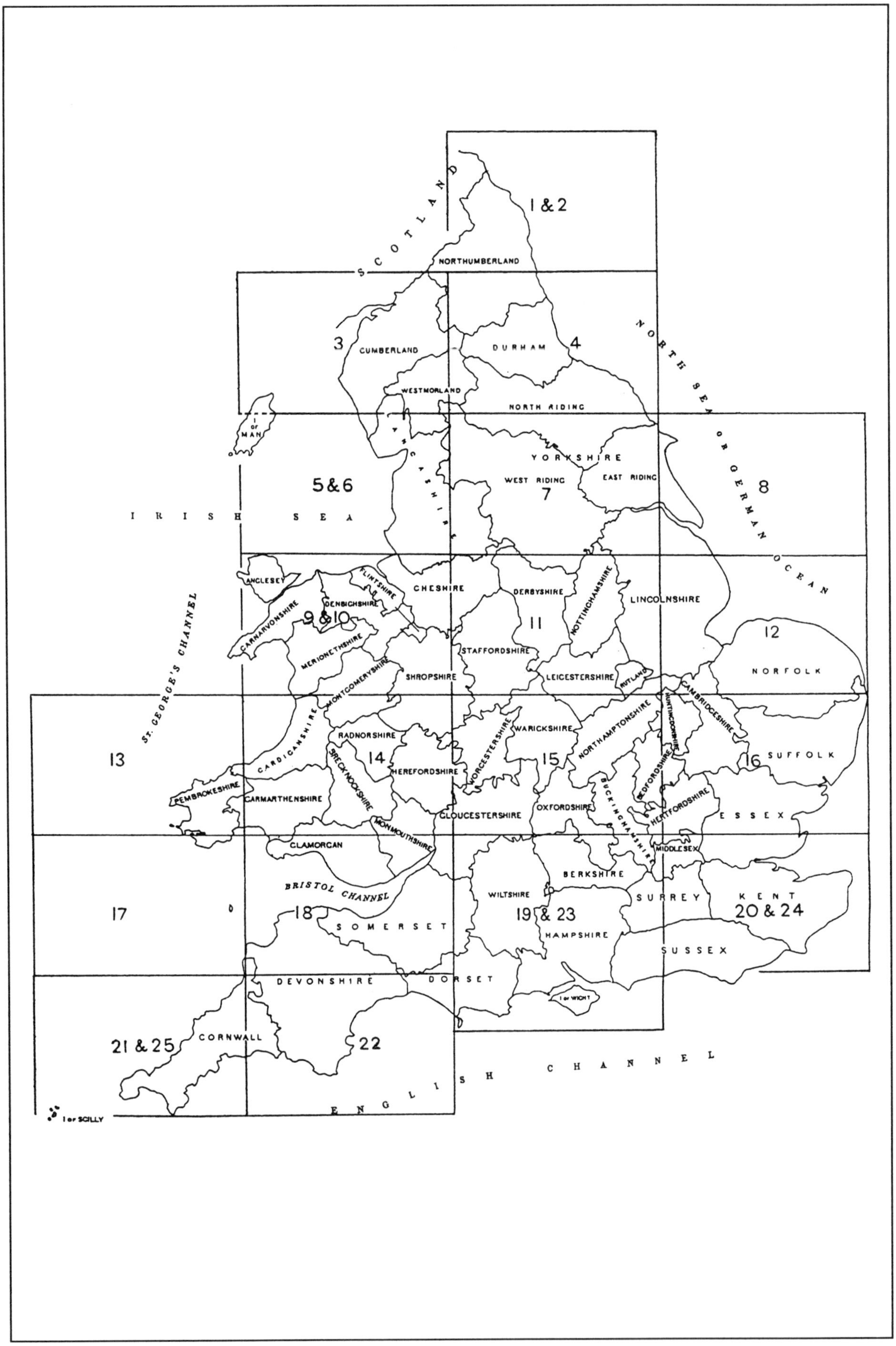

52. Quarter-inch Second Edition Map of England and Wales : small sheet series

52. Quarter-inch Second Edition Map of England and Wales : small sheet series

Laid out (as ✚**51**) in 25 sheets, reduced on publication to nineteen as a consequence of sheet combinations. With a graticule at 20' intervals. Produced from the second national revision of 1901-12. With a coastal outline of Scotland on Sheet 3 and Ireland on Sheet 13. Heading: *Ordnance Survey of England and Wales (Second Edition).* The words "small sheet series" do not appear.

The Scottish portions of Sheets 1/2 and 3 are blank. Sheet 5/6 has an extrusion from 3 to complete the Isle of Man.

1. Outline edition, 1908-14. By engraving. All 25 sheets in 19: 1/2, 3, 4, 5/6, 7 (1917), 8, 9/10, 11-18, 19/23, 20/24, 21/25, 22.
   Sheet 17 was printed but may not have been published [▮RGS]. Its land areas are anyway covered by unattributed extrusions on Sheets 13 and 18. Otherwise publication was complete by 1914 but for Sheet 7 which was delayed until 1917.

2. Coloured edition, with hill shading, 1911. Sheet 19/23 only.

3. *Aero Map,* dated 1911. Sheet 19/23 only [▮RGS].
   Coloured edition, with hill shading. The publication information given is that of the source map [✣2], and is thus no indication of the actual date of issue. See ✚**51**.3 for further details.

Geological Survey of England and Wales: see ✚**51**.5, **51**.6.

The outline map was transferred into the nine-sheet GSGS 2631 *The Distribution of the Territorial Forces in England & Wales 1911,* 1912.

Symbols **:** a **bold** number prefixed with ✚ is a cross reference to another section of the book; a number prefixed with ✣ is a cross reference within the current section; a reference number in ( ) at a district map identifies the next, or previous, such map listed with the same sheet lines; the ▮ symbol accompanies a source reference for maps rarely encountered (library sigla are listed on page 241); ❍ warns that there are noted exceptions to the information given in headings; ↑ identifies what is referred to here as War Office marginalia (for a description see page xxii); ❋ refers to the exceptional use of the heading *Ordnance Survey of Great Britain.*

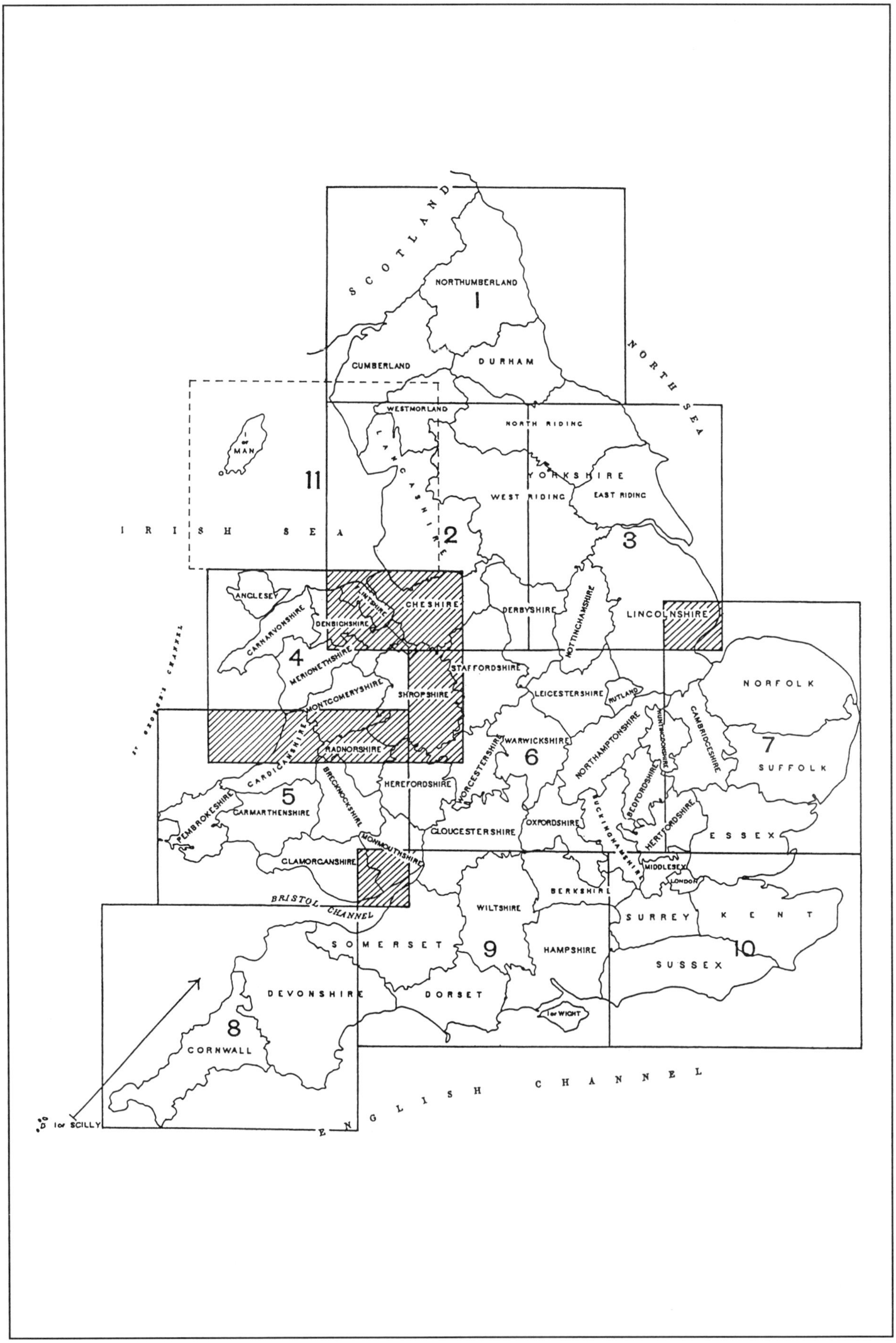

53. Quarter-inch Second Edition Map of England and Wales (Large Sheet Series)

53. Quarter-inch Second Edition Map of England and Wales (Large Sheet Series)

Constructed on Cassini's Projection on the origin of Delamere, and published in ten sheets. Map ✣**52** was recast on to larger sheets, with no standard sheet size. Usually with a graticule at 20' intervals. Heading: *Ordnance Survey of England and Wales (Second Edition).* The 1915 new edition of Sheet 1 replaces *(Second Edition)* with *(Large Sheet Series).* This map does not cover the Isle of Man (but see Air Packets [✣8.4]). Its inclusion was subsequently planned as Sheet 11, which appears on the indexes from 1915. However no copy is recorded.

There is an inset of the Isles of Scilly on Sheet 8.

1. Coloured edition, with hill shading and blue inland water. All sheets.
   1. Published with Scotland blank, 1912. Sheet 1.
   2. Published complete, 1912-15. All sheets, including a new edition of Sheet 1.

2. Coloured edition, with hill shading and black inland water. ?All sheets.
   Printed by Waterlow, apparently in 1914, though not all sheets are so dated.
   1. Published with Scotland blank. Sheet 1.
   2. Published complete. 6 sheets recorded: 2, 3, 6, 7, 9, 10.

3. *Black Outline Edition,* 1912-15 (published 1918). All sheets complete.

4. *Aeroplane Raid October 31st/ 17,* no date. Sheet 10 [▮BL].

5. *London Area* district map.
   1. Coloured edition, with hill shading, 1916.
   2. Outline edition, dated 1916 [▮Wn].

Military and aeronautical issues

6. Coloured edition, with hill shading, overprinted with military grid. Sheet 9 ?only [▮Lraf].
   The sides of the red squares are 10 miles long and are parallel and perpendicular to the Mean Magnetic North (Var[iatio]n 15°4'W). There is no reference system.

7. GSGS 2861: *England (Aviation Map),* 1918. Sheet 9 recorded [▮PRO*].
   Drawn and printed at the War Office. Without reference system. Roads, lettering and other detail are reversed out in white. Coverage extends into France; British coverage is uncertain, though Sheets 5, 6, 8-10 appear on the adjoining sheet diagram.

8. Air Packets.
   These comprised contemporary quarter-inch mapping without hill shading or graticule, sectioned usually into twelve-inch square flying maps, including marginalia at the top. They were issued by the Admiralty War Staff Intelligence Division for the use of pilots of the Royal Naval Air Service. Four packets covered the British Isles. Sheet indexes may either be printed on the reverse, or issued as key plans. All packets were accompanied by explanatory sheets. See also ✣**109**.8.
   1. AWS (ID 1054) Air Packet No.25, March 1916: *Sleaford, Midland and Eastern Counties.* 17 sheets [▮PC: 13, 14, 16].
      Including a special circular map centred upon Sleaford.
   2. AWS (ID 1083) Air Packet No.46, July 1916: *Scotland, North of England, and North of Ireland.* 36 sheets. Not found [▮Lraf: explanatory sheet only].
   3. AWS (ID 1084) Air Packet No.47, April 1916: *South of England.* 10 sheets [▮PC].
   4. AWS (ID 1090) Air Packet No.53, June 1916: *Wales, Isle of Man, and Ireland (South of Donegal Bay).* 32 sheets [▮Lraf].
      Twelve sheets, 7, 8, 13, 14, 19, 20, 25-27, 30-32, cover Wales and part of England; Sheet 6 covers the Isle of Man; nineteen sheets, 1-5, 9-12, 15-18, 21-24, 28, 29, cover Ireland south of Donegal Bay.

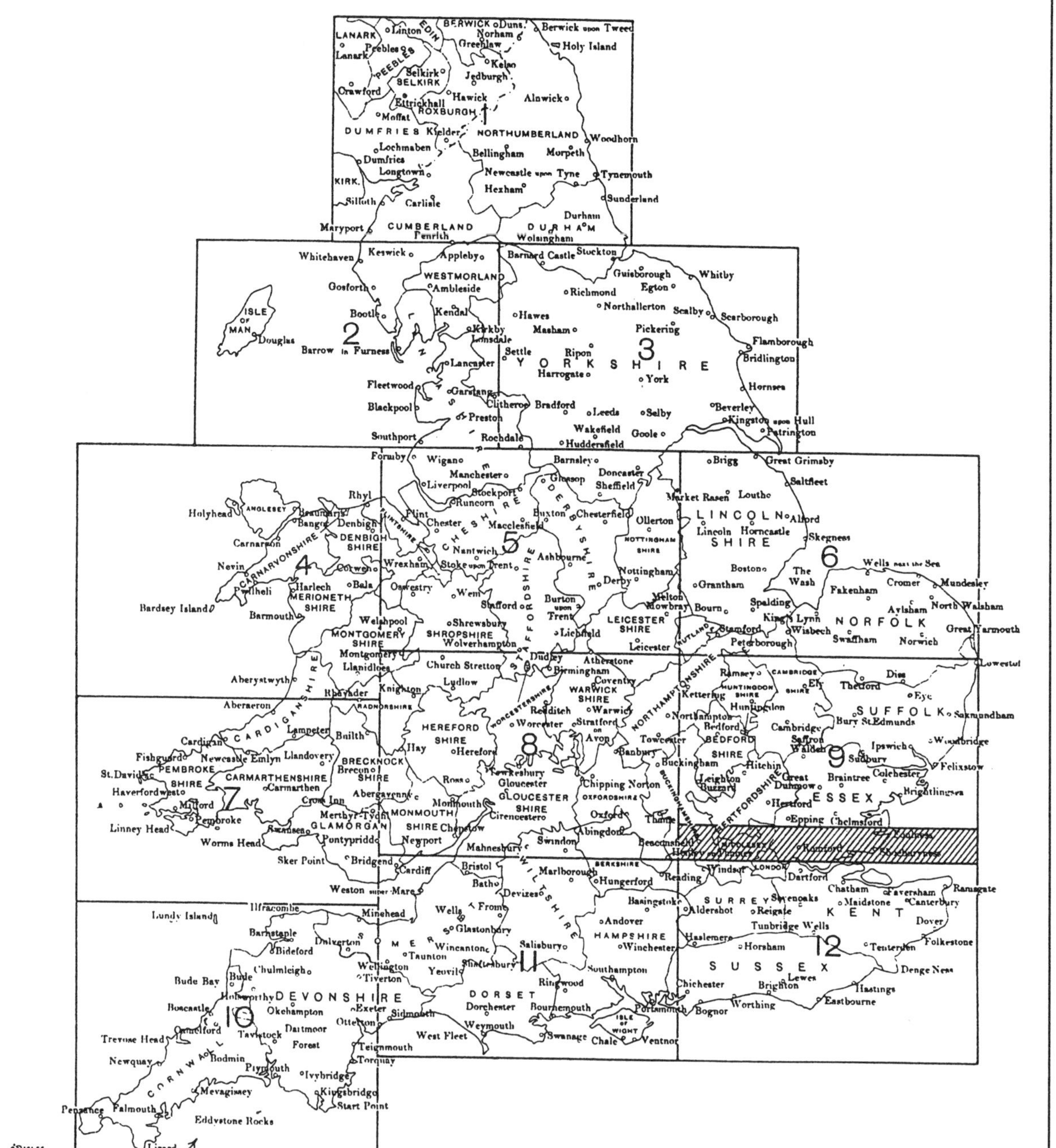

54. Quarter-inch Third Edition Map of England and Wales

54. Quarter-inch Third Edition Map of England and Wales

Constructed on Cassini's Projection on the origin of Delamere, and published in twelve sheets. Standard sheet coverage 108 by 72 miles, which is the area covered by sixteen one-inch *Popular Edition* sheets. Mostly produced from the third national revision of 1912-23 and compiled from drawings at the half-inch scale. Sheet 12 was based on an engraved map until redrawn as the other sheets for heliozincography and reissued in 1926. With an alpha-numeric squaring system unless otherwise noted. Heading: *Ordnance Survey of England and Wales* (Sheet 1 *Ordnance Survey of Great Britain*) : *¼-Inch to One Mile, Third Edition.*

Sheet 1 is common to both England and Scotland [✚**59**.A].

The Isles of Scilly are inset on Sheet 10.

1. Coloured edition, with layers, 1919-21. All sheets.
   Also published as an Ordnance Survey atlas, 1922. Special printings of Sheets 5 and 12 appear in *Report on War Office Exercise Nos.1,2,4 (1930)* and *No.3 (1930) Crowborough...* [▮PRO (WO 279/71, 279/72)], and of Sheet 1 in Brigadier-General W. Sitwell *The Border*, Newcastle-upon-Tyne, Andrew Reid, 1927.

2. *Outline* edition, with water in blue, 1919-21 (published 1923). All sheets.
   Until about 1929 sheets are headed *Third Outline Edition*, thereafter usually *Third Edition*, with *(Outline)* on the water plate.

3. Megalithic series, 1922. Sheet 8 *Long Barrows and Stone Circles.*
   In *Ordnance Survey Professional Papers - New Series, No.6.* The title appears on the map reprint in O.G.S. Crawford *The Long Barrows of the Cotswolds*, Gloucester, John Bellows, 1925. The map is in grey outline, with layers but without contours, and with water in blue. Sites are overprinted in black numbered in red. See also ✚**55**.3, **56**.4.

4. Experimental outline editions, headed in red *New ¼-Inch Series*, 1920 [▮Bg, LDg, Sg].
   A series of experimental outline issues presumably in some way related to similar issues of the one-inch *Popular Edition* [✚**10**.8.2.1, **10**.8.2.2].
   1. *Drawn on ½-inch - reduced and heliozincographed plate for direct printing.* Sheet 4.
   2. *Heliozincographed.* Sheet 7.
   3. *Three fundamental plates printed together. All heliozincographed.* Sheet 7.
      Incorporating outline, water and contour plates.
   4. *Drawn ½-inch - reduced to ¼-inch. Photo-etched and transferred to stone.* Sheet 8.
   5. *Transferred from copper (engraved).* Sheet 12.

5. District map. Coloured with layers.
   South Central, 1924. Another edition, 1929.
   Used for training in the Staff College. The 1929 issue also appears in *Report on War Office Exercise No.1 (1929) Aldershot.....* [▮PRO (WO 279/66)].

M. Aeronautical and military issues

With a graticule at 20' intervals in black

1. *British Isles Aeronautical Series, Provisional* [edition]. 2 sheets recorded: GSGS (Air) 114 Sheet 11 (1923) [▮PRO*], GSGS (Air) 117 Sheet 12 (?1922) [▮RGS, defective].
   Produced by the War Office from the Ordnance Survey map, though largely redrawn and completely relettered. Without contours, but with hill shading in grey, railways and town infill in red. Twin borders show true and magnetic compass bearings from the centre of the map. With air information in black. It has yet to be confirmed whether the Sheet 12 overlap with Sheet 9 is present or not.

With an alpha-numeric squaring system in black

2. *Royal Air Force Special Edition,* 1925. ?All sheets.
   At least one sheet in this edition was also used in *Sectional Maps for Fighter Squadrons.* For information on these see ✣M.4.

With a graticule at 20' intervals overprinted in purple

3. *Civil Air Edition,* 1928-29 (published 1929-30). All sheets.

With War Office Cassini Grid

4. *Royal Air Force Edition,* 1928-?29. All sheets.
   With War Office Cassini Grid (British System) overprinted in purple and air information in red. Sheets 6, 8, 9, 11, 12 are also recorded mounted into sixths of sheets (nine-inch squares) in *Royal Air Force Special Edition : Sectional Maps for Fighter Squadrons,* 1928 [▮PC] wherein the copy of Sheet 6 recorded is a member of the 1925 edition [✣M.2]. In this format Sheet 12 lacks its twelve-mile overlap with 9.

5. [Military exercise map], [1928]. Sheet 3.
   Without air information. Referencing is by a variant of the War Office Cassini Grid (Modified British System), already introduced on some overseas series prior to its introduction in Great Britain. The grid is in black, square with the sheet lines, and springs from a false origin situated near Atherton. Grid values are overprinted in purple across the sheet. In *Report on War Office Exercise No.5 (1928) Harrogate....* [▮PRO (WO 279/64)]. See also ✣**10**.M.4.

6. GSGS 3933: *Military Edition.* Not found.
   Entered as "Gridded" in the *Register of GSGS Maps* in 1933. There is no record that this edition was ever issued, one possibility being that it was planned using the regular *Third Edition* sheet lines, and eventually issued, as GSGS 3950, using the extended sheet lines lately required of aeronautical maps [see ✣M.7].

Aeronautical and military issues with extended sheet lines

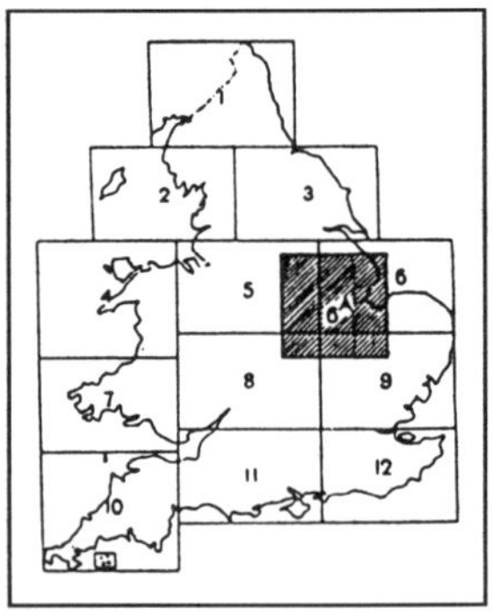

Eight-mile overlaps with sheets adjoining east and north were added as required in military and aeronautical editions starting in 1932.
Sheets with extensions east: 2, 4, 5, 7, 8, 10, 11.
Sheets with extensions north: 2, 3, 5-11.

Contours were omitted from *Civil Air Editions* in 1934, but later restored. The clearance of unnecessary background detail and the addition of more air information was completed between 1935 and 1938. Air information is overprinted in red. Printed publication dates are unreliable and sometimes revert to those on earlier states. Sheet 6A *Grantham* was published in 1936. It forms an additional member of at least two Royal Air Force editions.

With War Office Cassini Grid (Modified British System) overprinted in purple

Coloured editions with brown layers unless noted otherwise.

7. GSGS 3950: *Military Edition,* 1934. ?All sheets.

8. *Royal Air Force Edition.* All sheets.
   Some sheets have *(Aeronautical Map)* supplementing the heading.
   1. Coloured with brown layers, 1932-?34. All sheets.
   2. Coloured with purple layers, ?1936. All 13 sheets: 1-6, 6A, 7-12 [▮Lraf: 6A].
      A copy of Sheet 12 is recorded with GSGS 3950 marginalia [▮PC] [see ✣M.7].

With a graticule at 20' intervals overprinted in purple

9. *Civil Air Edition.* All sheets.
    1. Coloured with brown layers, without contours, 1934. All sheets.
    2. Coloured with brown layers, with contours, 1935-37. ?All sheets.
    3. Coloured with purple layers, 1937. 2 sheets recorded: 11, 12.

With a graticule at 10' intervals overprinted in purple ❍

Coloured editions with purple layers unless noted otherwise. In most cases *(Aeronautical Map)* supplements the heading.

10. *Civil Air Edition,* ?1938. All sheets.

11. *RAF Edition.* All sheets.
    1. Coloured with layers, 1937-38. All 13 sheets: 1-6, 6A, 7-12 [▮Lraf: 6A].
    2. Coloured with shadowing, 1938. Sheet 3 recorded [▮PC].
       Presumably an experimental map, with shadowing applied to the west and south of river valleys, though by no means consistently so.

12. *RAF Edition (War),* 1940-41. All sheets.

13. *RAF (War),* 2nd Edition, 1942. All sheets.
    With War Office Cassini Grid overprinted in brown in the borders at 10 km intervals and at intersection points across the sheets.

14. *Aeronautical Map Training,* 1942. Sheet 5 ?only [▮Ob].
    See also ✛**59**.M.10. This was presumably a map for the training of air crews in the use of GSGS 3982 1:250,000 *Europe (Air)* [✛**46**], the specification of which is similar. The graticule is black.

Without reference system

15. MBAM 3761: *Great Britain : Road Obstructions [(Bridge Head-room)],* [1940-41]. All sheets.
    Outline diagrams prepared by the Map Branch, Air Ministry showing skeleton information only. Later issues are referenced ADI(Maps) 3761. Sheet 12 is classified MBAM 3798. The *Bridge Head-room* reference is present only on some sheets. Similar maps were made for Scotland and Northern Ireland [see ✛**59**.M.11, **70**.5].

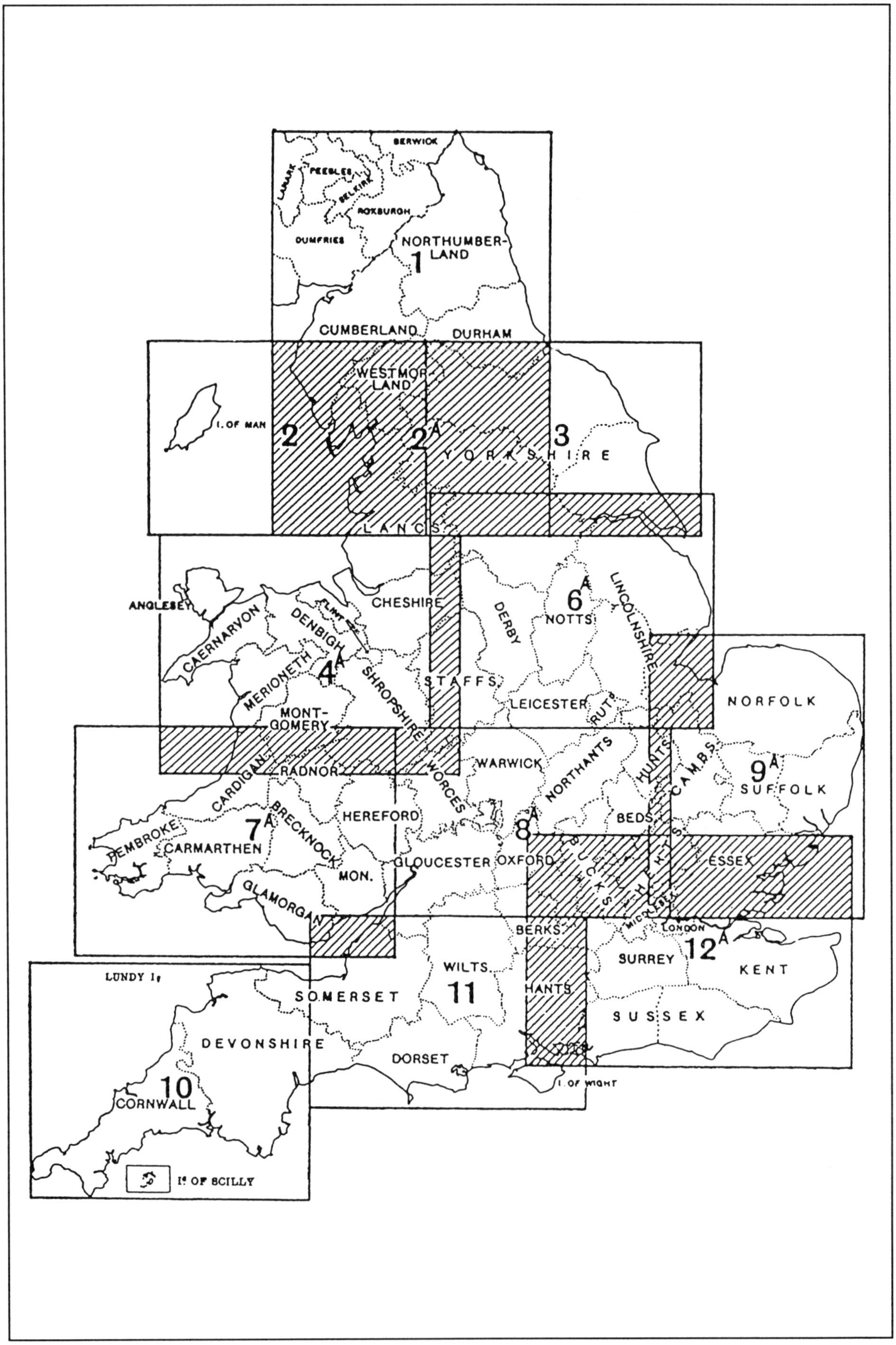

55. Quarter-inch Third Edition (New Series) Map of England and Wales

55. Quarter-inch Third Edition (New Series) Map of England and Wales

Constructed on Cassini's Projection on the origin of Delamere. The *Third Edition* map [✢**54**] was recast and published in twelve sheets: 1, 2, 2A, 3, 4A, 6A, 7A, 8A, 9A, 10, 11, 12A; Sheet 5 was thus discontinued. The sheet lines of 1, 2, 3, 10, 11 are unchanged, but there is no standard sheet size. The epithet *New Series* was used by the Ordnance Survey both in marketing and indexes by 1930, but it was an expression quickly abandoned as within five years the Third Edition was superseded by the Fourth. This edition is now usually referred to as the *A Series*. Coloured issues are recognised most easily by the addition of road numbers. With an alpha-numeric squaring system, unless noted otherwise. Heading: *Ordnance Survey of England and Wales* (Sheet 1 *Ordnance Survey of Great Britain*) : *¼-Inch to One Mile, Third Edition.*

Sheet 1 is common to both England and Scotland [✢**59**.B].

The Isles of Scilly are inset on Sheet 10.

Sheets 2A (1926) and 4A (1928) as first issued preceded the development in specification characteristic of this series, but because of their sheet lines they are treated here.

1. Coloured edition, with layers, 1919-30 (published 1926-31). All sheets as listed above.
   Special printings of Sheets 3, 7A, 8A appear in *Report on War Office Exercise No.3 (1929) Harrogate...* and *Nos.1 and 2 (1931)* [▮PRO (WO 279/68, 279/73, 279/73)].

2. *Outline* edition, with water in blue, 1919-30 (published 1926-30). 10 sheets recorded: 1, 2A, 3, 4A, 6A, 7A, 8A, 9A, 11, 12A.
   Sheet 10 (published if at all in 1931) has not been found, nor Sheet 2, which is improbable. Until about 1929 sheets are headed *Third Outline Edition,* thereafter usually *Third Edition,* with *(Outline)* on the water plate.

3. Megalithic series.
   The base map is grey outline, with layers and contours, and water in blue, overprinted in black. See also ✢**54**.3, **56**.4.
   1. With an alpha-numeric squaring system, 1932. Sheet 11 *Neolithic Wessex.*
      With a commentary by O.G.S. Crawford. In addition to the megalithic sites the overprint includes a depiction of the areas covered by marshland and forest.
   2. With an alpha-numeric border, 1933. Sheet 6A *The Trent Basin : Showing the distribution of Long Barrows, Megaliths and Habitation-sites.*
      With a commentary by C.W. Phillips.

4. Outline edition in grey, 1931. Sheet 9A [▮PC].
   For the Le Play Society.

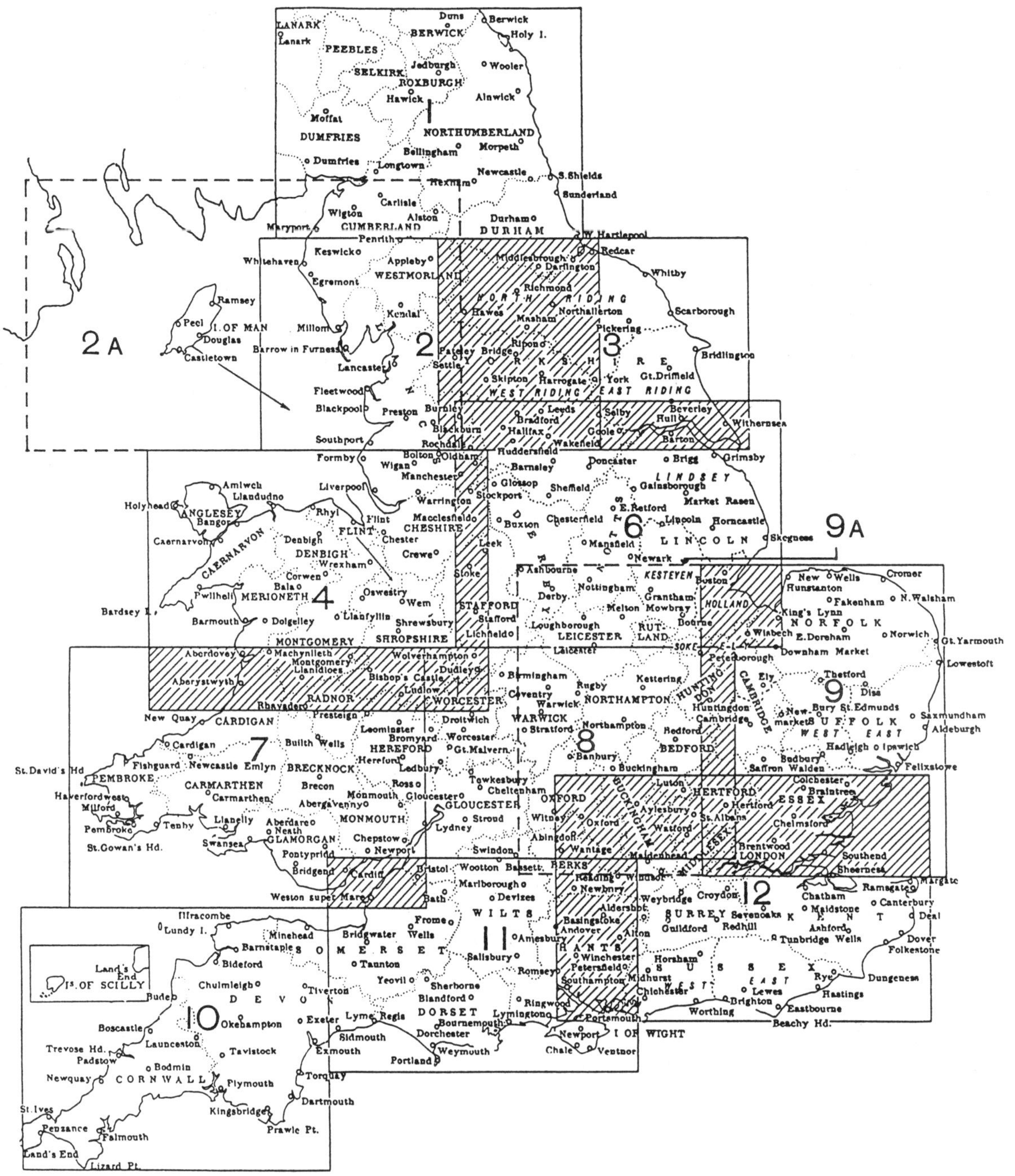

See military issues for Sheets 2A and 9A

56. Quarter-inch Fourth Edition Map of England and Wales

56. Quarter-inch Fourth Edition Map of England and Wales

Constructed on the national Transverse Mercator Projection on the origin of 49°N,2°W, and published in eleven sheets on National Yard Grid sheet lines: 1-4, 6-12. Sheet 5 was intentionally omitted, presumably in order to relate sheet numbers more closely to those of the *Third Edition (New Series)* [✣**55**], the map on Cassini's Projection from which the mapping was transferred (see page xiii). There is no standard sheet size. Heading, if present: *Ordnance Survey of Great Britain* : *Fourth Edition, England & Wales.*

With insets of the Isle of Man on Sheet 2, Isles of Scilly on 10. The Smalls are not covered.

A. With National Yard Grid at 10,000 yard intervals O

1. Coloured edition, with layers, 1934-35. All sheets.

2. *Black* [outline] edition. All sheets.
   Most sheets are lacking in OSPR, so publication dates are at present deduced from the print code on the earliest known state of each sheet.
   1. With uncoloured woods, 1935. 5 sheets recorded: 3, 4, 7, 10, 11.
   2. With woods in grey, 1935-37. 6 sheets recorded: 1, 2, 6, 8, 9, 12.

3. Outline edition, with water in blue. All sheets.
   1. With uncoloured woods, 1941. Sheet 7 recorded.
   2. With woods in grey, with grid, 1941. 2 sheets recorded: 2, 6.
   3. With woods in grey, without grid, 1941-46. 9 sheets recorded: 1, 3, 4, 6, 8-12.

4. Megalithic series, 1936. Sheet 7 *South Wales* : *Showing the distribution of Long Barrows and Megaliths.*
   The base map is grey outline, with water, layers and contours, overprinted in black. With a commentary by W.F. Grimes. See also ✣**54**.3, **55**.3.

5. Water and contour issues.

6. Outline edition, with water in blue, contours in brown, 1933. Sheet 4 recorded [▮RGS].
   A defective copy, presumably an experimental printing with trial specification. Without price or grid, though grid values are present.

B. With National Grid

Heading: *Fourth Edition (National Grid), England & Wales* (not ✣B.3).

1. Coloured edition, with layers, 1945-46. All sheets.

2. *Outline Edition,* with woods in grey, 1945-46. All sheets.

3. Outline edition, with water in blue, 1940-42. All sheets [▮Wc].
   Unpublished: for wartime official use. The expression *Ordnance Survey Grid* is used.

4. *Administrative Areas Edition,* 1950 (published 1951). Sheet 1 only.
   In brown outline. Two versions recorded, showing:
   1. County, burgh, district boundaries (red), civil parishes (purple).
   2. As ✣B.4.1, together with parliamentary constituencies (green).

   See Scotland [✣**60**.B.3] for the remainder of the set.

5. Water and contour issues.

Geological Survey of England and Wales: *Fourth Edition* mapping is noted in ✣**51**.5, **51**.6.

M. Military issues overprinted with War Office Cassini Grid in purple

With *Fourth Edition* marginalia, and layer colouring, where present, in brown

Air information, where given, is in red. The *Military Edition* heading is sometimes lacking.

1. GSGS 3957: *Military Edition.* All sheets.
   Sheet 9A *East Anglia* was introduced in 1940. Its coverage is that of Sheet 9 extended some 63 miles west. First issues of this sheet lack air information.
   1. Coloured edition, with layers, 1937. ?11 sheets: 1-4, 6-12.
      With full air information tabulated in the right-hand margin.
   2. Coloured edition, with layers, 1939. All sheets: 1-4, 6-9, 9A (?1941), 10-12.
      With much reduced air information, tabulated in the bottom margin.
   3. Coloured edition, 1940. All sheets: 1-4, 6-9, 9A, 10-12.
      Most issues include air information.
   4. Outline edition, with water in blue, 1941. ?8 sheets: 6-9, 9A, 10-12 [▮PRO*, Wc].
      Other outline sheets are on the *War Revision* base [see ✣M.2.4].
   5. *Sales Copy,* coloured with layers, published 1943. 2 sheets recorded: 4, 9.

   The following issue dependent on ✣M.1.2 is recorded:
   6. Overprinted showing ?Yorkshire Manoeuvre Area, 1939. Sheet 3 [▮PRO*].

2. GSGS 3957: *War Revision,* 1940. 11 sheets.
   Sheet 12 is not recorded in some editions, probably because their immediate issue was possible in *Second War Revision* [✣M.3].
   1. *Military Edition,* coloured with layers, 1940-41. 11 sheets: 1-4, 6-12.
   2. [AMS M521]: AMS 1, coloured with layers, 1942-43. 10 sheets: 1-4, 6-11 [▮Wn].
      Sheet 6 is also recorded as "Reprint 1942", in advance of AMS 1 [▮Wc].
   3. *Military Edition,* coloured, 1940-?41. 10 sheets recorded: 1-4, 6-11.
   4. *Military Edition,* outline with water in blue, 1941. 2 sheets recorded: 2, 3 [▮Wc].
      Other outline sheets are on the *Military Edition* base [see ✣M.1.4]. It is thus uncertain which base was used for Sheets 1 and 4, or whether they exist.
   5. GSGS 3957[B]: *Grid/Graticule Edition,* 1941. 11 sheets: 1-4, 6-12 [▮PRO*].
      An outline edition with water in blue, overprinted in addition with a graticule at 10' intervals and *RAF Edition* [**✚54**.M.11] sheet lines in red. Sheet 3 and 1943 reprints are classified GSGS 3957B.
   6. *Sales Copy,* coloured with layers, published 1943. 10 sheets recorded: 1-4, 6-11.

3. GSGS 3957: *Second War Revision,* 1941.
   The Nord de Guerre Grid overprinted in blue appears on late printings.
   1. *Military Edition,* coloured with layers, 1941. Sheet 12.
   2. [AMS M521]: AMS 1, coloured with layers, 1942 (issued 1943). Sheet 12 [▮Wn].
   3. *Military Edition,* coloured, 1942. Sheet 12.
   4. GSGS 3957B: *Grid/Graticule Edition,* 1943. Sheet 12 [▮PRO*].
      An outline edition with water in blue, overprinted in addition with a graticule at 10' intervals and *RAF Edition* [**✚54**.M.11] sheet lines in red.
   5. *Sales Copy,* coloured with layers, published 1943. Sheet 12.

With War Office marginalia↑, and layer colouring in purple ○

With air information in red, except where noted. Sheet 2 is replaced by 2A *Irish Sea.* The Irish area is mapped, with the War Office Irish Grid in black, numbered in red.

4. GSGS 3957 (Air) editions. All sheets.
   A quarter-inch *Third Edition* style border [**✚54**] was used for Sheets 1, 3, 4, 6-12.
   1. *Ground Air* edition, 1942. Sheet 6 ?only [▮PC].
      The copies seen have *Ground Air* ruled through and *Air* overprinted in red.
   2. *Air* edition, 1942 (issued 1942-43). All sheets: 1, 2A, 3, 4, 6-12.
   3. [AMS M521]: AMS 2, 1944. 10 sheets: 1, 3, 4, 6-12 [▮Wn].
      For the companion issue of Sheet 2A (in edition AMS 1) see ✣M.6.2.

5. GSGS 3957 (Air): *War Revision,* 1940 : *Air,* First Edition, 1943. 2 sheets: 6, 7 [▮BSg].
   These sheets were proved in 1944, but were probably not issued.

6. GSGS 3957: *War Revision,* 1940 : *Military,* 1942.
   1. GSGS issue. Not found.
      It is unlikely that this edition was issued, though Sheet 2A was presumably proved for it to have been made available to the Army Map Service.
   2. [AMS M521]: AMS 1, 1943. Sheet 2A [▮Wn].
      For companion issues of Sheets 1, 3, 4, 6-12 (in edition AMS 2) see ✣M.4.3.

7. GSGS 3957: *2nd War Revision* : *Air,* 1943. All sheets.
   1. GSGS 3957 (Air): *Air* edition, 1944. All sheets: 1, 2A, 3, 4, 6-12.
      The Nord de Guerre Grid is overprinted in blue on Sheet 12.
   2. [AMS M521]: AMS 3, 1944. All sheets: 1, 2A (AMS 2), 3, 4, 6-12 [▮Wn].
   3. GSGS 3957 (Graticule): *Graticule Edition,* 1944. All sheets: 1, 2A, 3, 4, 6-12.
      Overprinted with a graticule at 10' intervals. Grids are shown by intersections and in the border. *Air* is replaced by *Graticule* at the GSGS number.

8. GSGS 3957: *2nd War Revision* : *Military.* All sheets.
   The Nord de Guerre Grid is overprinted in blue on Sheet 12.
   1. Coloured edition, with brown layers, 1942. Sheet 11 recorded [▮BSg].
      Proved in 1943, but probably not issued. Without air information.
   2. Coloured edition, with purple layers, 1943 (issued 1944). All sheets: 1, 2A, 3, 4, 6-12.
      Sheets 6 and 11 were reprinted in 1947 [▮PRO*].
   3. Third Edition, 1948 (issued 1949). Sheet 8 recorded [▮Bg].
      With air information in black.

   The following issues dependent on ✣M.8.2 are recorded:
   4. *Exercise Ubique IV,* 1947. Sheet 11 [▮Ob].
   5. GSGS Misc.299: *Exercise Ubique II,* 1947. Sheet 11 [▮Ob].
      See also ✚**10**.M.12.11.
   6. GSGS Misc.365: *Exercise Viking* : *Situation 19 Sep 49,* 1949. Sheet 11 [▮Ob].
      See also ✚**10**.M.12.13.

Military issues with National Grid (Military System) ○

The grid was initially numbered in purple, with air information printed independently in blue from 1952. The colour plates were united in about 1956. Sheets 1-4, 6-12 were issued.

9. GSGS 4628, later M521, coloured edition, with brown layers. All sheets.
   1. *War Office Edition,* 1948 (issued 1950). All sheets.
      With graticule intersections at 20' intervals.
   2. Fourth Edition-GSGS, 1948 (issued 1950). 3 sheets recorded: 4, 10, 12.
      With revised isogonals. The decision would appear to have been taken to implement a system of edition numbers incremental upon the civilian *Fourth Edition.*
   3. First Edition-GSGS, 1948 (issued 1951). Sheet 6 recorded.
      Using a base map that continues to display the numerical reference system of the National Grid, blocked out by overprint. The edition number is difficult to justify.
   4. Fifth Edition-GSGS, 1951 (issued 1951-52). ?9 sheets: 1, 3, 4, 7-12.
      Using base maps displaying the letter reference system of the National Grid.
   5. With air information and a graticule at 30' intervals overprinted in blue, 1952-53. All sheets.
      Sheets 2 and 6 did not appear as ✣M.9.4 issues so were issued here in Fifth Edition-GSGS. Sheets 1, 3, 4, 7-12 were increased to Sixth Edition. Each sheet was thereafter updated in numbered GSGS editions.
   6. AMS M521 (GSGS 4628), 1960 (Sheet 2 1955). All sheets [▮Wn].
      Without air information.

The following dependent issues are recorded:

7. GSGS Misc.490: *Exercise Hereward,* 1950. Sheet 9 [▮Ob].
   See also ✣**19**.M.3.8.
8. GSGS Misc.1663: *Exercise Quicksilver,* 1954. 2 sheets: 3, 6 [▮Ob].
   See also ✣**19**.M.3.15.

10. GSGS 4628 coloured edition.
    1. *War Office Edition,* 1948 (issued 1950). 3 sheets recorded: 4, 7 [▮PRO*]; 10 [▮Wc].
    2. AMS M521 (GSGS 4628): Fourth Edition-GSGS, 1951. All sheets [▮Wn: not 2].

11. GSGS 4735: [Topographical Air Map], 1955. Sheet 12 only [▮PC].
    Issued by the War Office, for the Ministry of Transport and Civil Aviation. With a graticule at 30' intervals and air information overprinted in blue. The grid has no military overprint. 1954 proof copies of Sheets 3 and 8 are also recorded [▮PC] which retain the National Grid (Military System). Superseded by GSGS 4736 [✣**61**], a similar map covering the whole of the United Kingdom.

12. GSGS 4857: *RAF Topographical Map..... (Radar),* 1956-57. All sheets [▮PRO*].
    With air information overprinted in blue. The grid has no military overprint.

13. GSGS 4863: *RAF Topographical Map,* 1955-56 (issued 1956). All sheets [▮BL].
    With a graticule at 30' intervals and air information overprinted in blue.

- As Sheets 10-20 in GSGS 4736 see ✣**61**.

14. *England, South.* District map, coloured with layers, unless noted otherwise.
    1. GSGS 4628: First Edition-GSGS, untitled, 1951. Unpublished proof [▮PRO*].
       A handwritten note is appended: *Stock of these will have an o/p* (ie ✣M.14.3).
    2. GSGS Misc.1709: *England, South,* Edition 1-GSGS, 1955 [▮Ob].

       With overprinted title *Exercise Surprise Packet.*
       See also ✣**19**.M.3.10.
    3. GSGS Misc.1561: *Manoeuvre Area,* 1951 [▮Og].
    4. GSGS Misc.1563: *Traffic Routes,* 1951 [▮Ob]. Outline.
    5. GSGS Misc.1563/1: *Traffic Routes, Control HQ, and Umpires' Report Centres,* 1951 [▮Ob]. Outline.

Symbols **:** a **bold** number prefixed with ✣ is a cross reference to another section of the book; a number prefixed with ✣ is a cross reference within the current section; a reference number in ( ) at a district map identifies the next, or previous, such map listed with the same sheet lines; the ▮ symbol accompanies a source reference for maps rarely encountered (library sigla are listed on page 241); ❍ warns that there are noted exceptions to the information given in headings; † identifies what is referred to here as War Office marginalia (for a description see page xxii); ⊛ refers to the exceptional use of the heading *Ordnance Survey of Great Britain.*

57. Quarter-inch General Map of Scotland

Constructed on Bonne's Projection on the origin of 57°30'N,4°W, and published in nine sheets, plus an unnumbered title sheet and one entitled *Margins for 4 mile map of Scotland* consisting of extensions to Sheets 3, 5, 7 and 9 to permit the map to be mounted whole as a rectangle. Standard sheet coverage 120 by 90 miles, which is the area covered by 25 one-inch sheets. Reduced from blue impressions of the one-inch map [**✤13**] and usually printed by photozincography. With a graticule at 20' intervals. The full title is *A General Map of Scotland on the scale of one inch to four statute miles Showing the County Boundaries, Rivers, Lochs, Canals, Railways, Leading Roads and Principal Demesnes.* A *Table of Reference* was published in 1892. The sheets have no Ordnance Survey heading.

With an inset of St Kilda and Boreray on Sheet 4, and an extrusion for Housay on Sheet 1. With coastal outlines of Ireland and England. The English portion of Sheet 9 is blank.

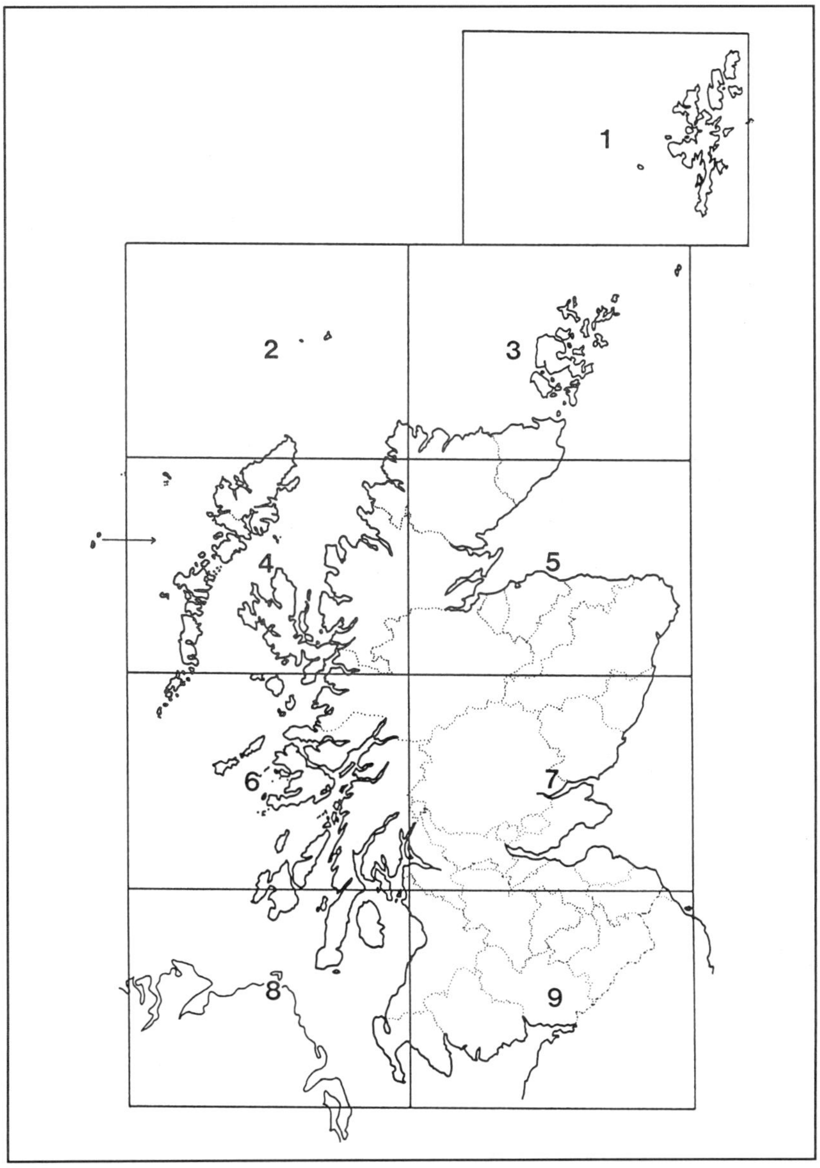

1. Outline edition, with water in blue, 1890-91 (published 1891). All sheets.

2. *Temporary Edition,* 1891-92, reprinted 1892-93. ?9 sheets: 1-9 [▮RML, Wc].
   This heading was added to reprints of the maps in ✣1. The reprints of Sheets 1-9 in ▮RML are later, and dated 1898-1900. In this issue Sheets 3 and 4 were printed by heliozincography, the others by photozincography.

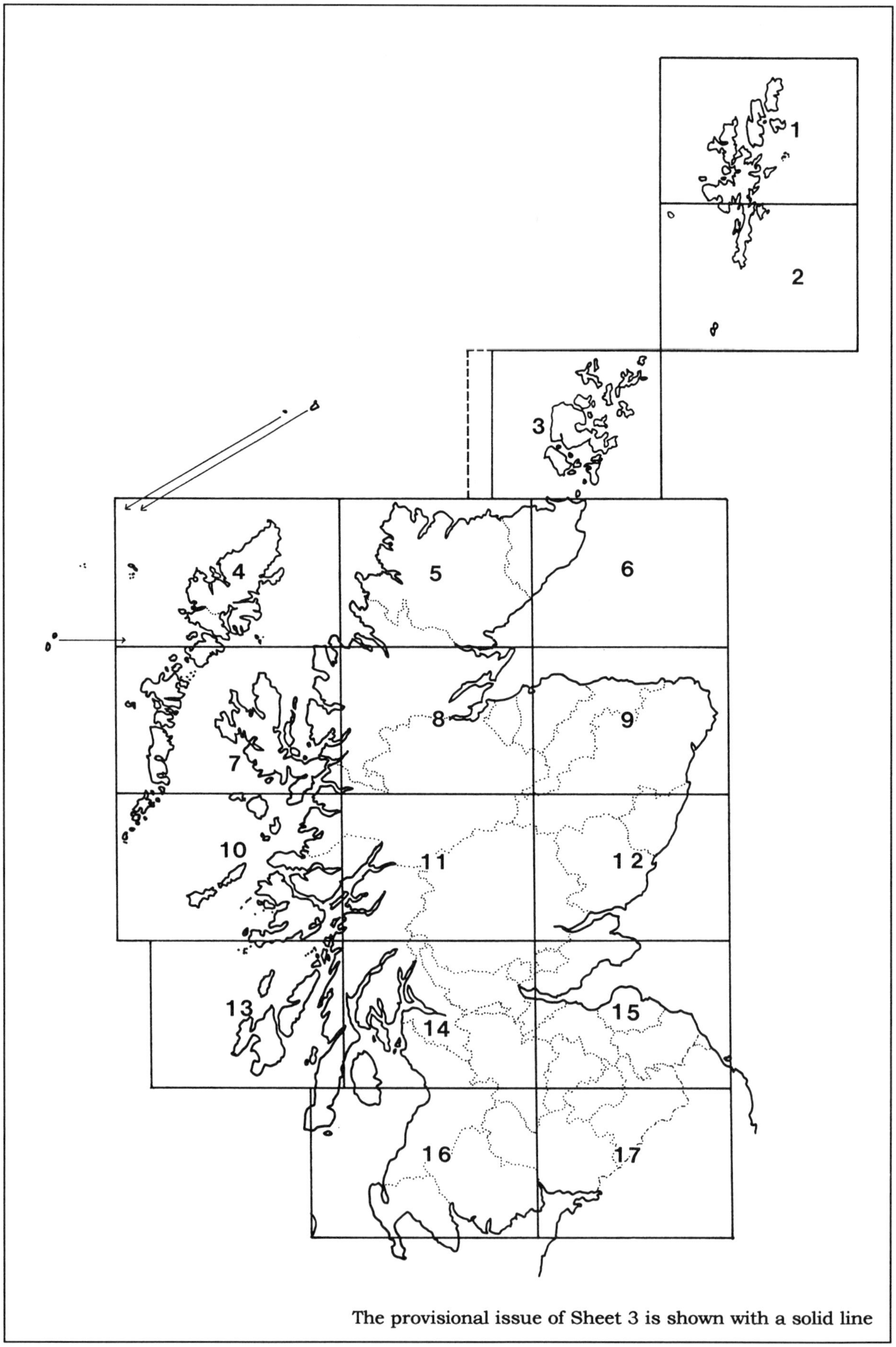

58. Quarter-inch Map of Scotland

58. Quarter-inch Map of Scotland

Constructed on Bonne's Projection on the origin of 57°30'N,4°W, and published in seventeen sheets. Standard sheet coverage 72 by 54 miles, the area covered by nine one-inch sheets [see **+13**]. Sheets 1-15 were newly drawn at the one-inch scale and reduced by heliozincography. It is unclear how the engraved plates for Sheets 16 and 17 were originated, but the sheets were printed from transfers to zinc. With a graticule at 20' intervals, except where noted. Heading: usually *Ordnance Survey of Scotland,* though those issues of Sheets 15 and 17 filled with mapping of England, also Geological Survey Sheets 1/2 and 10, have *Ordnance Survey of Great Britain.*

There are insets of Sula Sgeir, Rona, and Boreray and St Kilda on Sheet 4. With extrusions on Sheet 6 from Sheet 3, and on Sheet 16 of the Mull of Kintyre, Mull of Galloway and Burrow Head. With a coastal outline of Ireland on Sheet 16. Sule Skerry and Stack Skerry appear only in Geological Survey of Scotland issues of Sheet 5.

A. First Edition

The words "First Edition" do not appear in the heading.

1. Outline edition, with blue coastal tint. All sheets.
    1. [Provisional edition], 1901. Sheet 3 only.
        The contemporary *Orkney* district map [✢A.4.2] with hill shading and sheet number added. The price is altered from 9d to 1/-.
    2. Published with England blank, 1901. Sheet 17 only.
    3. Published complete, 1901-02. All sheets.
        Sheets 3 and 17 apparently followed in 1906 when reprints were required. Sheet 3 was remade with a standard border and dimensions.

2. Coloured edition, with hill shading, 1902-03. All sheets complete.

3. Outline edition, with overprint, 1910. Sheet 5.
    In *Sutherland* (Royal Commission on Ancient and Historical Monuments and Constructions of Scotland, Volume 2), Edinburgh, HMSO, 1911.

4. District maps.
    1. Coloured with hill shading.
        The Cairngorm Mountains, the Upper Dee and the Upper Spey Valleys, 1904.
        The Trossachs, 1904.

- No special *Orkney Islands* map of this type as listed in Ordnance Survey catalogues has been recorded. Series Sheet 3 [✢A.2] was probably offered.

    2. Outline with coloured main roads and water: county maps.
        Aberdeen, Banff and Elgin, 1903.
        Caithness and Sutherland, 1901.
        Dumfriesshire, Kirkcudbrightshire and Wigtownshire, 1901.
        Forfar and Kincardine, 1903.
        Orkney, 1901.
            With sheet lines identical to Sheet 3 in ✢A.1.1.
        Perthshire, 1903.
        Selkirk, Roxburgh, Berwick, Peebles and Haddington, 1903.
        Zetland, 1901.
            With an inset of Fair Isle.

3. Outline with coloured main roads and water.
   Argyll and the Isles (North), 1903.
   Argyll and the Isles (South), 1903.
   Edinburgh District, 1903.
   Glasgow District, 1903.
   Inverness District, 1903.
   Isle of Lewis, 1903.
   Skye and Inverness, 1902.
   Skye and the Western Islands, 1903.

- For Air Packets see **✢53**.8.2.

Geological Survey of Scotland

Planned in seventeen sheets, but only thirteen sheets in twelve were published. Sheets 16 and 17 use First Edition base maps, Sheets 3, 5, 6, 9, 10, 12-15 *Second Edition* [✢B], Sheet 1/2 *Fourth Edition (with National Grid)* [**✢60**.B]. The National Grid was also applied to reprints of the earlier editions.

Sheet 5 has an inset of Sule Skerry and Stack Skerry.

5. Colour printed edition. 13 sheets in 12.
   1. Published with England blank. 2 sheets: 15 (1912), 17 (1904, published 1907).
   2. Published complete, 1904-34 (published 1907-34). 11 sheets in 10: 1/2 (1963), 3, 5, 6, 9, 10 (1969), 12-14, 16.
      The eight existing sheets, 3, 5, 6, 9, 12-14, 16, were all reprinted in 1948-49, Sheet 9 again in 1974.

6. Overprinted with one-inch sheet lines and numbers. Sheet 3, 1932, printed 1934.
   In G.V. Wilson *The Geology of the Orkneys* (Memoirs of the Geological Survey, Scotland), Edinburgh, HMSO, 1935.

7. All published sheets were available uncoloured.

The mapping was also used as a base for indexes to large-scale maps. Other specially constructed maps were issued for specific military purposes, especially army manoeuvres.

B. Second Edition

Heading: *Ordnance Survey of Scotland (Second Edition).* Produced from the second national revision.

1. Outline edition, with blue coastal tint, 1914. 2 sheets ?only: 7 [▮RML], 14 [▮RGS, RML].
   Production of this edition was interrupted by the First World War and never resumed. Other plates were made, and apparently passed to the Geological Survey of Scotland. They were presumably unused by the Ordnance Survey in view of the wartime embargo on publishing updated topographical information.

Geological Survey of Scotland

- Nine sheets, 3, 5, 6, 9, 10, 12-15, use *Second Edition* base mapping, though of them only Sheet 14 is recorded as a topographical map. The English portion of Sheet 15 is blank. For further details see the notes above ✢A.5.

59. Quarter-inch Third Edition Map of Scotland

Constructed on Cassini's Projection on the origin of Delamere, and published in ten sheets. Standard sheet coverage 108 by 72 miles. Mostly produced from the third national revision of 1912-23 and compiled by reduction from drawings at the half-inch scale. With an alpha-numeric squaring system unless otherwise noted. Heading: *Ordnance Survey of Scotland* (Sheet 1 *Ordnance Survey of Great Britain*) : *¼-Inch to One Mile, Third Edition.*

Sheet 1 is common to both Scotland and England [**✣54, 55**].

There is an inset of Sula Sgeir and Rona on Sheet 8. The Irish area on Sheet 2 is mapped.

A. Third Edition

1. Coloured edition, with layers, 1921-23. All sheets.
   Also published as an Ordnance Survey atlas, 1924.

2. *Outline* edition, with water in blue, 1921-24 (published 1923-25). All sheets.

3. District map. Coloured with layers.
   British Association Topographical Map for the Glasgow Meeting 1928, 1928 (✣B.3).

B. Third Edition, revised

Revision comparable to that on the England and Wales *A Series* (such as the addition of road numbers on the red plate [see **✣55**]) affects the content, though not the sheet lines, of Scottish maps.

1. Coloured edition, with layers, 1921-23 (published 1930-34). 8 sheets ?only: 1-7, 10.

2. *Outline* edition.
   The sheets recorded are headed *Third Edition,* with *(Outline)* on the water plate.
   1. With water in blue, 1921-22 (published 1930-32). 2 sheets recorded: 1, 2 [▮Eu].
   2. With water in blue, contours in brown, 1923 (published 1931). Sheet 3 recorded [▮Eu].

3. District map. Coloured with layers.
   Glasgow and District, 1930 (✣A.3).
   The 1928 British Association map revised and put on public sale.

M. Aeronautical issues

Coloured editions with brown layers, and with air information overprinted in red.

With an alpha-numeric squaring system in black

1. *Royal Air Force Special Edition,* 1925-26. ?All sheets.

With War Office Cassini Grid (British System) overprinted in purple

2. *Royal Air Force Edition,* ?1929-30. ?All sheets.

With a graticule at 20' intervals overprinted in purple

3. *Civil Air Edition,* 1929-30 (published 1930-31). All sheets.

Aeronautical issues with extended sheet lines

Eight-mile overlaps with sheets adjoining east and north were added as required in aeronautical editions after 1932.

Sheets with extensions east: 2, 6, 8.
Sheets with extensions north: 2-6, 9.
Sheet 4 is repositioned eight miles west, reducing its overlap with Sheet 3 to twenty miles, in order to locate Tiree within the neat line.

The clearance of unnecessary background detail and the addition of more air information was completed between 1935 and 1938. Air information is overprinted in red. Printed publication dates are unreliable and sometimes revert to those on earlier states.

With War Office Cassini Grid (Modified British System) overprinted in purple

4. *Royal Air Force Edition.* All sheets.
   1. Coloured with brown layers, ?1934-35. ?All sheets.
   2. Coloured with purple layers, ?1935-36. ?All sheets.

With a graticule at 20' intervals overprinted in purple

5. *Civil Air Edition.* Coverage uncertain.
   1. Coloured with brown layers, without contours, 1934. Sheet 1.
      This sheet formed part of the English set. No Scottish sheet without contours has yet been recorded.
   2. Coloured with brown layers, with contours, 1935-?36. ?All sheets (1-3 recorded).
   3. Coloured with purple layers, 1937. Sheet 7 recorded.

With a graticule at 10' intervals overprinted in purple ○

Coloured editions with purple layers.

6. *Civil Air Edition,* ?1938. All sheets.

7. *RAF Edition,* 1937-38. All sheets.

8. *RAF Edition (War),* 1940-41. All sheets.

9. *RAF (War),* 2nd Edition, 1942. All sheets.
   With War Office Cassini and Irish Grids overprinted in brown in the borders at 10 km intervals and at intersection points across the sheets. With *(Aeronautical Map)* supplementing the heading.

10. *Aeronautical Map Training,* 1943. Sheet 5 ?only [▮BL].
    See also ✢**54**.M.14. This was presumably a map for the training of air crews in the use of GSGS 3982 1:250,000 *Europe (Air)* [✢**46**], the specification of which is similar. The graticule is black.

Without reference system

11. MBAM 3761: *Great Britain : Road Obstructions (Bridge Head-room),* [1941]. 5 sheets: 1-5.
    Outline diagrams prepared by the Map Branch, Air Ministry showing skeleton information only. Some issues are referenced ADI(Maps) 3761. Sheet 7 was also drawn but there is no evidence that the remaining sheets were made. Similar maps were made for England and Wales, and Northern Ireland [see ✢**54**.M.15, **70**.5].

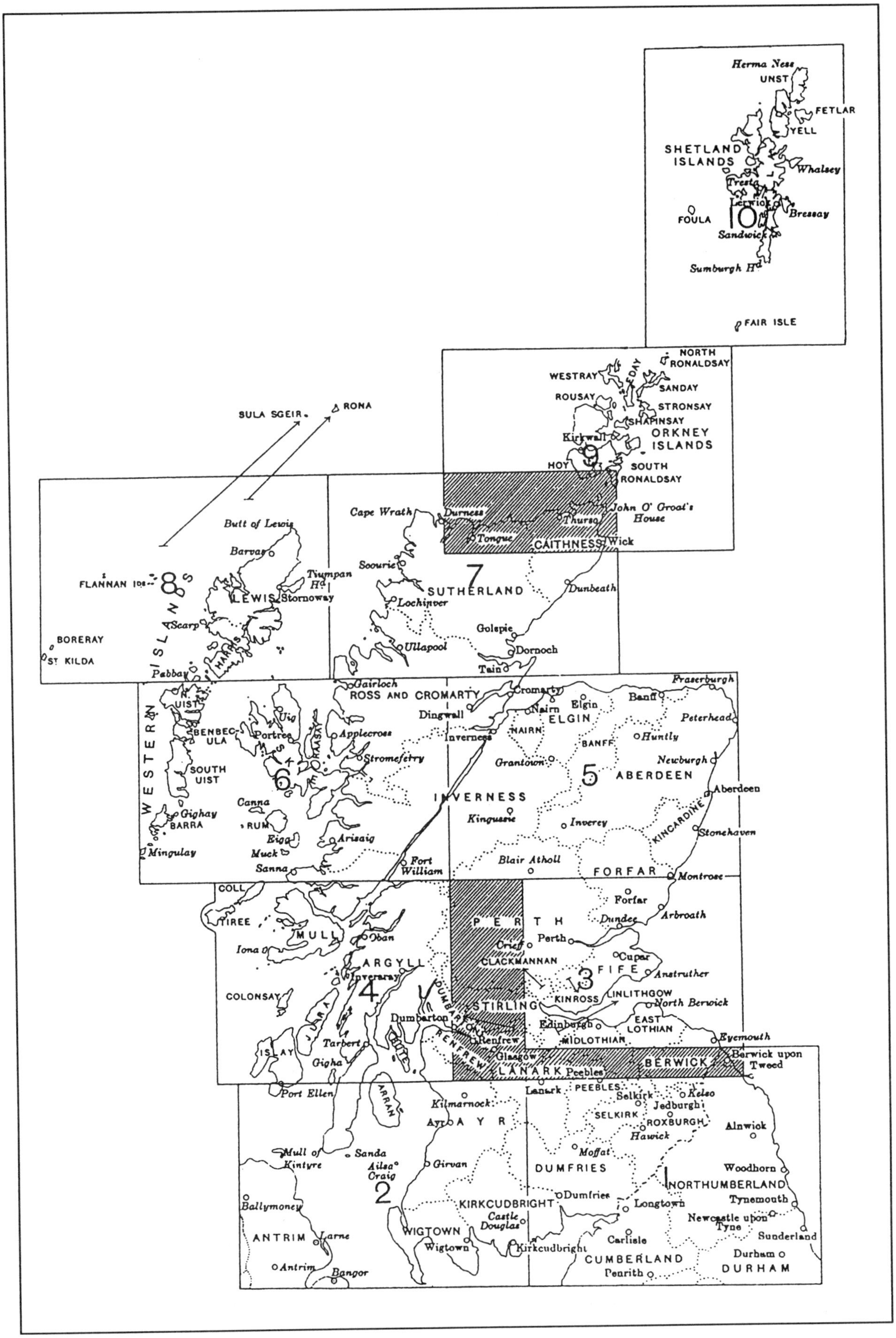

59. Quarter-inch Third Edition Map of Scotland

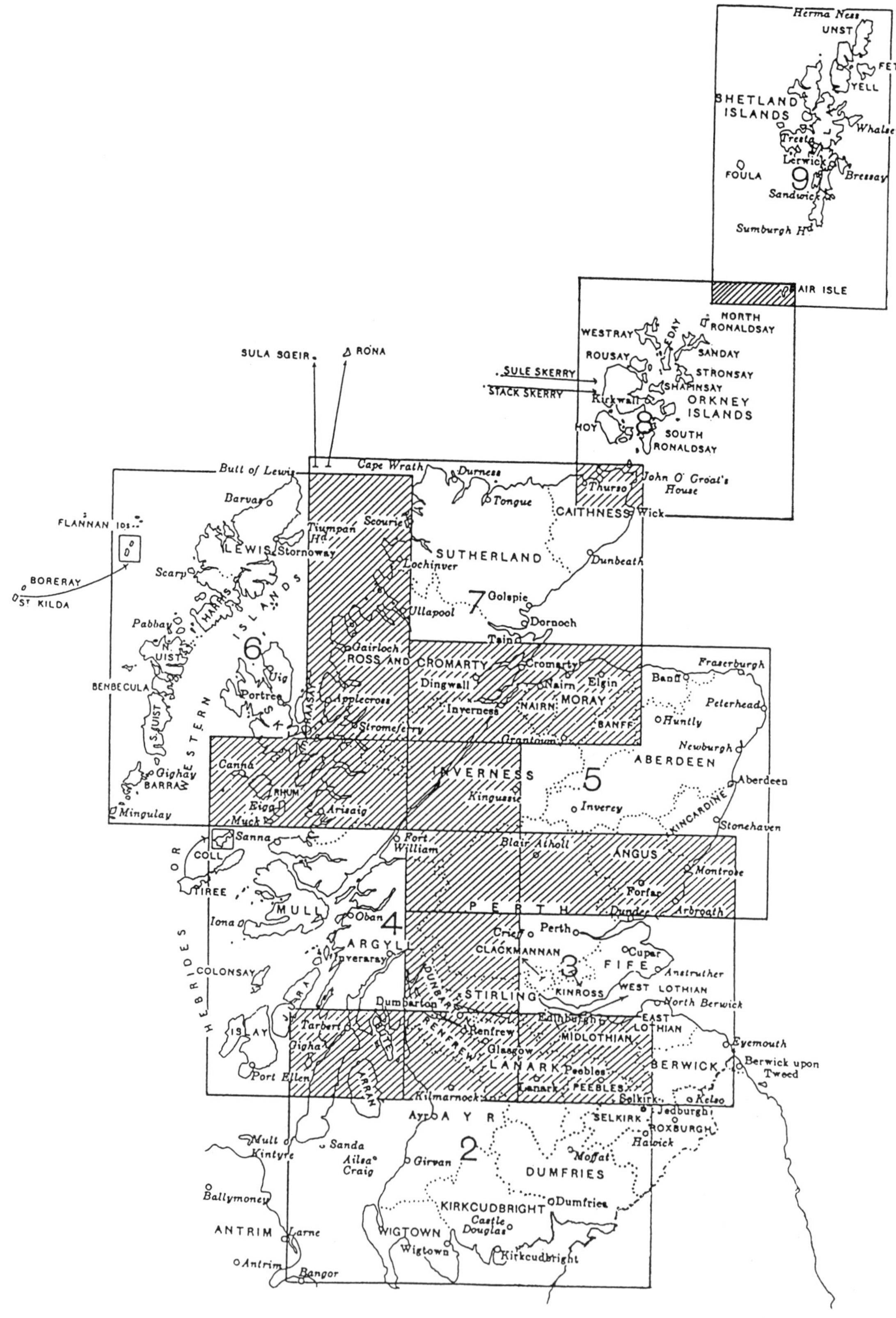

Sheet 4 was extended south in 1948, as shown (as Sheet 6) in diagram 61

60. Quarter-inch Fourth Edition Map of Scotland

60. Quarter-inch Fourth Edition Map of Scotland

Constructed on the national Transverse Mercator Projection on the origin of 49°N,2°W. Laid out in eight sheets numbered in the range 2 to 9 on National Yard Grid sheet lines, reduced on publication to seven by the combination of Sheets 8 and 9 (some military editions excepted). Mapping was transferred from the *Third Edition* map on Cassini's Projection [**✣59**] (see page xiii). There is no standard sheet size. Heading, where present: *Ordnance Survey of Great Britain : Fourth Edition, Scotland.* Though it appears on some Scotland indexes, Sheet 1 is designated an England and Wales, not a Scotland sheet. For information on Sheet 1 see **✣56**.

There are insets of Tiree on Sheet 4, St Kilda and Boreray on 6, Sula Sgeir and Rona on 7, Sule Skerry and Stack Skerry on 8. The Irish area on Sheet 2 is mapped.

A. With National Yard Grid at 10,000 yard intervals ❍

1. Coloured edition, with layers, 1935-37 (published 1936-38). All 8 sheets in 7.
   A *Forth & Tay* title panel was added to the reverse of copies of Sheet 3 used at the International Union of Geodesy and Geophysics, Edinburgh, 1936.

2. *Black* [outline] edition, with woods in grey, 1935-37 (published 1936-?38). All 8 sheets in 7 [▮BL: 2-7, LVg: 8/9].

3. Outline edition, with water in blue, woods in grey, 1941. Without grid. All 8 sheets in 7.

4. Roman series, distributed 1940-41. Sheet 3 *Scotland in Roman Times* [▮NLS].
   Compiled by O.G.S. Crawford. Publication was pending when most of the stock was destroyed in the bombing of Southampton in November 1940. Some fifty copies survived which Crawford had pulled out for distribution to libraries and colleagues.

5. Water and contour issues.

B. With National Grid

Heading: *Fourth Edition (National Grid), Scotland* (not ✣B.4). Sheet 4 was extended some sixteen miles south in 1948, covering the Kintyre peninsula. Rathlin Island was also mapped.

1. Coloured edition, with layers. All sheets.
   1. First issues, 1946. All 8 sheets in 7.
   2. Sheet enlarged by extension south, 1948. Sheet 4.

2. *Outline Edition,* with woods in grey. All sheets.
   1. First issues, 1946. All 8 sheets in 7.
   2. Sheet enlarged by extension south, 1948. Sheet 4.

3. *Administrative Areas Edition,* 1950-52 (published 1951-52). All 8 sheets in 7.
   Sheet 1 is listed at **✣56**.B.4. In brown outline. Two versions recorded, showing:
   1. County, burgh, district boundaries (red), civil parishes (purple).
   2. As ✣B.3.1, together with parliamentary constituencies (green).

4. Outline edition. ?All 8 sheets in 7.
   Unpublished: for wartime official use. The expression *Ordnance Survey Grid* is used.
   1. With uncoloured water, 1942. 2 sheets recorded: 2, 4 [▮PC].
   2. With water in blue, 1942. 3 sheets recorded: 5-7 [▮PC].

5. Water and contour issues.

Geological Survey of Scotland: for the use of *Fourth Edition* mapping see **✣58**.5.

M. Military issues overprinted with War Office Cassini Grid in purple

With *Fourth Edition* marginalia, and layer colouring, where present, in brown

Air information, where given, is in red.

1. GSGS 3958: *Military Edition.* All sheets.
    1. Coloured edition, with layers, 1939. All 8 sheets in 7.
    2. Coloured edition, 1939-40. All 8 sheets in 7.
    3. Outline edition, with water in blue, 1941. 6 sheets in 5: 2, 4, 6, 7, 8/9 [▮PRO*].

2. GSGS 3958: *War Revision,* 1940. All sheets.
    1. *Military Edition,* coloured with layers, 1940-41. All 8 sheets in 7.
    2. *Military Edition,* coloured, 1941-42. All 8 sheets in 7.
    3. *Military Edition,* outline with water in blue, 1941. 2 sheets: 3, 5 [▮PRO*].
    4. *Grid/Graticule Edition,* 1940-41. All 8 sheets in 7 [▮PRO*].
       An outline edition with water in blue, overprinted in addition with a graticule at 10' intervals and *RAF Edition* [✣**59**.M.7] sheet lines in red.
    5. *Sales Copy,* coloured with layers, published 1943. All 8 sheets in 7.

With War Office marginalia↑, and layer colouring in purple

With air information and War Office Irish Grid as needed in red. Sheets 8 and 9 are separate.

3. GSGS 3958 (Air): *Air,* 1943. 3 sheets in 2 recorded: 5, 8 with 9 [▮BSg].
   Probably not issued. Sheets 8 and 9 are on one sheet of paper prior to separation.

4. GSGS 3958 Army/Air: *Army/Air.* All sheets.
    1. GSGS issue, 1943. All sheets: 2-9.
    2. [AMS M524]: AMS 1, 1944. All sheets: 2-9 [▮Wn].

5. GSGS 3958 Army/Air: *2nd War Revision* : *Army/Air,* 1943 (issued 1944). All sheets: 2-9.

Military issues with National Grid (Military System) ❍

The grid was initially numbered in purple. Air information was added in blue in 1952. These colour plates were united in about 1956. With War Office Irish Grid overprinted in red (sometimes lacking). The extended form of Sheet 4 is used [see ✣B]. Sheets 8 and 9 are combined.

6. GSGS 4650 coloured edition, with brown layers. All sheets.
    1. *War Office Edition,* 1948 (printed 1948-49, issued 1950). All 8 sheets in 7.
       With graticule intersections at 20' intervals.
    2. Fifth Edition-GSGS, 1951 (issued 1952). Sheet 5.
       Using base maps displaying the letter reference system of the National Grid.
    3. With air information and a graticule at 30' intervals overprinted in blue, 1952 (issued 1952-53). All 8 sheets in 7.
       Sheet 5 is Sixth Edition-GSGS, Sheets 2-4, 6, 7, 8/9 Fifth Edition-GSGS.

7. AMS M524 (GSGS 4650): Fourth Edition-GSGS, coloured, 1951. All 8 sheets in 7 [▮Wc].

8. GSGS 4858: *RAF Topographical Map..... (Radar),* 1957. Sheet 2 recorded [▮PRO*].
   With air information overprinted in blue. The grid has no military overprint.

9. GSGS 4864: *RAF Topographical Map,* 1955 (issued 1956). All 8 sheets in 7 [▮BL].
   With a graticule at 30' intervals and air information overprinted in blue.

10. District map on National Grid sheet lines.
    GSGS 4982: *Hebrides Range Area,* 1966 [▮NLS].

- As Sheets 1/2, 3-7, 9, 10 in GSGS 4736 see ✣**61**.

61. Quarter-inch Military Map of the United Kingdom

Laid out in 21 sheets, reduced on issue to 20 by the combination of Sheets 1 and 2. The mapping used was the quarter-inch *Fourth Editions* of England and Wales, and Scotland [**✢56**, **60**], renumbered north to south 1/2, 3-10, 11A, 11-20 with, for coverage of Northern Ireland as Sheet 8, *The Quarter-inch Map (Provisional Edition)* [**✢76**.A], and, as Sheet 11A *Isle of Man*, a map with sheet lines almost identical with Sheet 2A in GSGS 3957 [**✢56**.M.4]. With British and Irish National Grids (the latter not on Sheet 6).

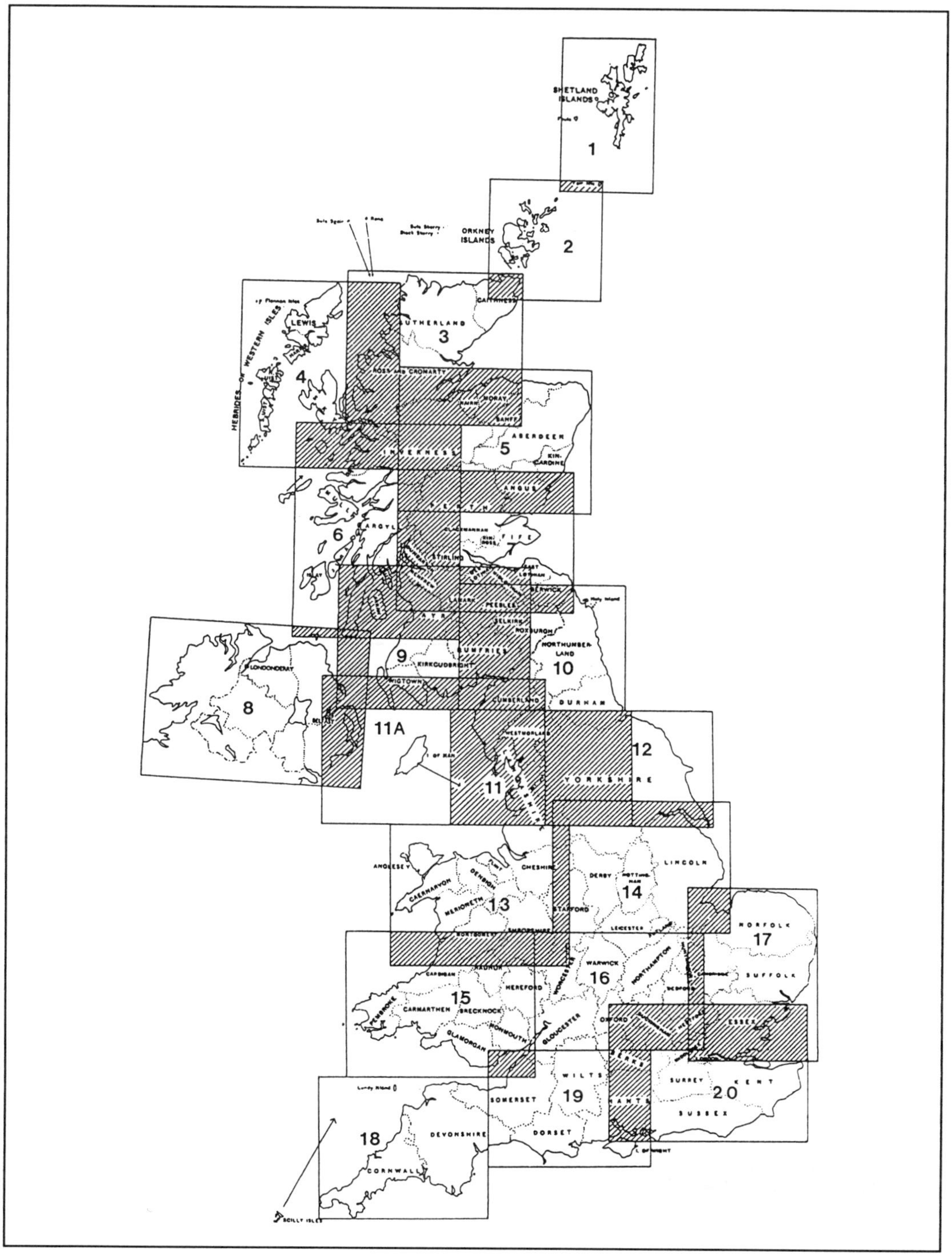

1. GSGS 4736: *Topographical Air Map of the United Kingdom*, 1955-59. All 21 sheets in 20. Issued by the War Office, for the Ministry of Transport and Civil Aviation. Coloured edition, with brown layers. With a graticule at 30' intervals and air information over-printed in magenta and control zones in blue.

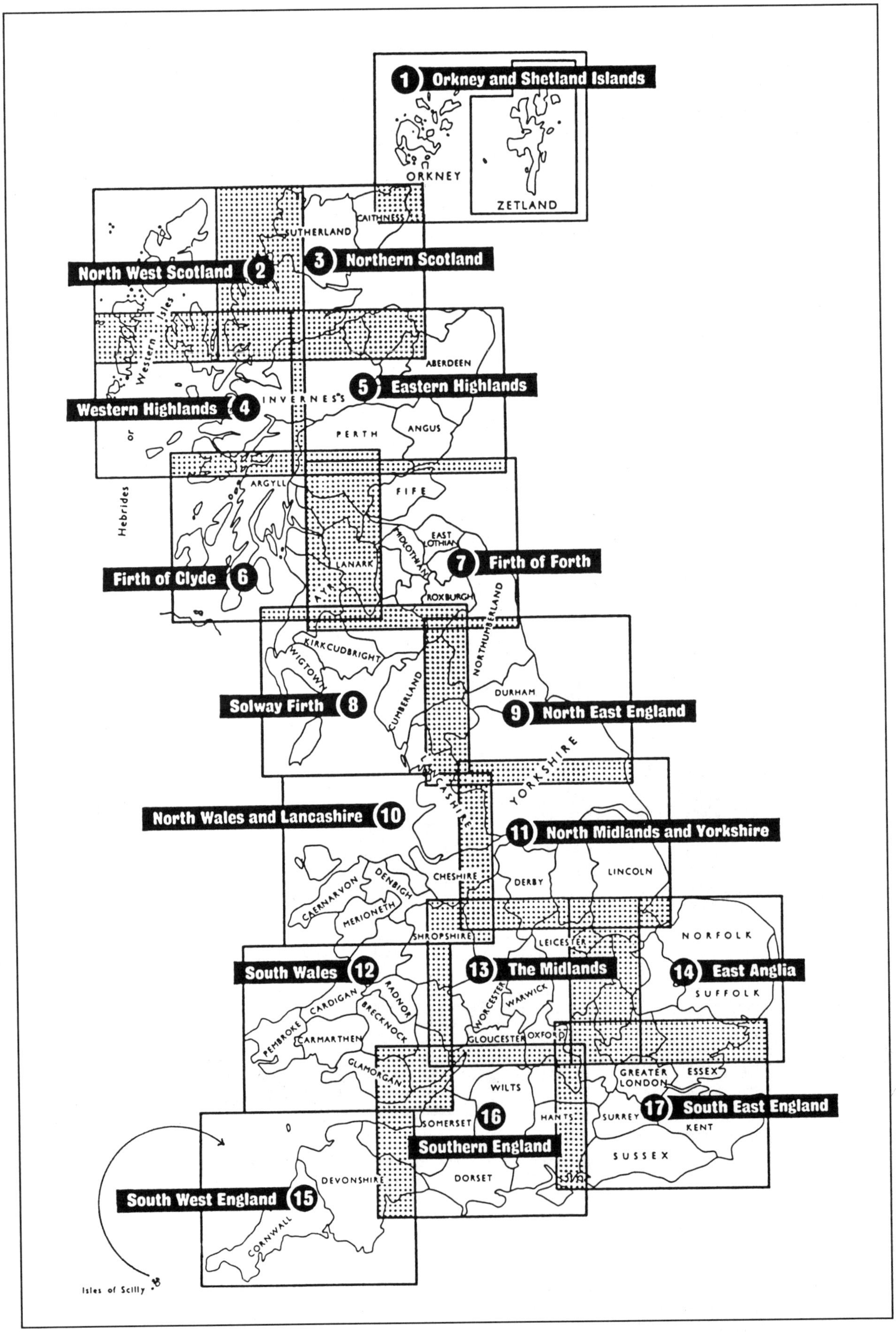

62. 1:250,000 Fifth Series Map of Great Britain

62. 1:250,000 Fifth Series Map of Great Britain

National Grid series. Published in seventeen sheets. Standard sheet coverage 190 by 150 km. Produced from 1944-61 revision. Newly drawn at the one-inch scale using one-inch *Seventh Series* [**✢20**] source material. Heading, where present: *Ordnance Survey of Great Britain : Quarter Inch Fifth Series,* though the scale is in fact 1:250,000. For military versions see **✢63**.

There are insets of Shetland Islands, Sule Skerry and Stack Skerry on Sheet 1, Sula Sgeir and Rona, St Kilda and Boreray on 2, Grassholm Island and The Smalls on 12, Isles of Scilly on 15. With the coastline of Ireland on Sheet 6.

1. Coloured edition, with layers and hill shading, without contours, 1957. Sheet 10 only.

2. Coloured edition, with layers and hill shading, with contours. All sheets.
   1. In twelve colours, 1960-62 (published 1960-63). All sheets.
      Sheet 10 is in edition *B*. The first printing of Sheet 11 was in thirteen colours.
   2. In ten colours, 1962-64 (published 1964-65). 7 sheets: 4, 7, 9, 11-13, 17.
   3. In eight colours, 1964-67. All sheets.
      Also issued as an Ordnance Survey loose leaf atlas, 1969.

3. *Outline Edition,* 1957-62 (published 1957-63). All sheets.

4. Water and contour issues.

5. *Conference of National Park Planning Authorities,* 1969. Sheet 5 recorded.
   With overprint supplied by the Countryside Commission.

6. *River Pollution Survey,* 1970. 10 sheets: 8-17, renumbered 1-10.
   Sheet 9 (renumbered 2) has an inset of the English section of Sheet 7. In *Report of a River Pollution Survey of England and Wales,* Volume 1, Directorate General Water Engineering, Department of the Environment and the Welsh Office, 1970.

7. Water Resources Board maps of England and Wales. 11 sheets.
   Outline editions with water in blue were used. Metric contours were supplied at 50, 200, 400 and 600 metres, and the *Relief* edition was layered at these levels. The maps were printed for the Water Resources Board by the Hydrographic Department, Ministry of Defence, Taunton.
   1. *Relief,* 1972. 11 sheets: 7-17.
   2. *Rainfall,* 1972. 11 sheets: 7-17.
      Rainfall information correct to August 1969 as supplied by the Meteorological Office was overprinted in black on the *Relief* edition.

8. *Outline Edition,* with water in blue, 1973-74. 3 sheets: 5-7 [▮RML].
   For the Scottish Development Department.

9. *Wales and the Marches* Special Sheet.
   With an inset of Grassholm Island and The Smalls.
   1. Coloured edition, with layers, hill shading and contours, 1959.
      Other editions, 1963, 1971, 1976.
   2. *Outline Edition,* 1959.
      Another edition, 1963.
   3. *Outline Edition,* overprinted in black with administrative boundaries, 1967 [▮RML].

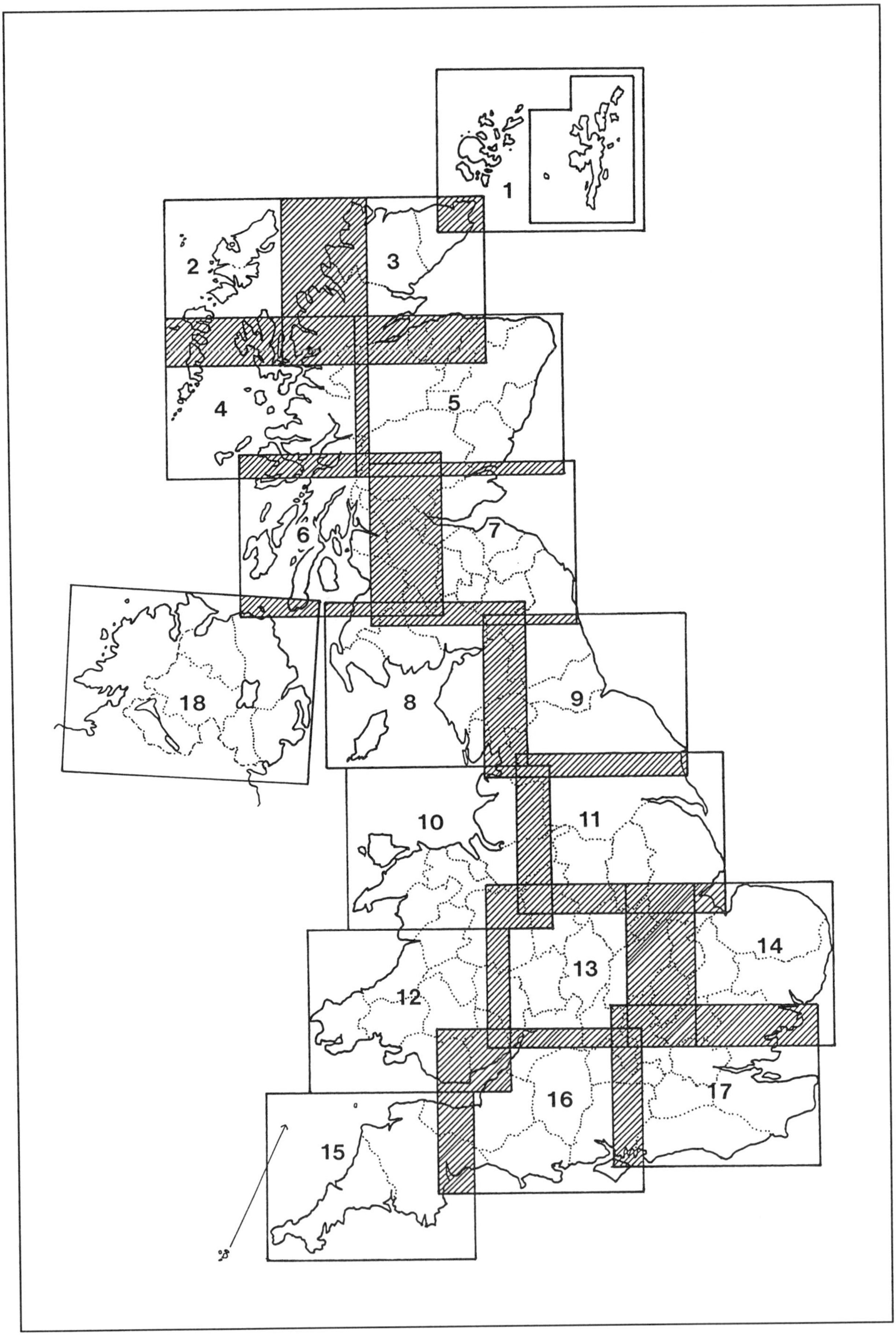

63. 1:250,000 Military Map of the United Kingdom

63. 1:250,000 Military Map of the United Kingdom

Issued for military and aviation use in eighteen sheets, using the seventeen sheets of the 1:250,000 *Fifth Series* of Great Britain [**✢62**], with a specially made map of Northern Ireland as Sheet 18. This was enlarged in 1963 from *The Quarter-inch Map* [**✢76**.B], extended 3 km south and 2½ km west. All sheets were first issued without hill shading. It was restored in some series to Sheets 1-17 in 1966, and applied to Sheet 18 apparently after 1980.

A. With British and Irish National Grids

A graticule at 30' intervals is usually overprinted in blue. On Sheet 18 Military Survey preferred the expression Irish TM Grid for the Irish National Grid.

1. M523 coloured edition, with layers [and hill shading]. All sheets.
   1. With overprint in blue, 1961-64. All sheets.
      Each sheet was updated independently (to 1968) in numbered GSGS editions. Edition 1-GSGS of Sheet 10 is the 1957 prototype [**✢62**.1], though with contours and the heading *Interim Specification*. Some reprints are recorded made by the Survey Production Centre, Royal Engineers (British Army of the Rhine), in which the words *Ordnance Survey of* are deleted from the heading. With grid and air information overprinted in blue.
   2. With overprint in magenta, 1968-69. ?17 sheets: 1-17.
      The overprint colour was altered to magenta on the first new edition issued for each sheet from 1968, blue being required for the M523 *Air* edition [✢A.3].

2. M523 coloured edition, 1964-65. ?All sheets [▮NLS, Wc: not 6, 13-15].
   Printed by the Army Map Service. Sheet 10 is Edition 2-GSGS, the remainder Edition 1-GSGS. 1964 issues have yellow town infill, 1965 (8, 16-18) screened black.

3. M523 Air, coloured edition, with layers and hill shading, 1968-69. All sheets.
   With air and other information overprinted in blue. The GSGS edition in M523 [✢A.1] for each sheet current in 1968-69 was used (Sheets 2, 15, 17, 18: Edition 2; Sheets 1, 3-8, 11, 12, 14, 16: Edition 3; Sheets 9, 10, 13: Edition 4). Each sheet was further updated independently in numbered GSGS editions.

   The following dependent issues are recorded:
   1. GSGS 5030: *RAF Topographic Decca Chart*, 1968-69. All sheets [▮BL].
      Various chains.
   2. GSGS 5162: *Topographic Dectrac Chart*, ?1972. ?All sheets [▮NLS: 14].

4. GSGS 5344: *Helicopter Aeronautical Chart (UK)*, c.1981. All sheets.
   With a graticule at 30' intervals in black and grids in blue.

   The following dependent issue is recorded:
   1. GSGS 5352: *RAF Topographic Decca Chart (UK)*, c.1981. ?All sheets [▮Mg: 13].

B. With a graticule at 10' intervals overprinted in blue

Air information is overprinted in blue. Printed by the Ordnance Survey.

1. GSGS 4941: *Topographical Air Map*, later *Topographical Air Chart of the United Kingdom*, 1962-64. All sheets.
   An ICAO series, published by the Ministry of Aviation, later the Board of Trade. Each sheet was updated independently in numbered GSGS editions.

2. *Topographical Air Chart of the United Kingdom*, 1975. All sheets.
   Published by the Civil Aviation Authority. Each sheet was updated independently in numbered editions, in sequence from those in ✢B.1.

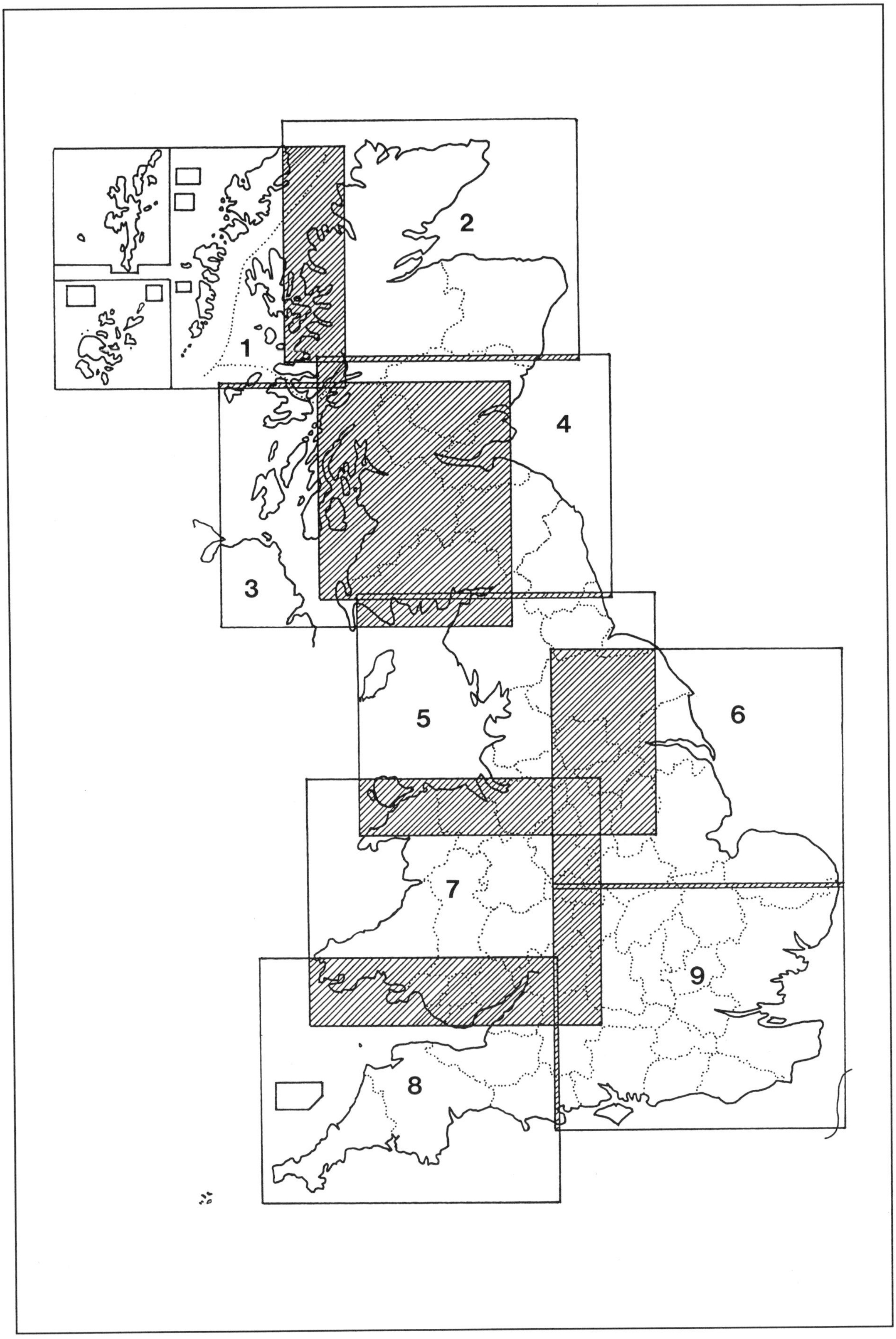

64. 1:250,000 Routemaster Series Map of Great Britain

64. 1:250,000 Routemaster Series Map of Great Britain

National Grid series. Published in nine sheets, Sheet 1 being a composite covering the Shetland Islands, Orkney Islands and Outer Hebrides in three boxes. Standard sheet coverage 270 by 220 km. Revised to December 1977 (Sheets 5-9) or April 1978 (Sheets 1-4), and compiled from quarter-inch (1:250,000) *Fifth Series* mapping [**✢62**]. Heading: *Ordnance Survey : Routemaster Series of Great Britain.*

The sheet lines of Sheets 7, 8, 9 are common with those of the *Travelmaster Series* [**✢65**].

There are insets of Stack Skerry and Sule Skerry, Fair Isle, Rockall, Rona and Sula Sgeir, St Kilda and Boreray on Sheet 1, Isles of Scilly on 8. With the coastlines of Ireland on Sheet 3 and France on Sheet 9.

The diagram to the right shows the sheet lines of the *1:250 000 Sixth Series* as developed in 1976. It was plotted in twelve sheets each covering an area of 200 by 200 km, with overlapping extensions bled off on two sides. Neighbouring sheets were to be printed back to back: 1 with 3, 2 with 4, 5 with 6, 7 with 10, 8 with 9, 11 with 12. Pilot Sheets 11 and 12 *London and South England* have been recorded issued in this form in coloured editions, with layers and hill shading [▮PC]. In its early stages of development the *Routemaster Series* was also referred to as the *1:250 000 Sixth Series.* Prototype sheets with this heading are recorded [▮PC].

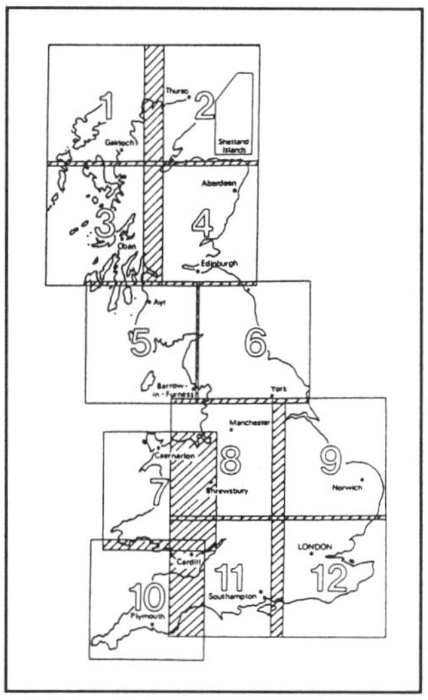

1. Coloured edition, with layers and hill shading. All sheets.
   Copies sold in covers were initially issued without borders to the east, divided in half along the horizontal axis and printed back to back.
   1. With National Grid in black, 1978-79. All sheets.
   2. With National Grid in blue, 1984. All sheets.

2. *Outline Edition,* 1980. All sheets.
   Sheets 5-9 apparently start at edition *B* (edition *A* not recorded).

3. Holiday Map (at scale 1:200,000).
   The West Country : showing Cornwall, Devon and part of Somerset, 1986.
   Compiled from *Routemaster* mapping. With an inset of the Isles of Scilly. National Grid 10 km squares are measured alpha-numerically from the south-west corner.

4. Touring Maps (at scale 1:158,400).
   Compiled from *Routemaster* mapping. National Grid 10 km squares are measured alpha-numerically from the south-west corner.
   Northumbria, 1989.
   Snowdonia and North Wales : Eryri a Gogledd Cymru, 1990. Another edition, 1994.
   Wessex, 1990.

5. City Link Maps (at scale 1:126,720).
   Compiled from *Routemaster* mapping. National Grid 10 km squares are measured alpha-numerically from the north-west corner.
   Birmingham and the Midlands, 1988.
   Edinburgh and Glasgow, 1989.
   Manchester, Sheffield, Leeds & York, 1987.
   M25 & London, 1986. Another edition, 1989.

Geological Survey of Great Britain (England and Wales)

6. District Map. Solid edition.
   Geological Map of Wales : Map Daearegol o Gymru, 1994.

65. 1:250,000 Travelmaster Series Map of Great Britain

National Grid series. Published in eight sheets numbered in the range 2 to 9, Sheet 1 being at 1:625,000 [✢**91**]. Standard sheet coverage 270 by 220 km. The National Grid is blue on coloured issues. With an alpha-numeric referencing system. Revised to August 1992, and produced from digital data. Heading: *Ordnance Survey* : *Travelmaster Series of Great Britain.*

The sheet lines of Sheets 7, 8, 9 are common with those of the *Routemaster Series* [✢**64**].

There are insets of Shetland Islands, Orkney Islands, Foula, Fair Isle (all at scale 1:400,000) on Sheet 2, Rockall, Rona and Sula Sgeir, Sule Skerry and Sule Stack, St Kilda and Boreray, Flannan Isles, Islay on 3, Isle of Man on 5, Grassholm Island, The Smalls on 7, Isles of Scilly on 8. With the coastlines of Ireland on Sheet 4 and France on Sheet 9.

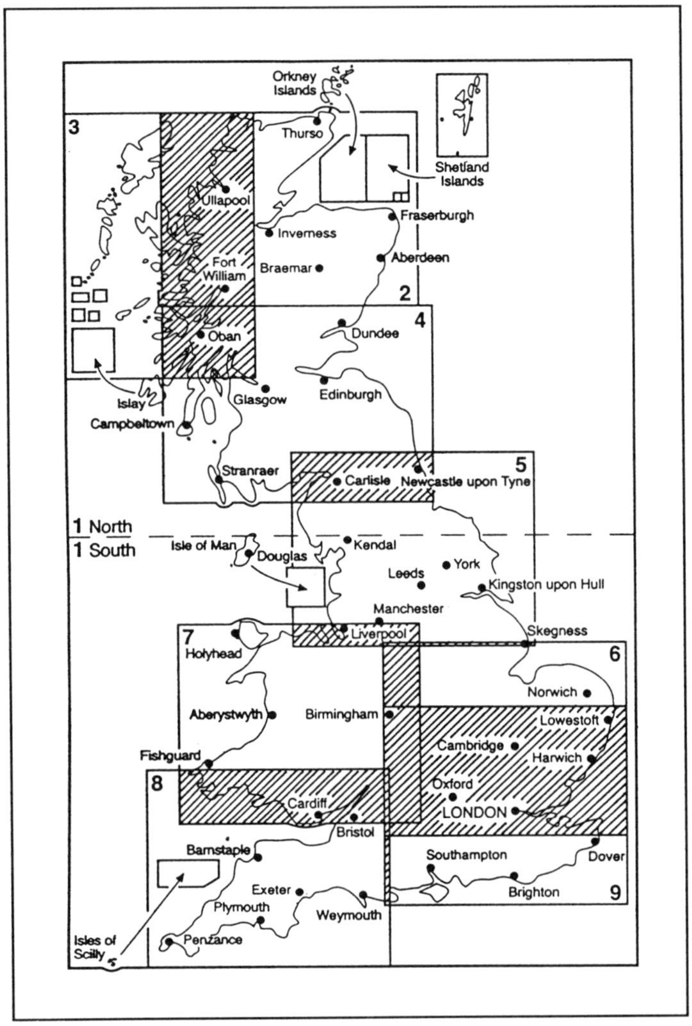

1. Coloured edition, with layers and hill shading, 1993. All sheets: 2-9.

2. *Outline Edition,* 1993. All sheets: 2-9.

3. *Administrative Boundary Map,* 1996. All sheets: 2-9.
   Showing national boundaries (blue), county boundaries (brown), unitary boundaries (red), district boundaries (green).

4. Touring Map (at scale 1:207,070).
   Devon and Cornwall : *showing part of Somerset,* 1992. Another edition, 1994.
   Compiled from *Travelmaster* mapping. With an inset of the Isles of Scilly. National Grid 10 km squares are measured alpha-numerically from the south-west corner.

66. 1:250,000 Soil Survey Maps

National Grid series. Based on *Routemaster* mapping. Published by the Ordnance Survey.

A. Soil Survey of Scotland

Published in seven sheets. The Shetland and Orkney Islands share Sheet 1. English areas are not treated.

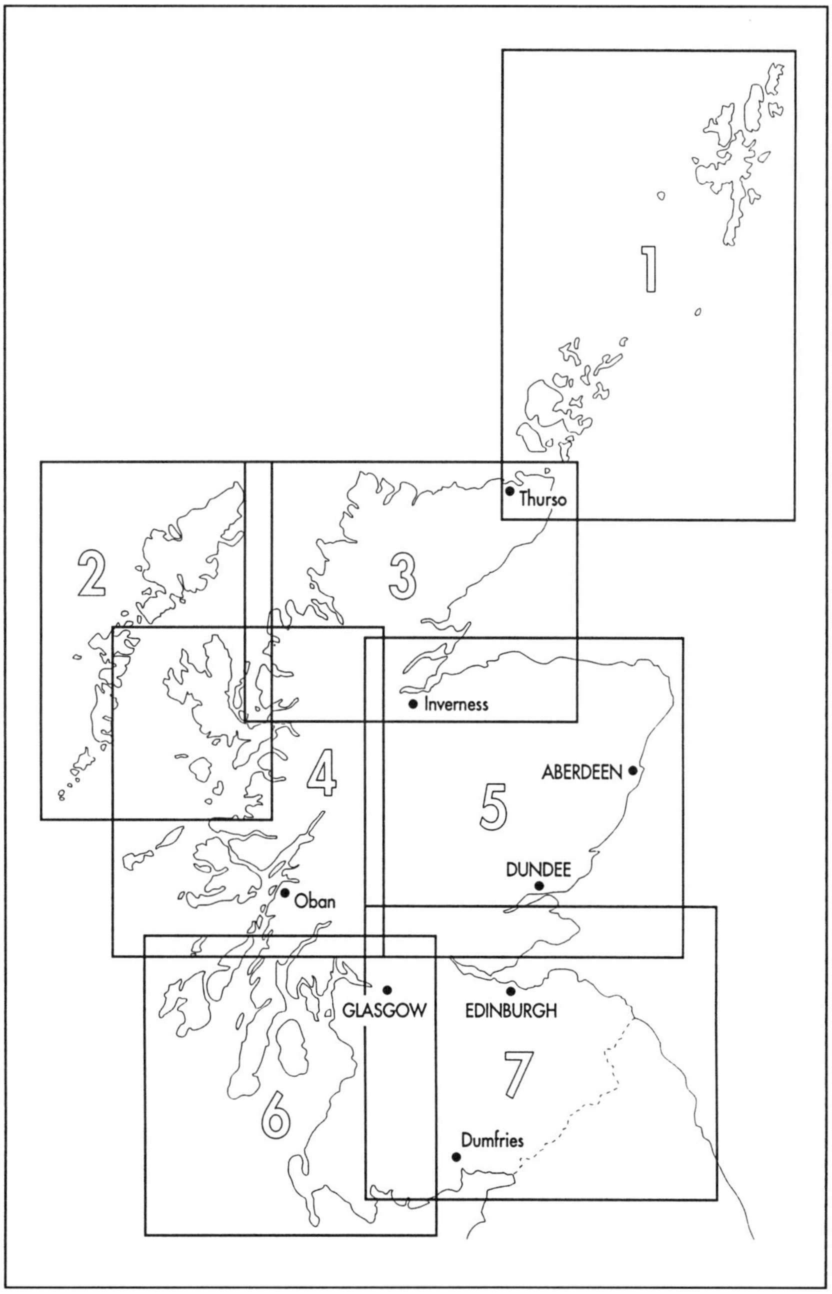

1. *Soil,* 1982. All sheets.

2. *Land Capability for Agriculture,* 1983. All sheets.

B. Soil Survey of England and Wales

Published in six sheets. Scottish areas are not treated.

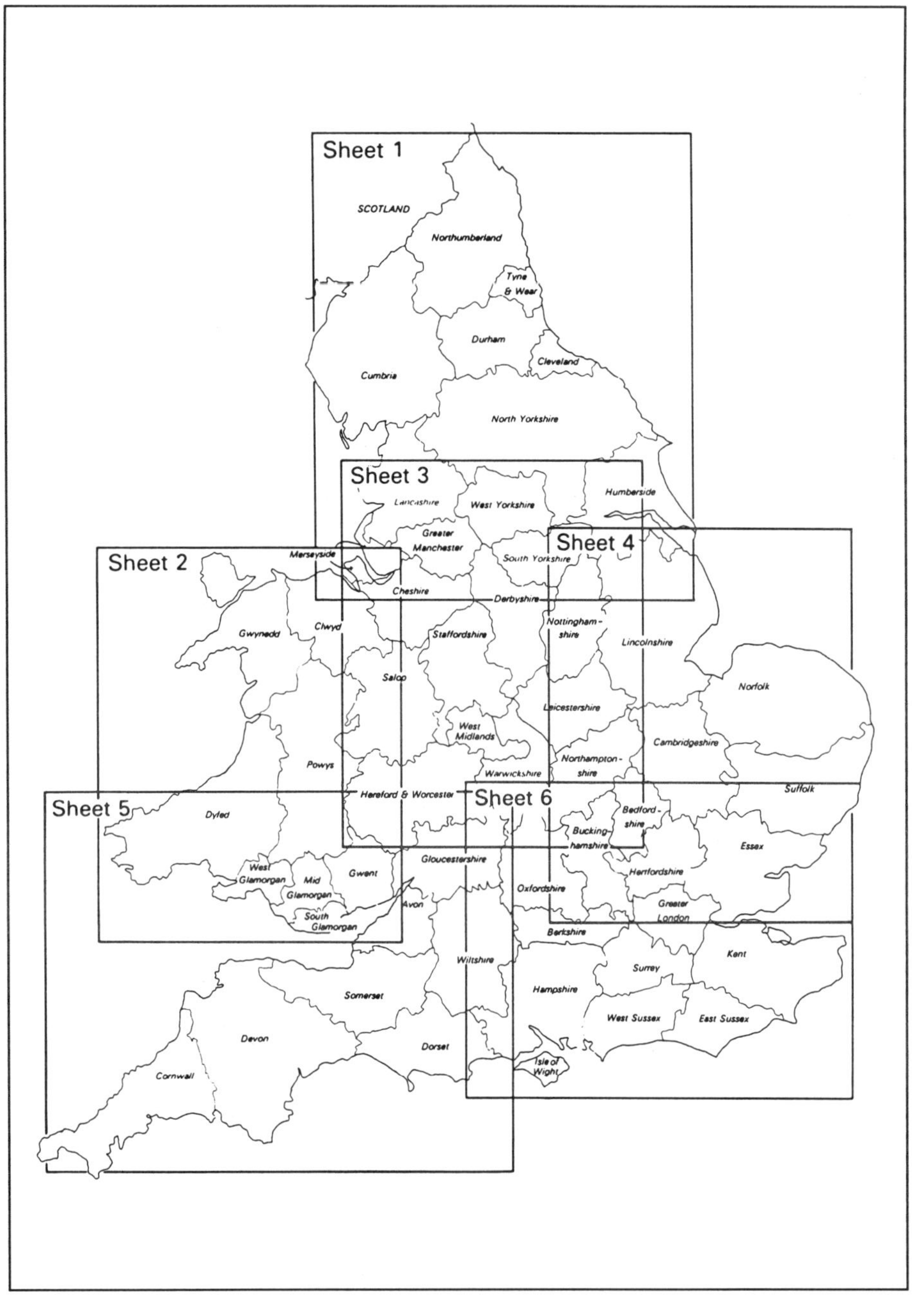

1. *Soil,* 1983. All sheets.

2. *Soil Suitability For Straw Incorporation,* published 1986. Sheet [4].

67. Quarter-inch General Map of Ireland (1)

Constructed by Thomas Larcom in 1836 and engraved with hachures in 1837-38 by the Ordnance Survey at Phoenix Park, Dublin, in six (initially unnumbered) sheets. The geological lines were laid down by Richard Griffith. It was prepared under the aegis of the Railway Commissioners but issued too late to be included with their report. Standard sheet size 29 by 24 inches, including a graduated border on the outer edges only. With a graticule at 30' intervals. British mapping is lacking.

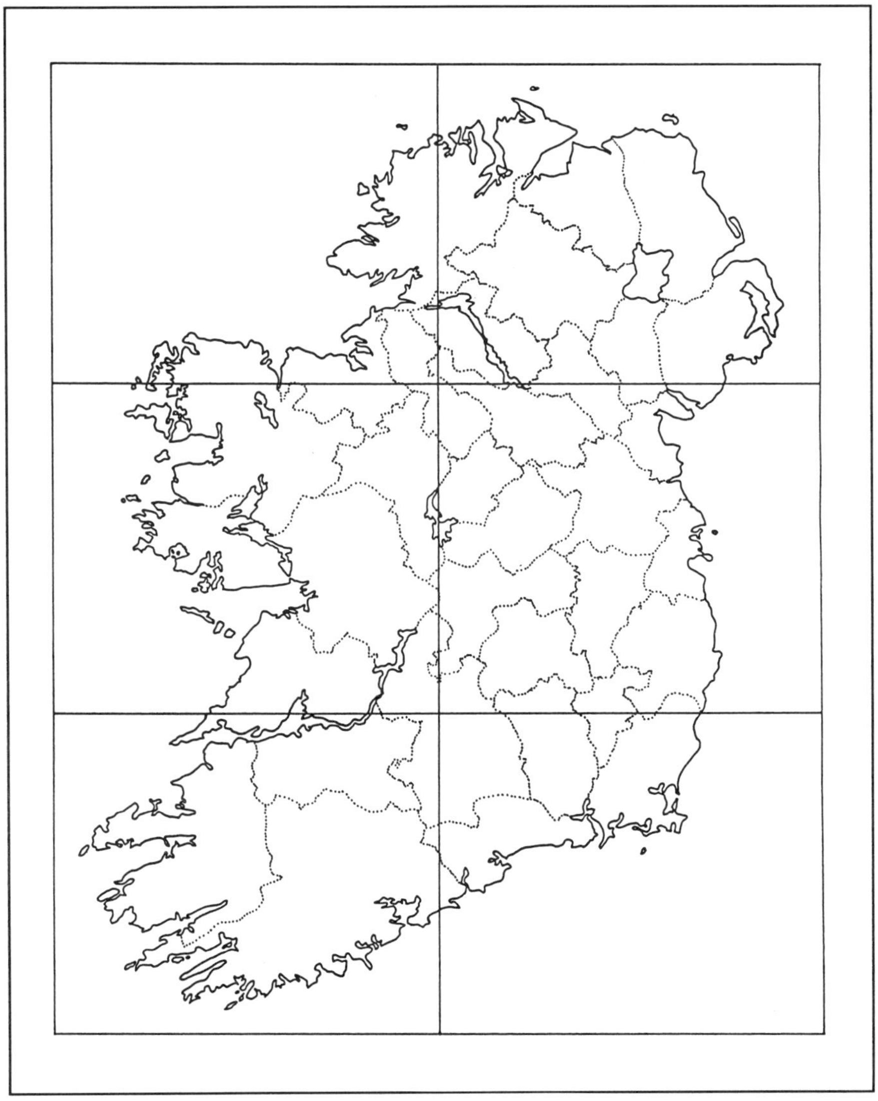

1. *A General Map of Ireland to Accompany the Report of the Railway Commissioners shewing the Principal Physical Features and Geological Structure of the Country.*
   Published by Hodges and Smith, Dublin, and James Gardner, London (later Longman & Co). Ordnance Survey responsibility for the map was not acknowledged.
   1. As first issued, signed *Dublin March 28th 1839 Richard Griffith,* 1839. All sheets.
   2. As ✣1.1, with geological hand colouring, 1839. All sheets.
   3. Revised (undated) to 1852, with Griffith's signature deleted. All sheets [▮Dtl].
   4. *The geology revised and improved in 1853,* 1853. All sheets [▮Dn: 1-3, 5].
   5. *The geology revised and improved in 1855,* 1855. All sheets.

2. *A General Map of Ireland for the Use of the Commissioners of Public works, exhibiting the Boundaries of Counties, Baronies, Poor Law Unions and Electoral Divisions, with the Principal Physical Features of the Country. 1847,* 1847. All sheets.
   Published by the Ordnance Survey.

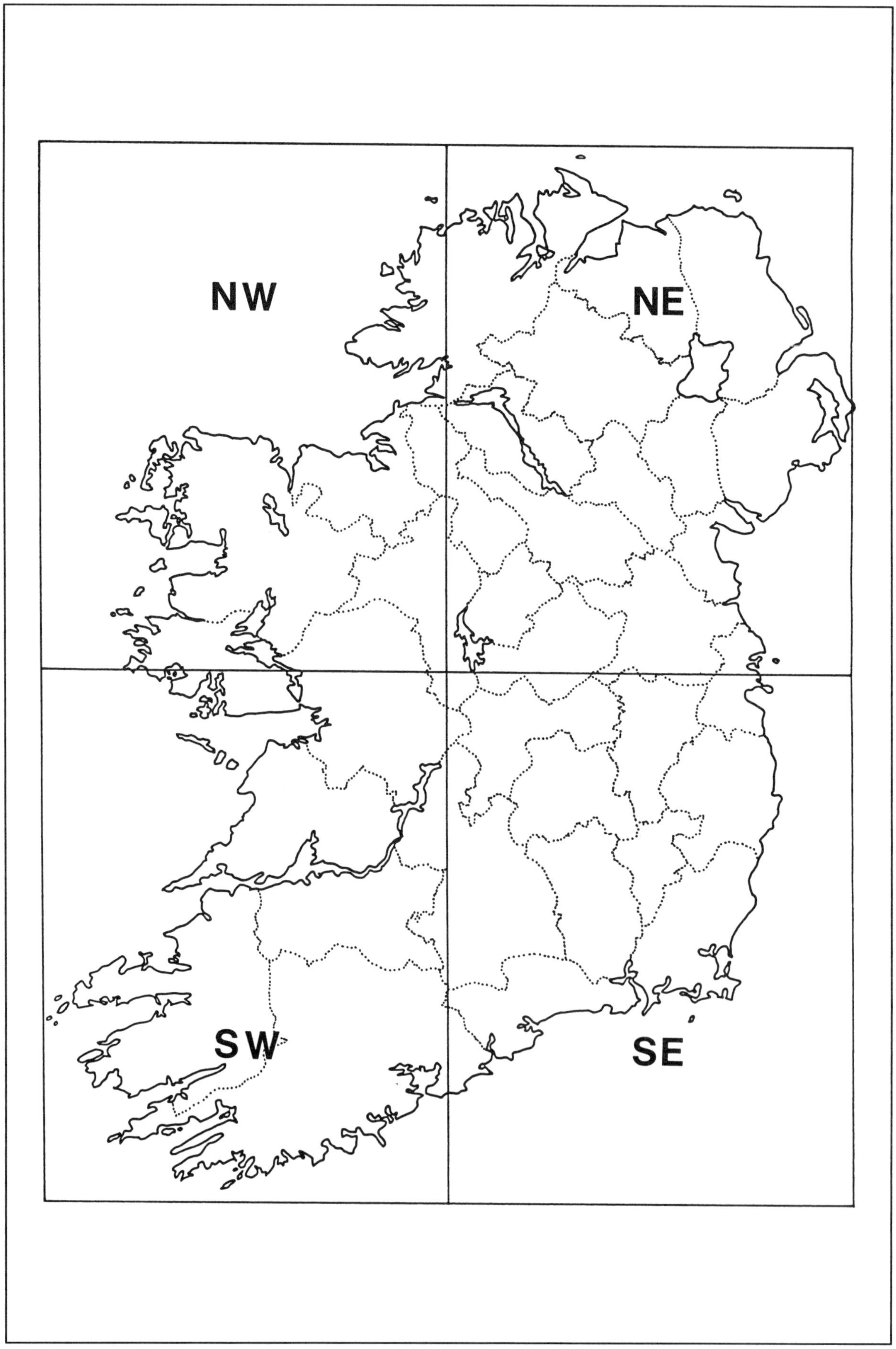

68. Quarter-inch General Map of Ireland (2)

68. Quarter-inch General Map of Ireland (2)

Constructed on Bonne's Projection on the origin of 53°30'N,8°W, and published 23 years after its inception in four sheets, *NW, NE, SW, SE,* meeting at the junction of one-inch Sheets 97, 98, 107, 108 [see ✦**22**]. Standard sheet coverage 108 by 144 miles, with extrusions for Burr Point and Tearaght Island on the NE and SW sheets. Based on the one-inch map. The full title is *A General Map of Ireland Showing the County and Barony Boundaries, the Rivers, Railways, Canals, Leading Roads and Principal Demesnes.* Lacking British mapping.

A. Topographical maps with a graticule at 30' intervals

With a graduated border on the outer edges only.

1. Outline edition, no date (published 1887). By engraving. All sheets.
   Called *New Edition.* Late reissues may be by litho- or zincography. A set with the title lettering engraved in outline only, fathom lines hand-drawn in blue in 1888 and contours in red in 1891, is in ▮Dna.

2. Outline edition, with hill shading. All sheets [▮Dna].
   Undated. Hill shading was by the triotint process. Evidently only two sets ever went on sale, in about 1898.

B. Skeleton maps without graticule

With a neat line border. Sheet sizes are approximate. Entitled *A General Map of Ireland* until 1962, with subtitles showing:

1. *Poor Law Union and Electoral Division Boundaries.* By zincography.
   1. Temporary edition for official use only, c.1874. ?All sheets. Not found.
   2. Reprinted for publication, published 1891. All sheets.

2. *County Boundaries, also County & District Electoral Division Boundaries Revised in January 1899.* All sheets [▮OSNI].
   Colour printed. For the Local Government Board for Ireland.

3. *County, Union & District Electoral Division Boundaries Revised in January 1899.* ?All sheets. Not found.
   Outline issues are listed in Ordnance Survey catalogues.

4. *Boundaries of Administrative Counties, Poor Law Unions, Urban & Rural Districts,* 1902. All sheets.
   Also 1917 edition, published 1918. For the Local Government Board for Ireland.

5. *Boundaries of Administrative Counties, Co. Boroughs, Urban, Rural & Dispensary Districts. & District Electoral Divisions,* 1912 (published 1913). All sheets.
   Also 1924, 1935 and 1962 editions. *Rural* was dropped from the title from 1935. For the Department of Local Government and Public Health. Railways are absent.

6. *Showing in respect of the 1911 Census Percentage of / Total Number of Irish Speakers in each District Electoral Division,* 1917. All sheets.
   Reprinted 1926 in *Coimisiún na Gaeltachta* : *Report,* Dublin, Stationery Office, 1926.

7. *Showing in respect of the 1925 Special Enumeration for the Counties of Donegal, Mayo, Galway, Kerry, Cork & Waterford, and parts of the Counties of Sligo, Roscommon, Clare, Limerick & Tipperary,* 1917 (published 1926).
   In *Coimisiún na Gaeltachta* : *Report,* Dublin, Stationery Office, 1926.

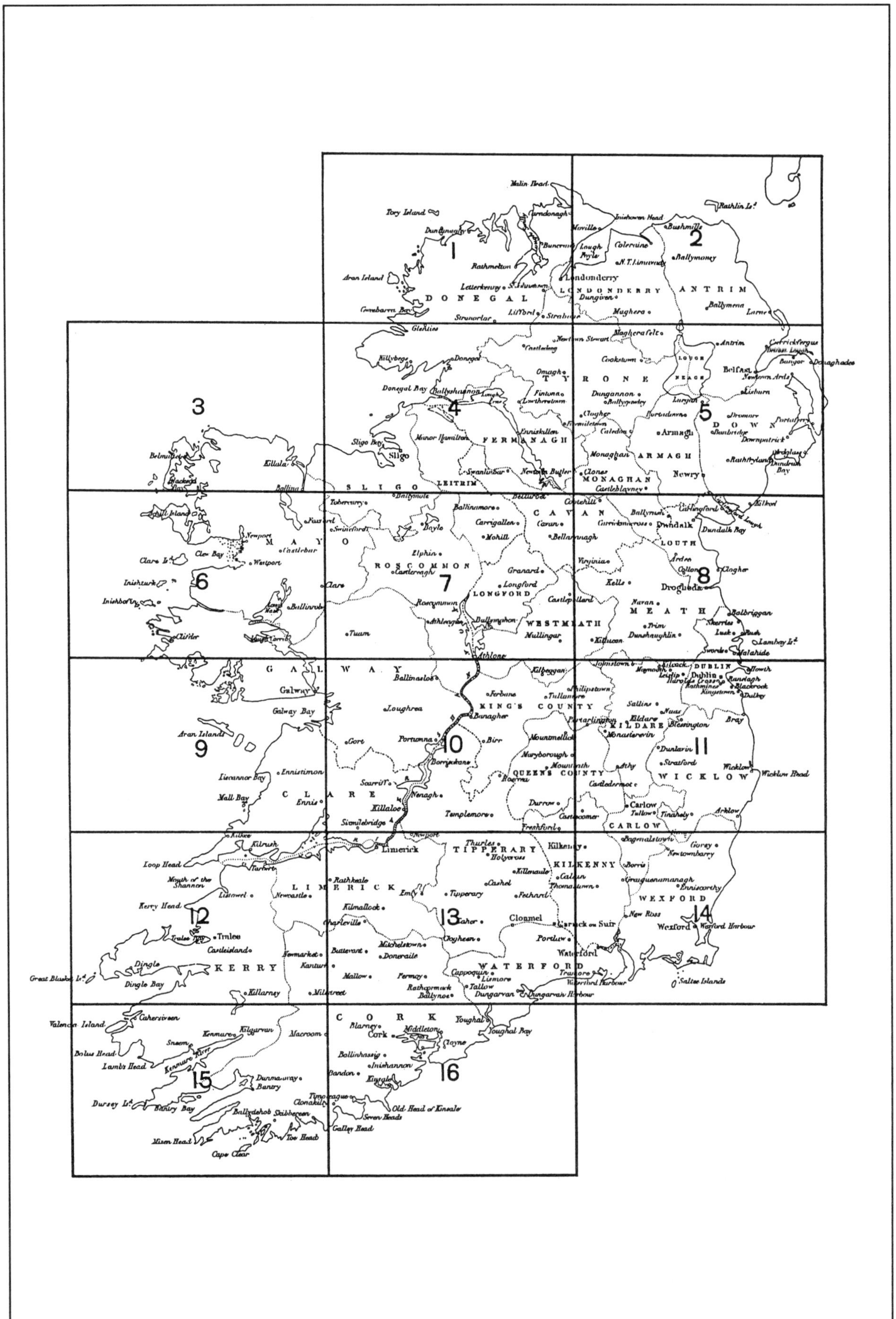

69. Quarter-inch Map of Ireland

69. Quarter-inch Map of Ireland

Constructed on Bonne's Projection on the origin of 53°30'N,8°W, and published in sixteen sheets. Standard sheet coverage 72 by 48 miles, the area covered by sixteen one-inch sheets [see **✣23**]. Newly drawn at the one-inch scale and presumably reduced by heliozincography. With a graticule at 20' intervals, unless noted otherwise. With the Scottish coastline on Sheet 2 and extrusions on Sheets 5 and 12. Heading, where present: *Ordnance Survey of Ireland.*

A. First Edition

The words "First Edition" do not appear.

1. Outline edition, with blue coastal tint, 1903-04. All sheets.
   This issue remained in Ordnance Survey catalogues until 1949.

2. Coloured edition, with hill shading. All sheets.
   1. Ordnance Survey issues, 1904-05 (published 1905). All sheets.
   2. Ordnance Survey of Ireland issues, 1927-51. 13 sheets recorded: 1-11, 13, 15.
   3. With roads and woods uncoloured. 2 sheets recorded: 8 (1907), 11 (1913).

3. Outline edition, with a simple border, 1918. Sheet 10 recorded [▮Dtc].
   The mapping is that of **✣68** which shows baronies. With a graticule at 30' intervals.

4. Outline edition, with water in blue, ?1930s. 5 sheets recorded: 4, 8, 11, 13, 16 [▮Dm].
   For the Department of Defence, from the coloured edition's outline and water plates.

- For Air Packets see **✣53**.8.2, 8.4; for the Northern Ireland district map see **✣73**.

Geological Survey of Ireland

Planned in sixteen sheets, but only four were issued. Sheets 2, 5, 11 use First Edition base maps, Sheet 16 the otherwise unrecorded *Second Edition* [✣B].

5. Colour printed edition, 1913-21 (published 1914-22). 4 sheets: 2, 5, 11, 16.
   Sheet 2 was reprinted in 1935 with the Scottish area coloured. Sheet 5 was *reprinted for the Government of Northern Ireland* in 1964. Manuscript or printed proof copies of all unpublished sheets except Sheet 9 survive [▮GSI].

6. All published sheets were available uncoloured.

B. Second Edition

Heading: *Ordnance Survey of Ireland (Second Edition).* Produced from the second national revision.

Geological Survey of Ireland: Sheet 16, 1915 (published 1921) only. For details see ✣A.5.

M. British military issues overprinted with War Office Irish Grid

1. GSGS 4142 coloured edition, with hill shading. All sheets.
   Usually printed by the 515th Corps Field Survey Company, Royal Engineers.
   1. [First Edition], with grid in purple, 1940. All sheets [▮Rg].
   2. Second Edition, with grid in blue, 1941. All sheets [▮PRO*, Ob, NLS].
      Classified roads as at 1 January 1942 are in red.
   3. Second Edition, with grid in red, reprinted by AMS, 1942. All sheets [▮NYp, Wn].
      Sheet 5 is atypical, being issued in Advance (1942) and AMS 1 (1944) editions.

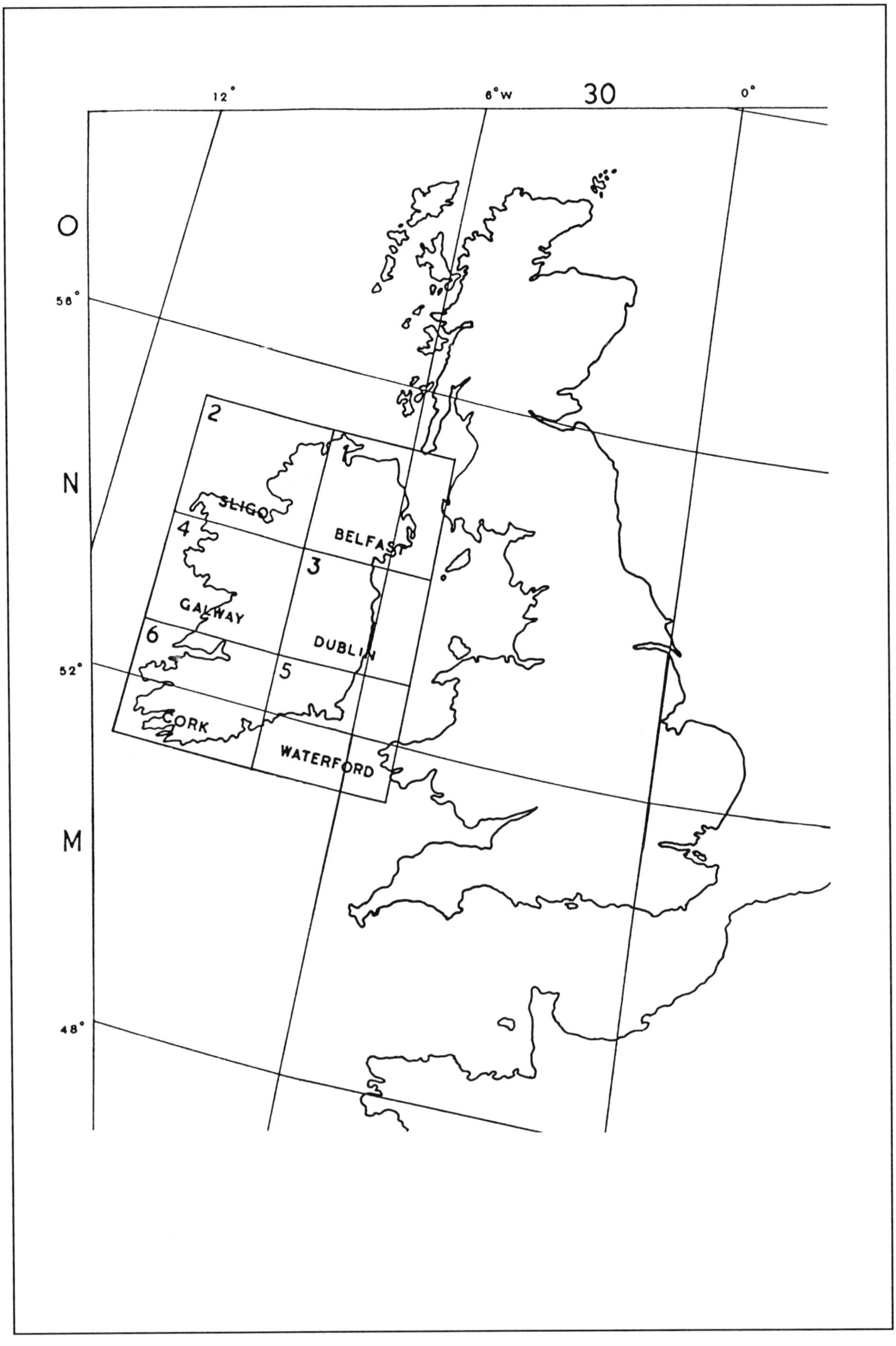

70. 1:250,000 Map of Ireland (Air)

70. 1:250,000 Map of Ireland (Air)

A separately numbered set of six sheets on non-standard sheet lines (forming a subsection of the parent GSGS 3982 *Europe 1:250,000 (Air)* [✣**46**]) covers Ireland. The sheet numbers, prefixed "Ireland", unusually increase from the north-east, not the north-west, corner. Laid out on graticule sheet lines, with overlaps with adjoining sheets, 10' to the north and 15' to the east. With a graticule at 10' intervals. The War Office Irish Grid overprinted in brown at 10 km intervals appears in the border: the grid lines nearest to the sheet edges are fully drawn. The British areas are mapped. With air information overprinted in black. The map was compiled and drawn by the Ordnance Survey. The *Ireland 1:250,000 (Air)* heading is high in the top right-hand corner, and usually trimmed off. The recorded editions are coloured, with purple layers. Only the sheet line information given here is relevant to GSGS (Air) 5015 [✣5].

1. GSGS 3982: [First Edition], 1940. All sheets: Ireland 1-6 [▮PC].

2. [AMS M502]: *Advance edition,* 1942. All sheets: Ireland 1-6 [▮Dna, Wn].
   Printed by the Engineer Reproduction Plant, United States Army.

3. GSGS 3982: 2nd Edition. All sheets.
   With isogonals in black. War Office Irish Grid intersections are added.
   1. GSGS issue, 1940 (issued 1942-43). All sheets: Ireland 1-6 [▮Bg, Wc].
   2. [AMS M502]: AMS 2, 1943. All sheets: Ireland 1-6 [▮Wn].

4. GSGS 3982 (Marine): 2nd Edition.
   Bathymetric layer colours are reversed, with orange used for under six fathoms.
   1. GSGS issue, 1943. Ireland Sheet 6 recorded [▮PRO*].
   2. [AMS M502]: AMS 3, 1944. Ireland Sheet 6 recorded [▮PRO*, Wn].

5. GSGS (Air) 5015: *Road Obstructions (Bridge Headroom),* 1942. All sheets [▮BL, PRO*].
   "Air" is deleted from the GSGS number on some copies. These are outline diagrams showing skeleton information only. They were prepared by the War Office, compiled and drawn by the Assistant Directorate of Maps, Air Ministry, in July 1942. They are related to the MBAM 3761 Great Britain series [✣**54**.M.15, **59**.M.11], also to a special 1:250,000 map AM 3761 *Northern Ireland* : *Road Obstructions (Bridge Headroom),* made in 1941. This was revised, reclassified GSGS 5015A, and printed in proof on 19 April 1943 [▮PRO*].

Symbols **:** a **bold** number prefixed with ✣ is a cross reference to another section of the book; a number prefixed with ✣ is a cross reference within the current section; a reference number in ( ) at a district map identifies the next, or previous, such map listed with the same sheet lines; the ▮ symbol accompanies a source reference for maps rarely encountered (library sigla are listed on page 241); ❍ warns that there are noted exceptions to the information given in headings; ↑ identifies what is referred to here as War Office marginalia (for a description see page xxii); ❁ refers to the exceptional use of the heading *Ordnance Survey of Great Britain.*

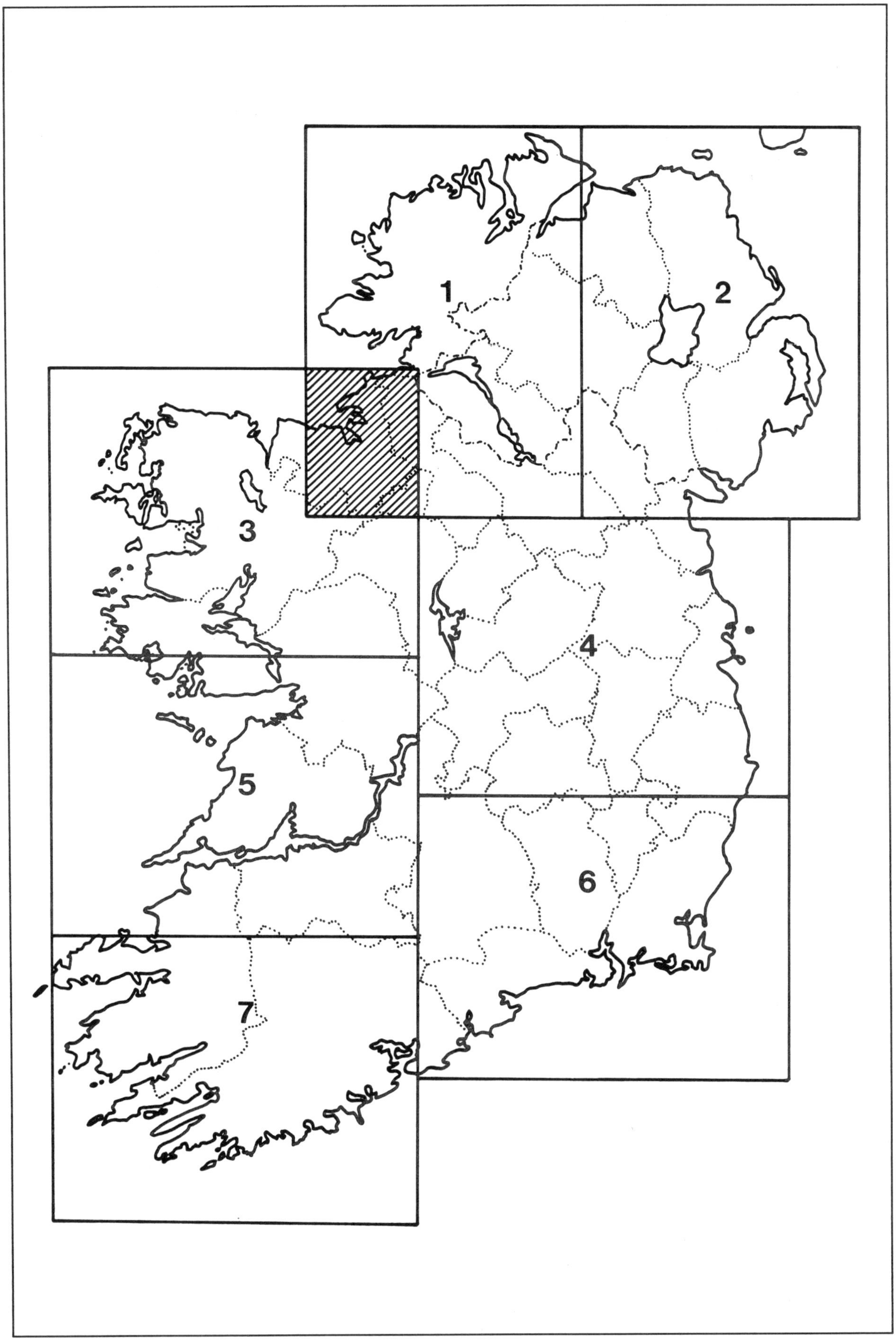

71. Quarter-inch Military Map of Ireland (Large sheet series)

71. Quarter-inch Military Map of Ireland (Large sheet series)

Issued in seven sheets on War Office Irish Grid sheet lines. Some sheet lines are common with those of the one-inch map GSGS 4136 [**✚28**]. Standard sheet coverage 160 by 120 km; Sheets 1 and 2 are portrait, the others landscape. Compiled and drawn by the Ordnance Survey based on GSGS 4142 mapping [**✚69**.M.1]. With outline mapping of Scotland on Sheet 2.

With extrusions on Sheet 7 for the Blasket Islands and Skellig Rocks.

1. GSGS 4338 coloured editions, with brown layers. All sheets.
   With War Office Irish Grid in black, numbered in red; the War Office Cassini Grid in British areas is numbered in purple. Without air information, though with isogonals overprinted in red. With classified roads, usually as at 1 January 1942, also in red.
   1. GSGS 4338: First Edition, 1942. 2 sheets recorded: 2 [■NLS], 4 [■BSg].
      Sheet 4 may be a proof copy.
   2. GSGS 4338: First Edition, *Ground/Air,* 1942. 6 sheets: 1, 3-7 [■NLS].
      With the "Black Arrow" magnetic variation diagram (see page xxii).

2. AMS M522 (GSGS 4338): AMS 1, coloured, 1950. All sheets [■Wn].
   With the "Black Arrow" magnetic variation diagram (see page xxii). With War Office Irish Grid in black, numbered in red; the War Office Cassini Grid in British areas is numbered in blue. The source map is described as *First GSGS Edition, 1942.*

3. GSGS 4338, later M522, reissued as *Northern Ireland and Eire.* All sheets.
   Coloured editions with brown layers. The grid is not named except as *Irish Grid* on sheet indexes; presumably the Irish National Grid (which was superficially similar to the War Office Irish Grid (see page 242)) is now in use. With the National Grid (Military System) over British areas. With air information overprinted in blue.
   1. GSGS 4338: Second Edition, 1953-54. All sheets [■Og, PRO*].
   2. M522: Edition 2-GSGS, 1953, printed by AMS, 1963. Sheet 4 recorded [■Wn].
   3. GSGS 4338: Edition 3-GSGS, 1954. 2 sheets: 1, 2 [■NLS].
   4. M522: Edition 4-GSGS, 1962. Sheet 2 [■Ob].
   5. M522: Edition 3-GSGS, 1963. 2 sheets: 3, 4 [■NLS].

4. GSGS 4865: *RAF Topographical Map,* 1956. All sheets [■PRO*].
   With a graticule at 30' intervals and air information overprinted in blue.

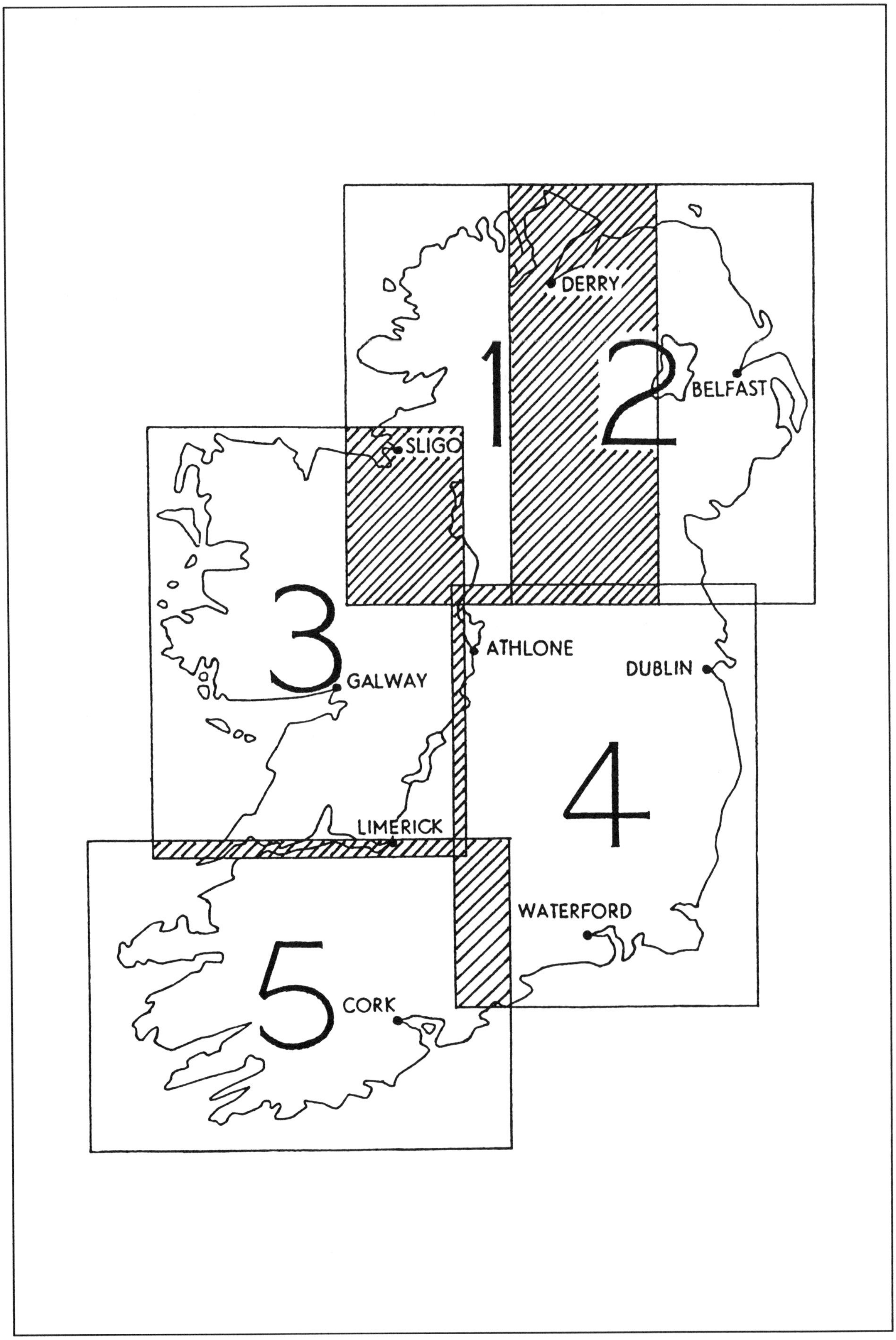

72. 1:250,000 Map of Ireland (1)

72. 1:250,000 Map of Ireland (1)

Irish National Grid Series. Published in five sheets. Standard sheet coverage 150 by 200 km: Sheet 5 is landscape. The Scottish area on Sheet 2 is omitted. Newly drawn. Issues are colour printed, with layers, unless noted otherwise. Published by the Ordnance Survey of Ireland.

1. *Provisional Edition,* no date (published June 1958). Sheet 4 only [▮Ob].

2. 1st Edition, 1959-60. 3 sheets: 1, 3, 5.
   With *Other roads* as single lines. For Sheet 2 see ✣3, for Sheet 4 see ✣1 - a note on the 2nd Edition reads: *The Provisional Edition of this Sheet - No.4 published June 1958 - is regarded as its First Edition.*

3. 2nd and subsequent editions, 1961-66. All sheets.
   With *Other roads* as unfilled double lines. The first issue of Sheet 2 is classified *1st-2nd Edition.* Each sheet was further updated independently in numbered editions:
   Sheet 1 editions. 2: 1966, 3: 1972, 4: 1976, 5: 1979.
   Sheet 2 editions. 1/2: 1962, 3: 1966, 4: 1974, 5: 1976.
   Sheet 3 editions. 2: 1964, 3: 1968, 4: 197x, 5: 197x, 6: 1977.
   Sheet 4 editions. 2: 1961, 3: 1965, 4: 1970, 5: 1972, 6: 197x, 7: 1977.
   Sheet 5 editions. 2: 1964, 3: 1966, 4: 1969, 5: 1974, 6: 1975, 7: 1976, 8: 1977.

4. Outline edition, with water in blue, contours in grey, 1966. Sheet 5 recorded [▮Dtf].
   In 3rd Edition. Other sheets presumably exist but this has yet to be confirmed.

5. *Gravity Anomaly Map* : *Bouguer Anomaly.* 2 sheets: 4 (1962), 5 (1960).
   By T. Murphy in *Geophysical Bulletin* 22 and 18 respectively, Dublin Institute for Advanced Studies, 1962 and 1960.

6. District map.
   Limerick Region, 1966 [▮BL].

British military issue

7. M524: Edition 1-GSGS, 1969. All sheets.

73. Quarter-inch Map of Northern Ireland

Made by the transfer to one sheet by lithography of the relevant sections of the sixteen-sheet map of Ireland [✣**69**]. With a graticule at 20' intervals. With a coastal outline of Scotland. Most issues have the international and county boundaries overprinted.

1. Outline edition, with water in blue, 1922 [▮Dtc, Ob].
   Without title or heading. Printed by the Ordnance Survey, Southampton.

2. *North Eastern Ireland* : *To Accompany the Report of the Irish Boundary Commission,* 1925 [▮PRO (MPI 402)].
   Coloured edition, with hill shading and overprint in red. Both report and map were suppressed; a modern edition appeared in 1969 [✣**76**.B.8]. See also ✣M.1.1.

3. *Ministry of Home Affairs* : *Northern Ireland Road Map,* 1926.
   Outline edition, with water in blue, classified roads in red and blue, boundaries in yellow. Also 1931 edition, which was further updated by overprinting to 1935. With heading *Ordnance Survey of Northern Ireland.*

4. *Average Annual Rainfall (1881-1915),* 1928.
   Outline edition, with water and overprinted information in blue. In *Ulster Year Book* (second edition), 1929. The rainfall data was supplied by the British Rainfall Organization, Meteorological Office, London.

M. Military issues overprinted with War Office Irish Grid in purple ❍

1. *North Eastern Ireland.*
   1. ?Coloured edition, with hill shading, 1925. Not found.
      Printed at Geographical Section, General Staff, War Office, 1925. This imprint information survives on ✣M.1.2. This map was probably the source of ✣2.
   2. GSGS 3942 coloured edition, with hill shading, 1933 [▮DGI].
      Printed by the Ordnance Survey. With the international border and index of the one-inch map GSGS 3917 [✣**27**] overprinted in purple.

2. *Essential Traffic Routes Map,* c.1940.
   A reduced area map on graticule sheet lines.

74. Quarter-inch Province Map of Northern Ireland

Enlarged from the ten-mile map [✚**94**.A.15.2]. Showing the province only. With a graticule at 1° intervals. Published by the Ordnance Survey of Northern Ireland.

A. Quarter-inch issues

1. Outline edition, 1928.

2. *Density of Population in District Electoral Divisions 1926*, 1928.

3. Untitled index showing *1" Standard Ordnance Sheets* (red), *6" County Sheets* (green), 1928 (printed 1938).
   In *A Preliminary Survey of the Ancient Monuments of Northern Ireland conducted by the Ancient Monuments Advisory Council for Northern Ireland*, Belfast, HMSO, 1940.

4. *Boundary Commission for Northern Ireland Constituted in accordance with the House of Commons (Redistribution of Seats) Act*, 1944.
   Showing administrative boundaries (red), imperial parliamentary constituencies (green). In *Boundary Commission for Northern Ireland constituted in accordance with the House of Commons (Redistribution of Seats) Act, 1944 : Initial Report* (BPP(HC) 1946-47 [Cmd.7231], X).

B. Issues at a reduced scale of approximately 5½ miles to an inch

The map was revised, from 1950 with the addition of Republic of Ireland mapping, shipping routes and enhanced railways. The scale is unspecified.

1. Coloured edition, by county, 1947.
   In *[The] Ulster Year Book* (sixth, seventh and eighth editions), 1947, 1950, 1953.

2. Outline edition, 1947 [▮OSNI].

---

75. Quarter-inch Road Map of Northern Ireland

Presumably constructed on Bonne's Projection on the origin of 53°30'N,8°W. Produced from the 1936-38 revision in Northern Ireland. Showing graticule intersections at 20' intervals. With a coastal outline of Scotland. Heading: *Ordnance Survey of Northern Ireland.*

1. *Road Map*, 1939.
   No issue before 1941 is recorded [▮Dtc]. Reprinted 1945. Legal deposit collections received 1947 reprints.

76. The Quarter-inch Map of Northern Ireland

Irish National Grid map (sheet co-ordinates 142.5 km E to 370 km E, 303 km N to 460 km N). Heading: *Ordnance Survey of Northern Ireland : Northern Ireland : The Quarter-inch Map (Provisional / Second / Third Edition).* Newly drawn. The Scottish area is mapped.

A. Provisional Edition

1. Coloured edition, with layers.
    1. With roads and woods uncoloured, 1956 [▮BFq].
    2. With roads and woods coloured, 1957.

2. Outline edition, with water in blue, 1957.

3. Water and contour issue.

4. *Administrative Map of Northern Ireland,* 1959.
    Showing administrative information (red), district electoral divisions (black).

5. *Parliamentary Constituencies of Northern Ireland,* 1959.
    Showing Northern Ireland parliamentary constituencies (red), imperial parliamentary constituencies (green), district electoral divisions (black).

- As Sheet 8 in GSGS 4736 see **✣61**.

B. Second Edition

1. Coloured edition, with layers, 1961.

2. Outline edition.
    1. With uncoloured water, 1961.
    2. With water in blue, 1961.

3. *Irish Grid 6-inch Sheet Lines & Sheet Nos.,* 1961.

4. *Index to the Irish Grid Six-inch Sheets and 1:2500 Plans,* 1961.

5. *Index to the Irish Grid 1:10,000 Sheets and 1:2500 Plans,* edition *E*, 1979.
    See ✣C.2 for edition *D*. Editions *A* to *C* were published in ✣B.4.

6. *Administrative Map of Northern Ireland,* 1967.
    Showing administrative boundaries (red), district electoral divisions (black).

7. *Parliamentary Constituencies of Northern Ireland,* 1969.
    Showing Northern Ireland parliamentary constituencies (red), imperial parliamentary constituencies (green), district electoral divisions (black).

8. Outline edition, with boundaries overprinted in red, published 1969.
    In G.J. Hand *Report of the Irish Boundary Commission 1925,* Shannon, Irish University Press, 1969. The original report had been suppressed [see **✣73**.2]. The sheet width is reduced to 190 km.

- In 1963 the map, enlarged to 1:250,000 and extended west to 140 km E and south to 300 km N, was employed as Sheet 18 in M523 etc [**✣63**].

Geological Survey of Northern Ireland

9. *Gravity Anomaly Map of Northern Ireland,* 1967.

10. *Magnetic Anomaly Map of Northern Ireland,* 1971.

C. Third Edition

1. Outline edition, with water in blue, 1974 [▮OSNI].
   Probably unpublished. A note is written on a copy owned by the Ordnance Survey of Northern Ireland: *Not in catalogues. This name* [ie Third Edition] *should have been 2nd Edition. The blank at NW corner of this map indicates it was made from components for an index map.*

2. *Index to the Irish Grid 1:10 000 Sheets and 1:2500 Plans,* edition *D,* 1974.
   Edition *E* reverts to the *Second Edition* base [✣B.5].

Symbols **:** a **bold** number prefixed with ✚ is a cross reference to another section of the book; a number prefixed with ✣ is a cross reference within the current section; a reference number in ( ) at a district map identifies the next, or previous, such map listed with the same sheet lines; the ▮ symbol accompanies a source reference for maps rarely encountered (library sigla are listed on page 241); ❍ warns that there are noted exceptions to the information given in headings; ↑ identifies what is referred to here as War Office marginalia (for a description see page xxii); ❁ refers to the exceptional use of the heading *Ordnance Survey of Great Britain.*

77. 1:250,000 Map of Ireland (2)

Irish National Grid series. Published jointly in four sheets by the Ordnance Surveys of Ireland and Northern Ireland. Standard sheet coverage 220 by 150 km. The sheet lines of Sheet 1 are irregular, depending on the size and location of title and explanatory panels. Its width ranges between the 150 and 380 km grid co-ordinates, the height occasionally extends beyond the standard 460 km to 470 km. The Irish and British National Grids are usually in blue on coloured issues.

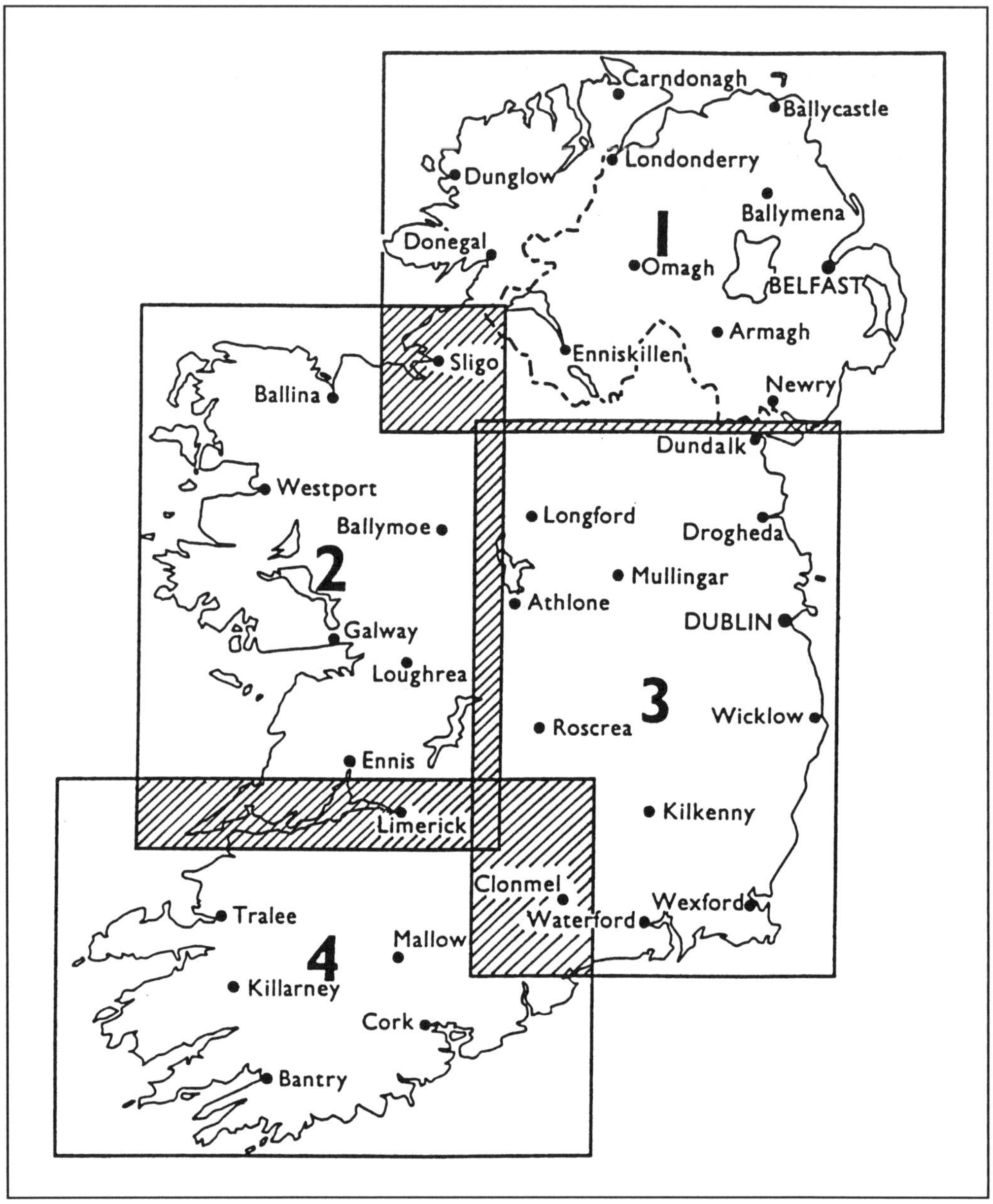

A. First Edition

Heading: *First Edition Ireland.* Newly drawn. In spite of the intention of producing a joint four-sheet map of Ireland, only Sheet 1 was published, in Belfast. The Scottish area is omitted.

1. Coloured edition, with layers, 1970. Sheet 1 only.

2. *Northern Ireland : A Map for Tourists,* published 1976. Sheet 1.
   A reissue of ✣A.1 with a title panel on the reverse. Motorway depiction is enhanced.

3. *General Soil Map,* 1970.

Geological Survey of Northern Ireland

4. Geological Survey, 1977. Sheet 1 (Solid).

5. *Bouguer Gravity Anomaly Map of Northern Ireland,* 1984.

Military issues

6. GSGS 5099: *Northern Ireland Road Map,* 1970.
   Superseded by M5218 *Northern Ireland Road Map,* 1975, a map on graticule sheet lines (not listed here).

7. GSGS 5101: *Royal Ulster Constabulary Divisions and Stations,* 1970.
   Editions 1 and 2-GSGS are apparently on this base map. Edition 3-GSGS, 1975, is a new map on graticule sheet lines (not listed here).

B. Holiday Map

The series title *Holiday Map* appears on map covers but has only irregularly been applied to the map. With a coastal outline of Scotland on Sheet 1.

1. Coloured edition, with layers. All sheets.
   1. Ordnance Survey of Northern Ireland publication, 1980. Sheet 1.
      Having used the expression *First Edition* on ✣A.1, Belfast chose not to reuse it here. At least five updated reprints with amendments were issued, but they were not promoted as new editions.
   2. Ordnance Survey of Ireland publications.
      1. 1st Edition, 1981-82. 3 sheets: 2-4.
      2. 2nd Edition, 1993. 3 sheets: 2-4.

2. Coloured edition, with layers. All sheets.
   With new mapping produced presumably from the 1:50,000 digital database, though derivation information is not supplied. The sheets are prominently named but lack the series title. They are also unnumbered except on the adjoining sheet diagrams of the south and east sheets. The series title on covers is modified to *Holiday Map : New.*
   1. Ordnance Survey of Northern Ireland publication, 1998. Sheet [1] *Ireland North.*
   2. Ordnance Survey of Ireland publications, 1998. 3 sheets: [2] *Ireland West,* [3] *Ireland East,* [4] *Ireland South.*

3. Outline edition, 1980. Sheet 1.
   Published by the Ordnance Survey of Northern Ireland.

4. *Éire thuaidh : Ireland North,* 1988. Sheet 1.
   A bilingual version of ✣B.1.1, produced by the Ordnance Survey of Northern Ireland and published by the Department of the Environment for Northern Ireland. With a bilingual gazetteer of settlements in Northern Ireland.

Geological Surveys of Northern Ireland and Great Britain issues

5. *Quaternary Geological Map of Northern Ireland,* 1st Edition, 1991.

6. *Groundwater Vulnerability Map of Northern Ireland,* 1994.

7. *Hydrogeological Map of Northern Ireland,* 1994.

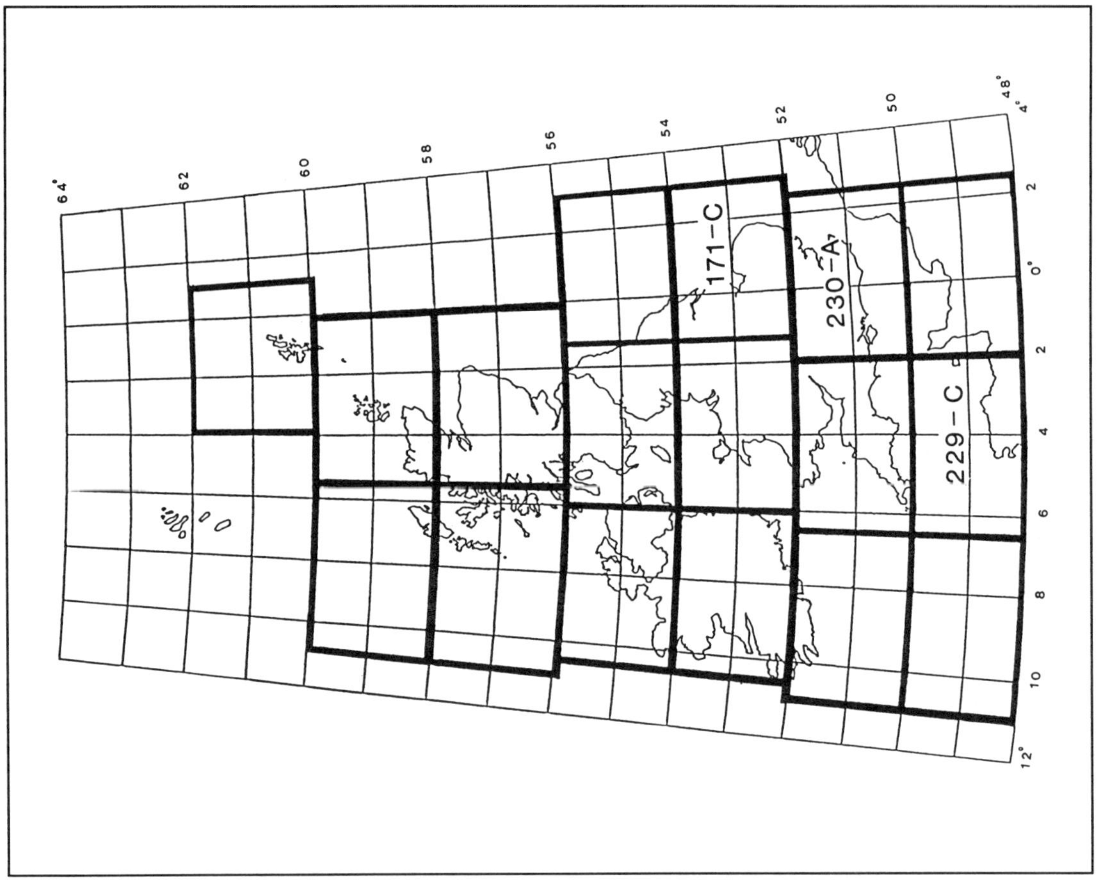

78. 1:500,000 RAF Aeronautical Chart

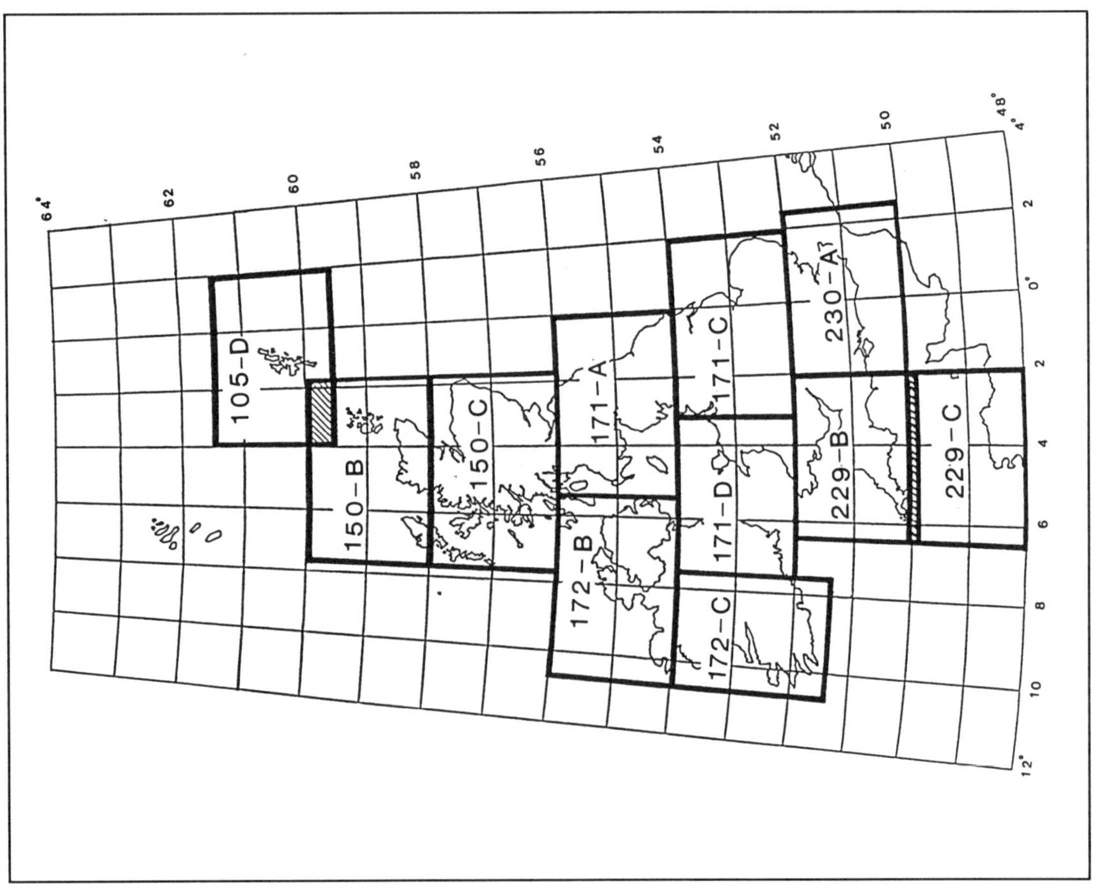

79. 1:500,000 Map of the World

78. 1:500,000 RAF Aeronautical Chart

Constructed on the Lambert Conformal Conical Projection. Laid out over the British Isles on graticule sheet lines in sheets usually of 2° in latitude by 4°30' in longitude, numbered as quarters *A* (NW), *B* (NE), *C* (SE), *D* (SW) of the 1:1,000,000 *RAF Aeronautical Chart* [**✚107**]. Another official index shows the quarters of Sheet 172 extended north-south to cover Ireland, and Sheet 229-A consequently reduced, but this is academic since it appears that only three sheets, 171-C *Norwich*, 229-C *Brest*, 230-A *London*, were published. War Office and Military Survey issues only are listed here. Sheet lines are common in Series 1404 for Sheets 229-C (without overlaps) and 230-A [**✚79**]. With a graticule at 10' intervals. Heading: *RAF 1:500,000 Aeronautical Chart (based on USAF Pilotage Chart)*. With air information overprinted in blue.

1. GSGS 4715 coloured edition.
   Military grid values and intersections are overprinted in brown.
   1. Without contours, 1954. Sheet 171-C *Norwich*, First Edition-GSGS [▮RGS].
   2. With contours, 1954. Sheet 230-A *London*, First Edition-GSGS [▮RGS].

2. GSGS 4715 coloured edition, 1957. Sheet 230-A *London*, Edition 2-GSGS [▮RGS].
   The military grid references are cleared. A 1962 reprint is recorded made by the Survey Production Centre, Royal Engineers (British Army of the Rhine) [▮DGI].

3. GSGS 4715 coloured edition, with purple layers, 1960. Sheet 229-C *Brest*, Edition 1-GSGS [▮RGS].
   With edges bled off north and east. A 1961 reprint is recorded made by the Survey Production Centre, Royal Engineers (British Army of the Rhine) [▮DGI].

Superseded by *Topographical Tactical Charts*, then *Tactical Pilotage Charts* (not listed here).

---

79. 1:500,000 Map of the World

Constructed on the Lambert Conformal Conical Projection. Laid out on graticule sheet lines rearranged from the regular pattern of **✚78** in order to achieve improved land coverage. Eleven sheets cover the British Isles: 105-D *Lerwick*, 150-B *Kirkwall*, 150-C *Aberdeen*, 171-A *Glasgow*, 171-C *Birmingham*, 171-D *Dublin*, 172-B *Belfast*, 172-C *Cork*, 229-B *Bristol*, 229-C *Brest*, 230-A *London*. These usually cover 2° in latitude but are of irregular width. All but Sheet 229-C were compiled from quarter-inch mapping and printed by the Ordnance Survey, and published by Military Survey. With British National and Universal Transverse Mercator Grids overprinted in purple, and Irish National Grid in red (in purple numbered in red on Sheet 172-B). A graticule in black at 1° intervals was supplied after early printings. GSGS 4830 was the number allocated in 1954, but the series was renumbered prior to the issue of the British sheets. It was also formerly classified Europe Series 6402.

There is an inset of St Kilda on Sheet 150-B.

1. Series 1404 coloured edition, with yellow base and brown layers. All sheets.
   1. Edition 1-GSGS, 1965-72. 10 sheets: 105-D, 150-B, 150-C, 171-A, 171-C, 171-D, 172-B, 172-C, 229-B, 230-A.
      A 1973 reprint of Sheet 172-B was made by Harrison and Sons (Hayes) Ltd.
   2. Edition 2-GSGS, 1970-71. 3 sheets recorded: 105-D, 171-C, 230-A.
      A 1972 reprint of Sheet 171-C was made by George Philip.
   3. L'Institut Géographique National publication. Sheet 229-C.
      With coverage of the Channel Islands. A civilian issue appeared in 1962, followed in 1963 by Edition 1 of a military issue *Type World Anglais 1404*, overprinted with the Universal Transverse Mercator Grid in purple. Both versions went to second editions in 1969 [▮RGS].

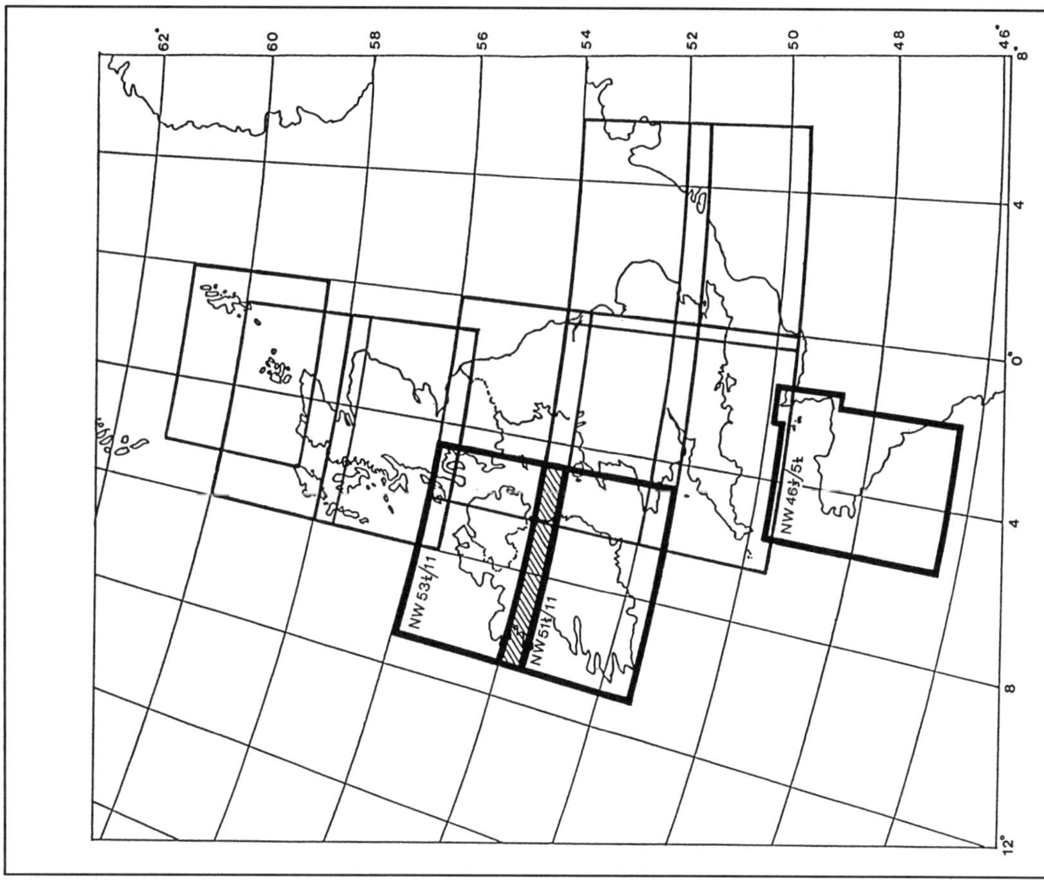

The sheet lines of GSGS 4072 set against those of GSGS 4369 [+83]

80. 1:500,000 Map of Europe (Air)

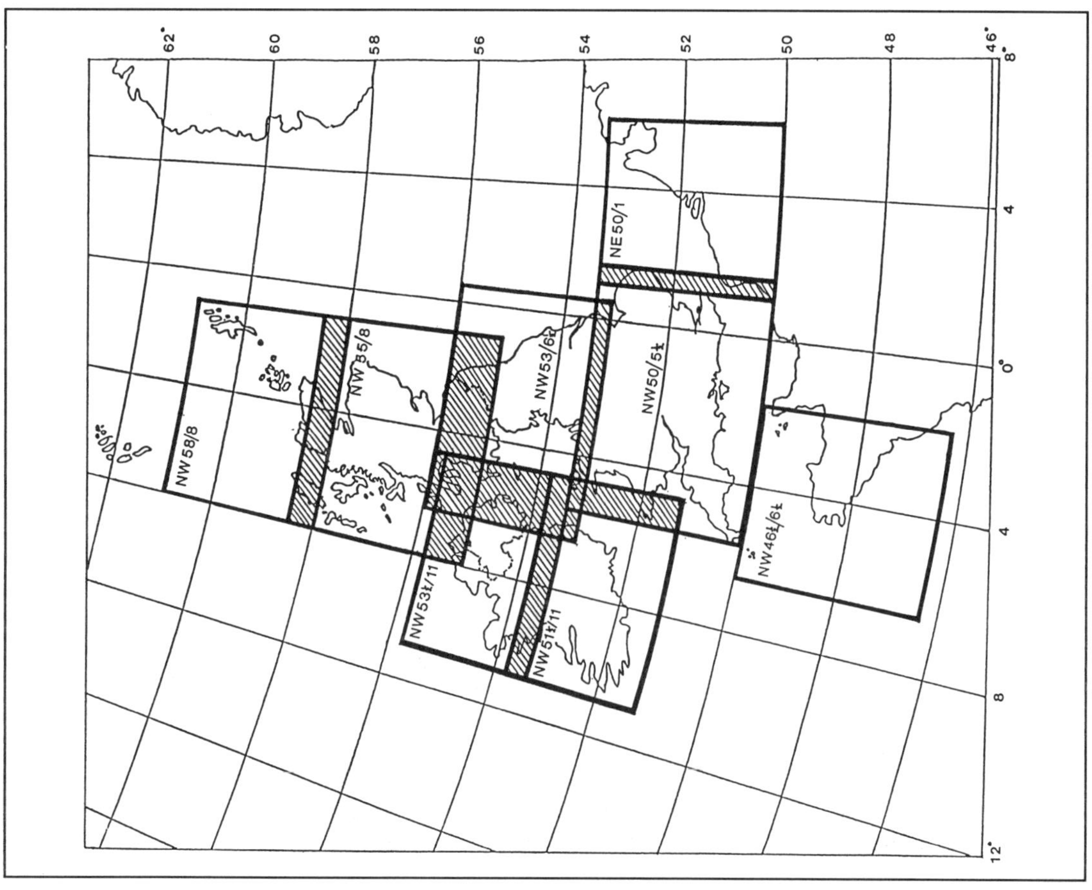

81. 1:500,000 Map of Europe

80. 1:500,000 Map of Europe (Air)

Constructed on the Lambert Conformal Conical Projection. Laid out on graticule sheet lines. Designed for the Royal Air Force, with topographical features selectively enhanced especially to meet the air navigational requirements of Bomber Command. In the British Isles area only Sheet NW46⅓/5½ *Brest* (covering the Channel Islands) and the two Irish sheets, NW51½/11 *Ireland South* and NW53½/11 *Northern Ireland,* later *Ireland North,* were required during the war years, Great Britain being covered by GSGS 4369 [**✚83**]. With a graticule at 10' intervals. The appropriate military grids were overprinted, initially in brown, later in red, in the borders at 10 km intervals and at intersection points across the sheets. With air information overprinted in black. Roads and contours were in brown, later red. Early issues had detailed marginalia regarding air information, adjoining sheets, etc, which was quickly dropped. The map was compiled and drawn at the War Office. The heading is usually *1:500,000 Europe (Air).* The Scottish area is mapped, and there is an extrusion for the Isle of Man. The editions recorded are coloured with purple layers. For the post-war continuation of this series on new sheet lines see **✚81**.A.1.

1. GSGS 4072: [First Edition].
   1. GSGS issues, 1940-41. 3 sheets: NW46⅓/5½, NW51½/11, NW53½/11.
   2. The first AMS editions were monochrome copies of ✣1.1 printings.
   3. [AMS M404]: *Unedited provisional edition,* 1942. Sheet NW46⅓/5½ [▮Wn].
   4. [AMS M404]: *Advance edition,* 1942. 2 sheets: NW51½/11, NW53½/11 [▮Wn].
      1942 reprints without the heading are recorded. One of Sheet NW51½/11 is overprinted in red with aeronautical radio information which was headed *Confidential* [▮Wn]. Sheet NW53½/11 is not recorded in this style but was implicitly required.
   5. [AMS M404]: AMS 2, 1943. Sheet NW46⅓/5½ [▮Wn].

2. GSGS 4072: Second Edition.
   1. GSGS issues, 1940-42 (issued 1942-44). 3 sheets: NW46⅓/5½, NW51½/11, NW53½/11.
   2. [AMS M404]: AMS 2, 1943. 2 sheets: NW51½/11, NW53½/11 [▮Wn].

3. GSGS 4072: Third Edition.
   Neither third nor fourth editions of Sheet NW46⅓/5½ have been recorded.
   1. GSGS issues, 1943. 2 sheets recorded: NW51½/11, NW53½/11.
      A 1952 reprint of Sheet NW53½/11 is recorded [▮PRO*].
   2. [AMS M404]: AMS 3, 1944. 2 sheets recorded: NW51½/11, NW53½/11 [▮Wn].

81. 1:500,000 Map of Europe

Constructed on the Lambert Conformal Conical Projection. For wartime issues of GSGS 4072 see **✣80**. Post-war, GSGS 4072 and GSGS 4649 shared graticule sheet lines which were larger, with edges bled off north and east. The British Isles were covered by seven sheets mostly with non-standard sheet lines: NW46½/6½ *Brest* (renumbered, with its pre-war dimensions extended to cover the Isles of Scilly and Lizard Point), NW50/5½ *Southern England and Wales* (with extrusions for Land's End and Lizard Point), NW51½/11 *Ireland South,* NW53/6½ *Northern England,* NW53½/11 *Ireland North,* NW55/8 *Scotland,* NW58/8 *Orkneys and Shetland.* Sheet NE50/1 *Low Countries,* later 2170D *Low Countries - Amsterdam,* overlaps East Anglia but is not listed in ✣A, B or D. The maps were compiled and drawn by the Ordnance Survey unless noted.

A. Europe RAF 1:500,000

With a graticule at 10' intervals. Overprinted with air information and Georef in blue. The points of intersection of military grids are marked, the National Grid in purple (red on Sheet NW46½/6½), the Irish Grid in red and Lambert Zone 1 or Universal Transverse Mercator Grid in brown, with values given in the border. For a description of Georef see the War Office *Manual of Map Reading,* London, HMSO, 1956, 79-86.

1. GSGS 4072 coloured edition, with purple layers. All sheets.
   Superseding both GSGS 4369 [**✣83**] and the wartime version of GSGS 4072 [**✣80**].
   1. Fifth Edition-GSGS, 1950. Sheet NW46½/6½.
      For the first two editions of this sheet see **✣80**. The third and fourth editions are not recorded. Compiled and drawn by the War Office. The Fifth Edition-GSGS was overprinted with French Lambert Zone 1 and National Grids but was without Georef. The Sixth Edition-GSGS, 1953 (issued ?1954), was overprinted with Georef and with Universal Transverse Mercator and National Grids. Edition 7-GSGS appeared in 1957; an issue with Georef but without grids is recorded.
   2. First Edition-GSGS, 1951 (issued 1952). 4 sheets: NW50/5½, NW53/6½, NW55/8, NW58/8.
      Sheet NW50/5½ was published in Second Edition-GSGS in 1953 (issued ?1954), Edition 3-GSGS in 1956, Sheet NW55/8 in Edition 2-GSGS in 1954.
   3. Fourth Edition-GSGS, 1953 (issued 1953-54). 2 sheets: NW51½/11, NW53½/11.
      For the first three editions of these sheets see **✣80**.
   4. Series M404 (GSGS 4072), printed by AMS, 1960. ?All sheets [▮Wc, Wn].
      The GSGS editions current in 1960 for each sheet printed were used. Layer colours are closer to brown than purple.

2. AMS M404 (GSGS 4072) outline edition, with water in blue, 1953. Sheet NW46½/6½ recorded [▮Wn].
   The Fifth Edition-GSGS base was used. With Universal Transverse Mercator Grid overprinted in blue. Other sheets presumably exist, perhaps in other editions, but this has yet to be confirmed.

B. Europe ICAO 1:500,000

With a graticule at 10' intervals. Coloured editions, with brown layers and air information overprinted in magenta. There is no British issue of Sheet NW51½/11 *Ireland South* in this edition. The Ordnance Survey of Ireland issued both Ireland sheets, but on different sheet lines: NW51¼/11 *Ireland South* and NW53¼/11 *Ireland North* [see ✣B.4]. Northern Ireland was thus covered twice. Sheet NW46½/6½ *Brest* was atypical [see ✣B.2].

1. GSGS 4649: *Europe ICAO 1:500,000.*
   1. *Provisional Edition,* 1948. ?4 sheets: NW50/5½, NW53/6½, NW55/8, ?NW58/8.
   2. Second Edition-GSGS, 1951 (issued 1951-52). 4 sheets: NW50/5½, NW53/6½, NW55/8, NW58/8.

2. GSGS 4649: *Europe ICAO 1:500,000,* 1950. Sheet NW46½/6½ [First Edition].
   Compiled, drawn and published by the War Office for the Ministry of Civil Aviation. Edition 2-GSGS was issued in 1960, printed by the Ordnance Survey.

3. GSGS 4649, reissued as *Aeronautical Chart ICAO 1:500,000 Europe,* 1954-55. 5 sheets: NW50/5½, NW53/6½, NW53½/11, NW55/8, NW58/8.
   Sheet NW53½/11 was issued in First Edition, the other sheets in Third Edition following the issues in ✣B.1. All sheets were constantly updated in sequentially numbered editions. Later issues of Sheet NW50/5½ have an inset of the Isles of Scilly and Sheet NW55/8 of St Kilda. The series title was revised on later issues.

4. *Aeronautical Chart ICAO 1:500,000,* 1951. 2 sheets: NW51¼/11, NW53¼/11 [▮Ob].
   Published by the Ordnance Survey of Ireland on independent sheet lines. The derivation of the base map is given as *Topographic Base 1950 edition,* though no such 1:500,000 map of Ireland in one or two sheets is recorded. The map is not dated, except by the air information date. Further editions followed. The 1967 issue, if no other, also appeared without the air information overprint.

United Kingdom coverage was replaced in 1972 by the four-sheet GSGS 5154: 2150ABCD *Scotland, Orkney and Shetland,* 2171AB *Northern England,* 2171CD *Southern England and Wales,* 2172AB *Northern Ireland,* printed for the Civil Aviation Authority by the Ordnance Survey. A new series without GSGS number commenced in 1974. Ordnance Survey sheets were reduced to three in 1984 with the amalgamation of Sheets 2171AB and 2172AB in 2171AB *Northern England and Northern Ireland.* Publication of the two Irish sheets on independent sheet lines continued; subsidiary sheet numbers 2172CD, 2172AB were added later. They were combined as Sheet 2172ABCD *Ireland* in 1995.

C. Europe [military]

With a graticule in black at 1° intervals. With Universal Transverse Mercator and National Grids overprinted in purple. British Isles coverage is excluded from this series.

1. GSGS 4782: Edition 1-GSGS, coloured with brown layers, 1954.
   1. Produced by the Ordnance Survey, 1954. 2 sheets: NW46½/6½, NE50/1.
   2. Printed by the Army Map Service, 1957-58. 2 sheets: NW46½/6½, NE50/1 [▮Wc].
      The series number of the Army Map Service edition is 6401 (GSGS 4782).

D. Radar

1. GSGS Misc.1575: *Radar Plotting Chart,* 1951 (issued 1952). 2 sheets: NW50/5½, NW53/6½ [▮PRO*].

2. GSGS 4859: *RAF Aeronautical Chart (Radar),* 1957. 2 sheets recorded: NW50/5½, NW53/6½ [▮PRO*].
   With purple layers and no contours. With air information overprinted in blue.

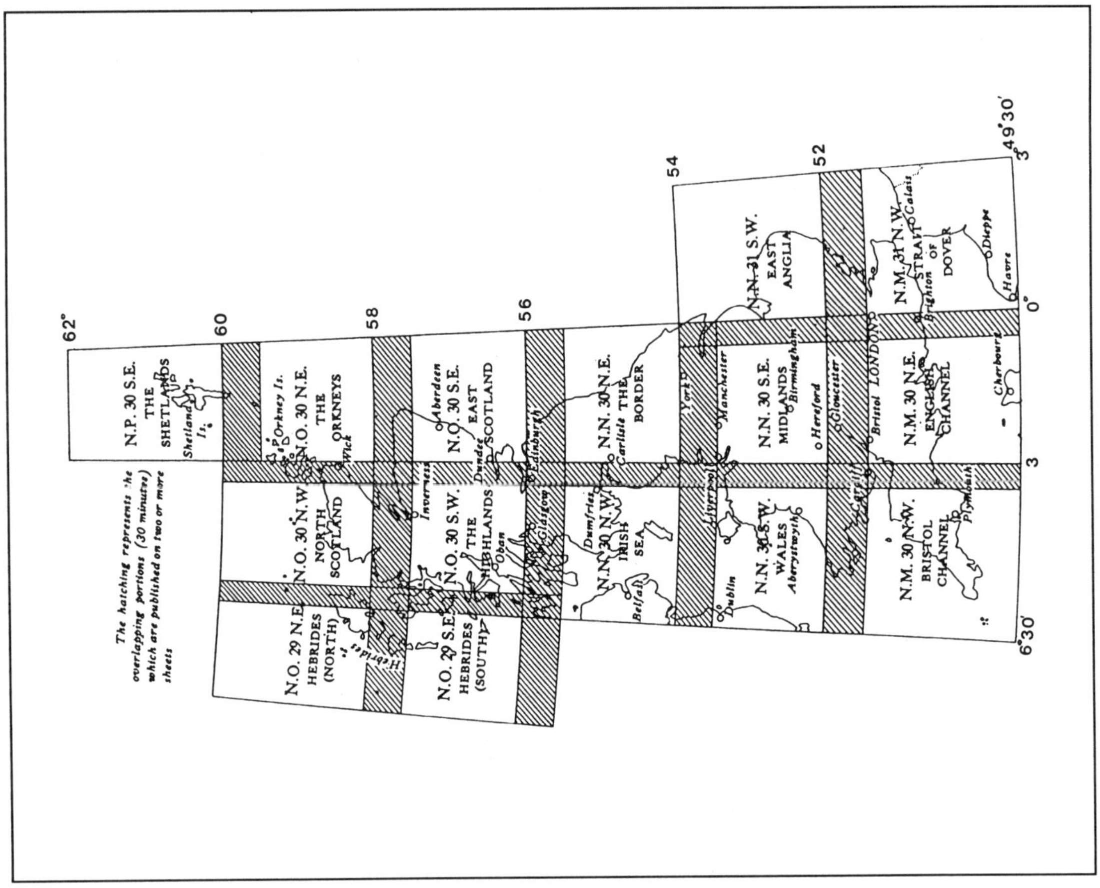

82. 1:500,000 Aeronautical Map of Great Britain (1)

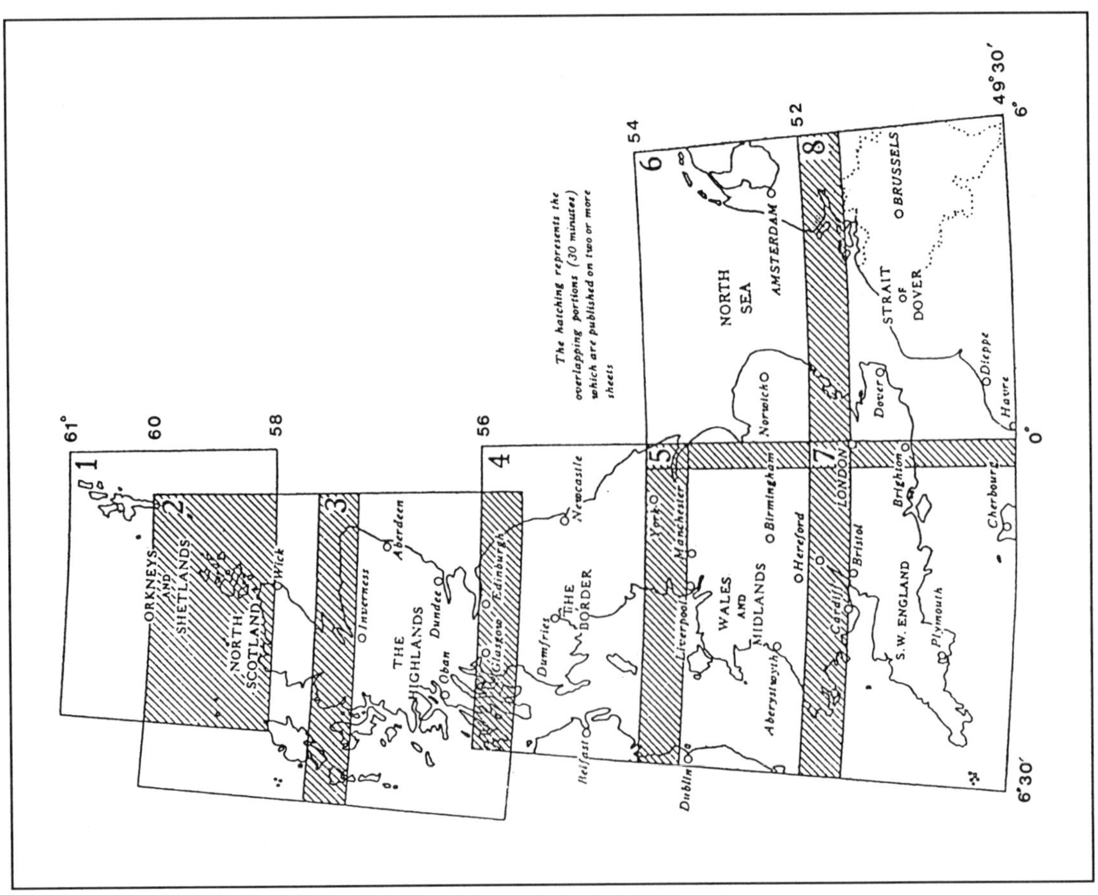

83. 1:500,000 Aeronautical Map of Great Britain (2)

82. 1:500,000 Aeronautical Map of Great Britain (1)

Based on the International Map of the World on 1:1,000,000. Laid out on graticule sheet lines, and published in fifteen sheets, each numbered as a quarter section of a sheet of the *International Map of the World* [✚**101**] with 30' overlaps with sheets adjoining south and west. With a graticule at 30' intervals. With air information overprinted in red. Heading: *Ordnance Survey of Great Britain (Aeronautical Map).* Coloured editions, with purple layers. Superseded by ✚**83**.

There is an extrusion on Sheet NM30NE for Guernsey to Sark. French and Irish areas are mapped.

1. First issues, 1937 (published 1938). All sheets.
   The air information shown was provided in the Air Ministry Notices to Airmen, for the use of both civil and service aviators.

2. *Civil Air Edition,* 1937 (published 1939). All sheets.

3. *RAF Edition,* 1937 (published 1939). All sheets.
   The additional air information given in Air Ministry Orders is shown; this was for the use of Royal Air Force crews alone. This edition was *de facto* the First Edition of the *RAF Edition (War)* recast on eight sheets in 1940 [✚**83**].

Symbols **:** a **bold** number prefixed with ✚ is a cross reference to another section of the book; a number prefixed with ✣ is a cross reference within the current section; a reference number in ( ) at a district map identifies the next, or previous, such map listed with the same sheet lines; the ▮ symbol accompanies a source reference for maps rarely encountered (library sigla are listed on page 241); ❍ warns that there are noted exceptions to the information given in headings; ↑ identifies what is referred to here as War Office marginalia (for a description see page xxii); ✺ refers to the exceptional use of the heading *Ordnance Survey of Great Britain.*

83. 1:500,000 Aeronautical Map of Great Britain (2)

Based on the International Map of the World on 1:1,000,000. Laid out on graticule sheet lines, and issued in eight sheets. This series provided complementary coverage of Great Britain to GSGS 4072 1:500,000 Map of Europe (Air) [**✚80**]. Superseding **✚82**: it was noted in the unpublished OSR 1939-40 that "A 2nd Edition has been prepared rearranged in eight sheets, instead of fifteen as previously." Sheets 4, 5, 7 were created by pairing sheets of **✚82**.3. Standard sheet coverage 2°30' in latitude by 6°30' or 7° in longitude, including 30' overlaps with sheets adjoining south and west. With a graticule at 10' intervals. Coloured editions, with purple layers, except where noted, with air information overprinted in black (blue on some Army Map Service issues). Heading: *Ordnance Survey of Great Britain (Aeronautical Map)*. Publication dates are generally lacking, print code dates being recorded.

With an extrusion on Sheet 7 for Guernsey to Sark. European and Irish areas are mapped.

1. *RAF Edition (War),* Second Edition. All sheets.
    1. Second Edition, 1940. All sheets.
        Published by the Ordnance Survey. With full legends in the lower margins of early printings, later cleared, perhaps to prepare for Third Edition marginalia.
    2. [AMS M422]: *Advance edition,* 1941-42. All sheets [▮Wn].
    3. [AMS M422]: AMS 1, 1942 (issued 1943). 4 sheets recorded: 1-4 [▮Wn].
        These issues carry the number GSGS 4369, in advance of British printings.

2. *RAF (War),* Third Edition. All sheets.
    With War Office Cassini and neighbouring military grids overprinted in brown in the borders at 10 km intervals and at intersection points across the sheets. Without legends in lower margins. The GSGS number was initially applied with a stamp.
    1. Third Edition, preceding application of GSGS number, 1941-42. All sheets.
    2. GSGS 4369: Third Edition, 1942. 4 sheets recorded: 1, 2, 4, 5.
    3. [AMS M422]: AMS 2, 1943. 2 sheets recorded: 5, 8 [▮Wn].

3. GSGS 4369: *RAF (War),* Fourth Edition. All sheets.
    The GSGS number was initially applied with a stamp (occasionally lacking).
    1. GSGS 4369: Fourth Edition (Provisional), 1943. 2 sheets recorded: 1, 5.
    2. GSGS 4369: Fourth Edition, 1942-44. All sheets.
        A 1947 reprint of Sheet 1 is recorded [▮DGI].
    3. [AMS M422]: AMS 2, 1943. ?6 sheets: 1-3, ?4, 6, 7 [▮Wc, Wn].
    4. [AMS M422]: AMS 3, 1944. 2 sheets: 1, 5 [▮Wn].

4. GSGS 4369: *RAF (War),* Fifth Edition. 7 sheets.
    1. GSGS 4369: Fifth Edition (Provisional), 1943. 7 sheets: 2-8.
    2. MDR 653/11096 (GSGS 4369), 1944. Sheet 6 recorded [▮PRO*].
        Reproduced by the 512th Field Survey Company, Royal Engineers.
    3. GSGS 4369: Fifth Edition, 1944. 7 sheets: 2-8.
    4. [AMS M422]: AMS 3, 1944. ?6 sheets: 2, 3, ?4, 6-8 [▮Wn].
    5. [AMS M422]: AMS 4, 1944. Sheet 5 recorded [▮Wn].
    6. AF 7308 (GSGS 4369), 1945. Sheet 3 recorded [▮BSg].
        Printed by Estab. Luigi Salomone for D.Svy AFHQ.

5. GSGS 4369: *RAF (War),* coloured, 1943. Sheet 8, Fifth Edition recorded [▮PRO*].
    Without hill or bathymetric layers.

6. GSGS 4369: *RAF (War),* outline with water in blue. ?All sheets [▮Og: 1-4 (1948), 6 (1943)].
    Details of issue are uncertain. Sheet 6 is in red with water in blue.

7. Special Sheet.
    GSGS 4369: *Southern England and Wales,* 1946 [▮Ob].
        Reprints dated 1947 and 1951 are recorded [▮PRO*].

84. Ten-mile Index

Engraved and published in three sheets, initially as an index to the one-inch *Old Series* of England and Wales [**✚2**], latterly also *New Series* [**✚3**] and Scotland First Edition [**✚13**].

1. *Index* [to the one-inch *Old Series* map]. 2 sheets.
   The south sheet (c.1816) as first laid out extended north to cover one-inch sheets 68-76, the middle sheet (?c.1824) from one-inch sheets 77-84. With neat-line borders. Neither sheet was completed in this form. The Isles of Scilly are not covered. Also offered (hand) coloured by county.

2. *Index*, later *Index to the Ordnance Survey of England and Wales.* 2 sheets.
   Redesigned c.1839 to relocate one-inch sheets 77-84 on the south sheet. South sheet (from 1885 Sheet 3) mapping was complete c.1841 when a piano key border was added on the west, south and east sides. The Isles of Scilly are not covered. Mapping of England on the middle sheet (from 1885 Sheet 2) was complete c.1866. The title was moved to the middle sheet c.1869 and reworded to reflect the addition of Scotland, initially a coastal outline only. Mapping north of this to Scotland Sheets 58-67 was added c.1873 when the sheet was also extended further west to encompass the Outer Hebrides. It was issued complete c.1881. Coastal outlines of France and Ireland were added c.1885. Also offered (hand) coloured by county.

3. *Index* [to the one-inch *New Series* map], ?1884. ?All sheets [▮Lgh: 1].
   Also offered (hand) coloured by county.

4. *Index to the New Series One Inch Map,* 1890. All sheets.
   Sheets 1 and 2 are slightly reduced in width in the west, and Sheet 3 extended westwards (so incorporating the Isles of Scilly) to the same dimensions, for mounting together. A tiny adjustment was made to the cutting line between Sheets 2 and 3. Also offered (hand) coloured by county.

5. *Eclipse of the Sun on the 15th March 1858.* South sheet only [▮BL, Mg, PRO (MPHH 310)].

6. *Plan of the Catchment Basins of the Rivers of England and Wales,* 1861. By zincography.
   South and partial middle sheets in the *Report of the Commissioners appointed to inquire into Salmon Fisheries (England and Wales)* (BPP(HC) 1861 [2768], XXIII).

7. District maps with reduced topography.
   England and Wales : Rivers and their Catchment Basins.
   1. By engraving, 1868.
   2. By zincography, 1870.
      In *Royal Commission on Water Supply : Report of the Commissioners : Appendix, Maps, Plans, and Index* (BPP(HC) 1868-69 [4169-II], XXXIII).

   Scotland : Rivers and their Catchment Basins, 1893. By photozincography. Reprinted 1946.

8. Geological Survey of Great Britain district map.
   Index to the Ordnance Geological Maps of Cornwall, Devon and West Somerset, 1839.
   Showing one-inch sheets 20-27, 29-33. Lithographed by Standidge & Co in H.T. de la Beche *Report on the Geology of Cornwall, Devon and West Somerset,* London, for HMSO, 1839.

The Index was also used whole or in parts for a variety of official uses. Military issues sometimes employed the Index sheets direct, but mostly the War Office took only those elements of the map it wanted, constructing their own maps on new sheet lines. One engraved and transferred to zinc by the Ordnance Survey is IDWO 1320 *Map of Great Britain prepared for the War Department,* 1898 (Sheets 1 to 3) [▮DGI]. See also **✚93**.12.

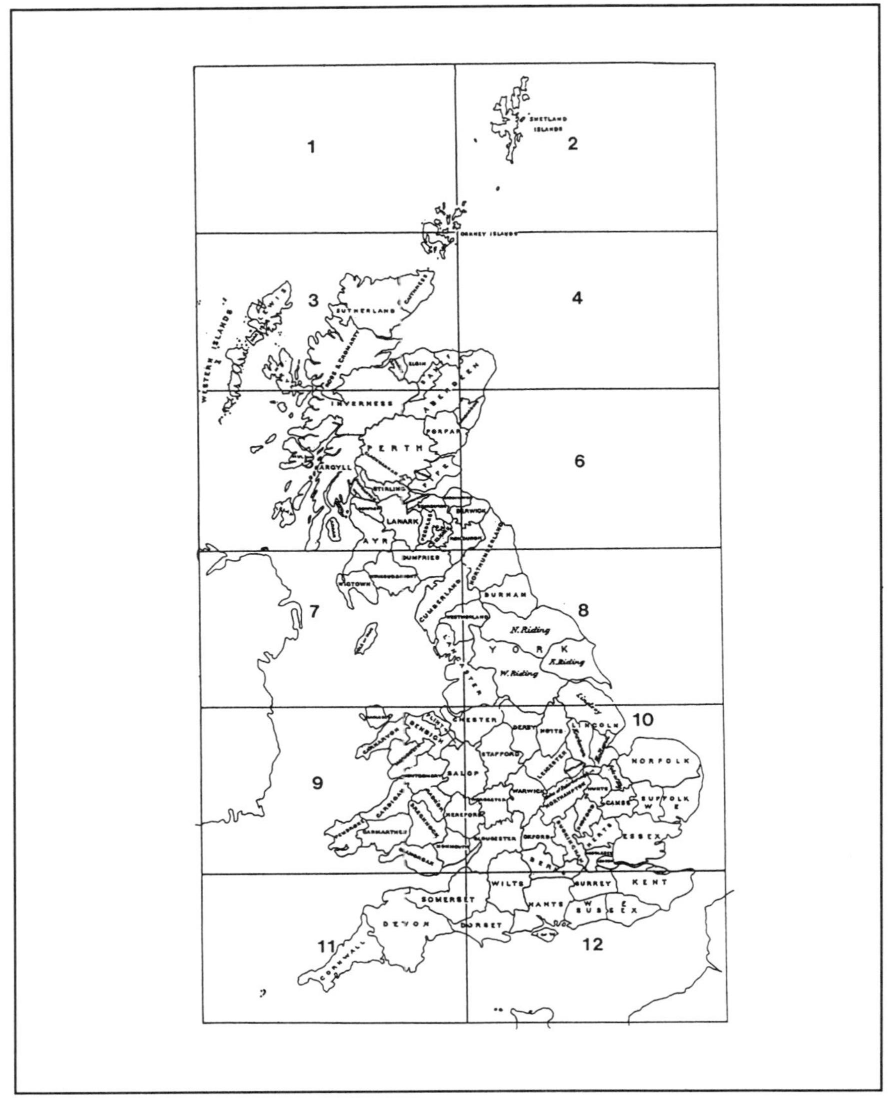

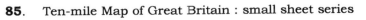

85. Ten-mile Map of Great Britain : small sheet series

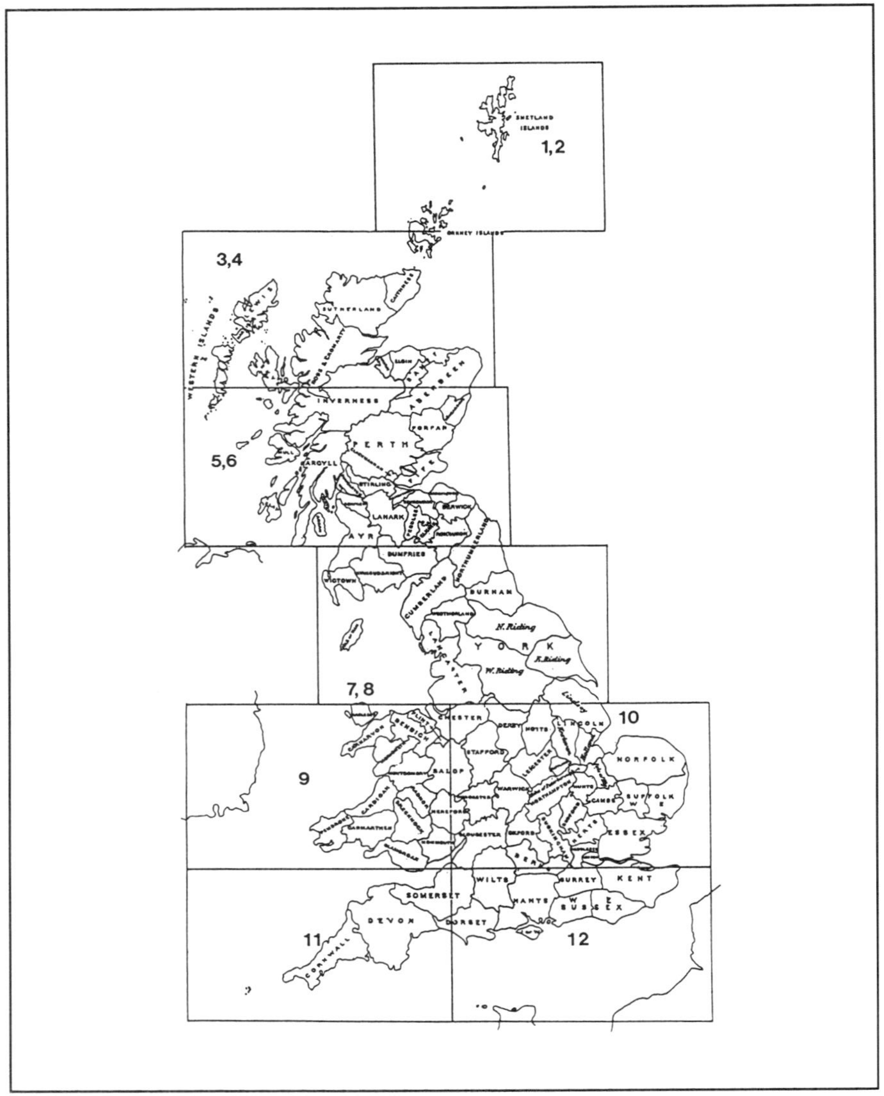

86. Ten-mile Map of Great Britain, in colour : small sheet series

85. Ten-mile Map of Great Britain : small sheet series

Reduced from the quarter-inch maps of England and Wales [✛**51**] on Cassini's Projection on the origin of Delamere, and of Scotland [✛**58**] on Bonne's Projection on the origin of 57°30'N, 4°W, and published in twelve sheets. Standard sheet coverage 200 by 130 miles (Sheets 1-8), 200 by 135 miles (Sheets 9-12). Sheets 9-12 have the same sheet lines as in the coloured edition [✛**86**]. Without grid or graticule; with a neat line border. With the coastal outlines of France and Ireland. Heading: *Ordnance Survey of Great Britain.* The words "small sheet series" do not appear.

1. Outline edition, with blue coastal tint, 1903. All sheets.
   With an illuminated title on Sheet 6.

2. *Air Raid, April 5th-6th, 1916,* 1917. Sheet [8] [▮BL].
   With overprint, and reduced sea area.

3. *Air Raid, March 13th, 1918,* no date. Sheet [8] [▮BL].
   With overprint.

The map also had a variety of official uses, especially in Royal Commission reports and other parliamentary papers.

86. Ten-mile Map of Great Britain, in colour : small sheet series

Reduced (as ✛**85**) from the quarter-inch maps of England and Wales [✛**51**] and of Scotland [✛**58**]. Laid out in the same twelve sheets but published in eight by virtue of four combined sheets 1/2, 3/4, 5/6, 7/8. Sheets 9-12 have the same sheet lines as in ✛**85**. Without grid or graticule; with a neat line border. With the coastal outlines of France and Ireland. Heading: *Ordnance Survey of Great Britain.* The words "small sheet series" do not appear.

1. Coloured edition, with hill shading, 1904. All 12 sheets in 8, as noted above.

2. Coloured edition, with hill shading. 7 sheets recorded, renumbered 1, 3-8.
   Late reprints were renumbered in the range 1 to 8 as required. The date of this change is uncertain, but it occurred no later than 1921.

3. Outline edition reprints, 1907 [see ✛**85**].
   None recorded, though OSPR 9/07 noted the appearance of Sheet 5/6, and the expectation of others to follow.

4. Military edition, overprinted with squaring system, 1916. 2 unidentified sheets documented, but not found.

The map also had a variety of official uses, especially in Royal Commission reports and other parliamentary papers.

87. Ten Mile Map of Great Britain (1)

Constructed on Cassini's Projection on the origin of Delamere, and published in three sheets, with sixty-mile overlaps. Standard sheet coverage 380 by 260 miles. Created presumably by reduction of quarter-inch *Third Edition* maps of England and Wales [**✢54**] and Scotland [**✢59**]. All editions are coloured, with brown layers and with an alpha-numeric squaring system, unless otherwise noted. Heading: *Ordnance Survey* : *Ten Mile Map of Great Britain.*

There are insets of Shetland Islands and Fair Isle, St Kilda and Boreray on Sheet 1. With the coastal outlines of France and Ireland.

1. Coloured edition, with layers, 1925-26 (published 1926). All sheets.
   A special printing of Sheet 2 is in *Report on War Office Exercise No.3 (1929) Harrogate...* [▮PRO (WO 279/68)]. Sheet 3 was reissued in 1935 based on a 1933 military printing [✢M.10].

2. *Outline Edition,* with water in blue, 1925-26 (published 1926). All sheets.

3. Water and contour issues, published ?1926. All sheets.

4. Physical issues, without black plate, published 1931. All sheets.

5. District maps.
   Scotland.
   With insets of Shetland Islands, St Kilda and Boreray.
   1. Coloured edition, with brown layers, 1927.
   2. *Outline Edition,* with water in blue, 1927.

   The Solar Eclipse 29th June, 1927, 1927.

M. Aeronautical and military issues

1. *Royal Air Force Edition,* pre-1927. ?All sheets. Not found.
   Noted in a 1934 Air Ministry document (PRO OS 1/456). The reference system is unknown (probably War Office Cassini Grid (British System)).

2. Coloured editions, with layers, overprinted for military exercises. Sheet 3, 1927, 1929, 1931.
   In *Report on War Office Exercise No.2 (1927) Winchester..., No.2 (1929) The War Office...* and *Nos.1 and 2 (1931)* [▮PRO (WO 279/59, 279/67, 279/73)].

3. *Main Overhead Electrical Grid Lines,* 1935. All sheets [▮Lraf].
   Outline editions, with air information in blue and overprint in red. Without squaring system.

Overprinted with a graticule at 30' intervals in purple

4. *Special Air Edition (Provisional),* 1928-29 (published 1929). All sheets.
   With air information and heading in red.

5. *Air Edition,* 1930. 2 sheets recorded: 2, 3.
   With air information and heading in blue.

6. *Civil Air Edition.* All sheets.
   With air information in blue.
   1. With heading in blue, 1932. Sheet 3 recorded [▮NLW].
   2. With heading in purple, without contours, 1934. All sheets.
   3. With heading in purple, with contours, 1935. All sheets.

Overprinted with War Office Cassini and Irish Grids in purple

7. *Royal Air Force Edition,* c.1931. All sheets. Not found.
   With air information in ?blue. Noted in OSR 1931-32.

8. *Royal Air Force Edition,* 1934. All sheets.
   With air information in blue. Sheet 1 is also recorded without overprint [▮BSg].

9. GSGS 3955: *Military Edition,* 1934. ?All sheets [▮PC: 3].
   With air information in blue.

10. Outline edition, overprinted in brown for a military exercise, 1933. Sheet 3 recorded.
    Printed by the 19th Field Survey Company, Royal Engineers.

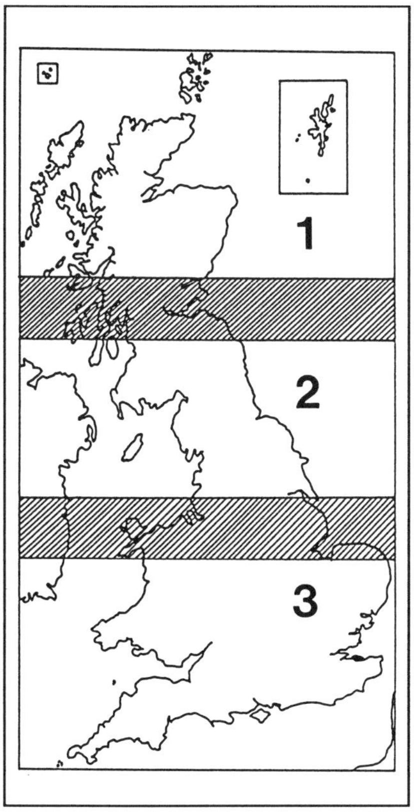

87. Ten-mile Map of Great Britain (1)

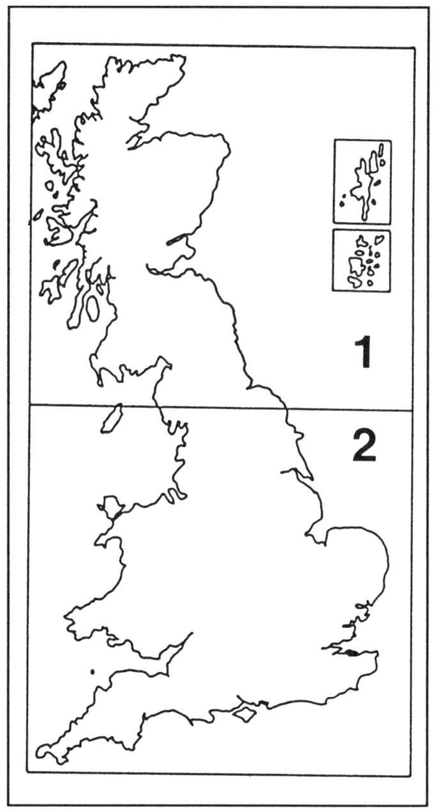

88. Ten-mile Road Map of Great Britain

88. Ten-mile Road Map of Great Britain

Constructed on the national Transverse Mercator Projection on the origin of 49°N,2°W, and published in two sheets on National Yard Grid sheet lines (sheet co-ordinates 680,000 yards E to 1,300,000 yards E, 1,120,000 yards N to 1,650,000 yards N to 2,180,000 yards N). Standard sheet coverage 620,000 by 530,000 yards. With National Yard Grid at 50,000 yard intervals. Superseded by ✢**89**.A.3.

There are insets of Shetland Islands, Orkney Islands on Sheet 1. The Isles of Scilly and most of the Outer Hebrides are not covered. Mapping of France and Ireland is omitted.

1. *Road Map,* relief edition, 1932. Both sheets.

89. Ten Mile Map of Great Britain (2)

Constructed on the national Transverse Mercator Projection on the origin of 49°N,2°W, and published in two sheets on National Yard Grid sheet lines (sheet co-ordinates 620,000 yards E to 1,300,000 yards E, 1,120,000 yards N to 1,650,000 yards N to 2,180,000 yards N). Standard sheet coverage 680,000 by 530,000 yards. Initially at 1:633,600 with National Yard Grid at 50,000 yard intervals, then at 1:625,000 with National [metric] Grid at 10 km intervals. Mapping was transferred from the 1926 map on Cassini's Projection [**✚87**] (see page xiii). Maps are without contours, unless noted. Both sheets were issued, unless noted.

There are insets of Shetland and Orkney Islands, Sule Skerry and Stack Skerry, Sula Sgeir and Rona, St Kilda and Boreray on Sheet 1, unless noted otherwise. There is an extrusion for the Isles of Scilly on Sheet 2. With the coastal outlines of France and Ireland.

A. Maps at 1:633,600, with National Yard Grid

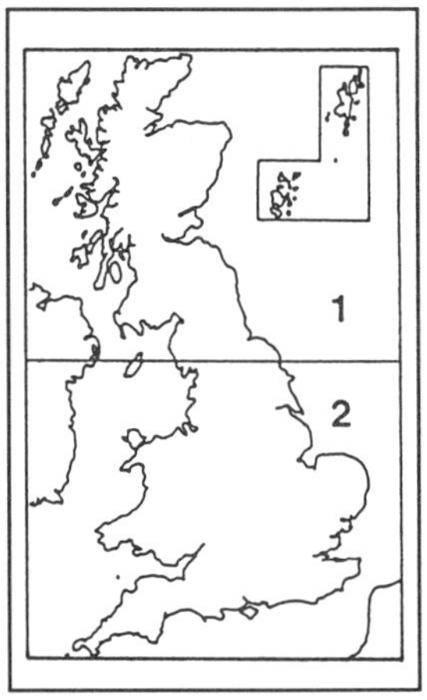

1. Coloured edition, with layers, 1936 (published 1937).
   Proof copies were printed with contours.

2. *Outline Edition,* with water in blue, 1936 (published 1937).

3. *Road Map.*
   Insets of Shetland Islands, Orkney Islands are on Sheet 1. French and Irish mapping is omitted. Superseding **✚88**.
   1. Relief edition, 1935 (published 1937). Both sheets.
   2. Coloured edition, 1935, reprinted 1947. Sheet 2 [▮RGS].

4. *Physical Features alone,* 1936 (published 1937).

5. *Outline Edition,* with water in blue, with overprint, 1936 (published 1939).
   Showing valuation regions. The map was prepared for the Central Valuation Board, Mines Department, under the provisions of the Coal Act, 1938.

6. *Monastic Britain,* 1939. Unpublished: the South Sheet was proved in 1940 [▮EH].

Land Utilisation Survey of Britain. Printed by G.W. Bacon.

7. *Land Utilisation Map of Great Britain,* published 1940. Sheet 2 [▮BL].

8. *Types of Farming Map of England and Wales,* distributed 1941. Sheet 2.
   Accompanied by a strip of Sheet 1 to complete northern England [▮BL].

M. Military issues overprinted with War Office Cassini Grid in purple

Early issues are overprinted with War Office Cassini Grid in all areas. By 1942 the War Office Irish Grid in purple was added, by 1943 all relevant adjacent grids were present, the Irish in red, the European red or blue. 1938 issues only have air information, overprinted in blue.

1. GSGS 3993: *Military Edition.*
   1. Coloured edition, with layers, 1938. Sheet 1 was reprinted in 1948.
   2. *Outline Edition,* with water in blue, roads in red, ?1938.
   3. *Outline Edition,* in monochrome grey, with contours, 1941-42. Reprinted 1948.

   The following dependent issues are recorded or documented:
   4. *War Office Skeleton Exercise, 1938,* 1938. Sheet 2 [▮ALm].
   5. GSGS 3993A: *Commands, Areas and Administrative Area Divisions,* ?1939.
   6. GSGS 3993B: *Essential Traffic Routes,* ?1940 [▮NLS: 1].
   7. GSGS 3993C: *Control of Flying in Balloon Areas,* 1941.

8. GSGS 3993/1/D: *Reserve Group Boundaries (RAF),* 19xx.
9. *Home Forces Boundary Map,* 1943 [▮BL].
10. GSGS Misc.501: *Air Ministry FC Maps,* 1944 [▮BL: 2].
11. GSGS Misc.502: *Overhead Electricity Cables,* 1944 [▮Ob: 1].
    In red outline. Overprinted with a graticule at 30' intervals.
12. GSGS Misc.505: *Security-released Airfields in the United Kingdom,* 1945 [▮RGS].
    In red outline. Overprinted with a graticule at 30' intervals.
13. GSGS Misc.506: *RAF Stations in the British Isles,* ?1945.
14. GSGS Misc.507: *Armament Training Areas,* ?1945.
15. GSGS Misc.517: *RAF Stations in the British Isles,* 1946.
16. *Geographical Organisation Static Engineer Force,* 1942 [▮DGI: 2].
    Printed by HQ Engr Ser. SOS ETO USA.
17. *Essential Railway Routes,* ?1940. Listed in OSR 1940-41.
18. *ARP Map,* ?1940. Listed in OSR 1940-41.
19. GSGS 4395: *Civil Aviation Edition.* Probably not issued.

Military issues overprinted with National Grid (Military System) in purple ❍

With War Office Irish Grid in red, European grids in blue.

2. GSGS 3993: *Second Military Edition.*
    1. Coloured edition, with layers, 1950.
    2. *Outline Edition,* in monochrome grey, with contours, 1950.

    The following dependent issues are recorded:
    3. GSGS 3993A: *Commands, Areas and Administrative Area Divisions,* Second Edition, 1951. Renamed *Home Commands Boundary Map* from 1955.
    4. GSGS Misc.1636: *Aerodrome and Royal Air Force Non-flying Unit Location Map,* Edition 1-GSGS, 1954 [▮Ob].
       With a graticule in blue at 1° intervals.

    The *Home Commands Boundary Map* [✣M.2.3] served as base for:
    5. GSGS 3993E: *Civil Defence Regional Boundaries,* 1961.

B. Maps at 1:625,000, with National Grid

Planning Series maps were made conjointly with the Ministry of Town and Country Planning, later the Ministry of Housing and Local Government. Printed publication dates are misleading and should be disregarded. The grid was named *Ordnance Survey Grid* on 1942-43 issues.

1. Outline edition, 1942.

    The outline edition [✣B.1] served as a base for Planning Series maps:
    1. *Administrative Areas,* 1944. With overprint in purple, red, green.
    2. *Administrative Areas,* 1944. With overprint in black.
    3. *Coal and Iron,* 1945 (published 1946).
    4. *Coal and Iron,* overprinted with names of colliery districts, 1945 (published 1946).
    5. *Electricity : Statutory Supply Areas,* 1946.
    6. *Gas and Coke,* 1951.
    7. *Igneous and Metamorphic Rocks,* 1955. Unpublished proofs [▮CCS, PC].
    8. *Iron and Steel,* 1945 (published 1946).
    9. *Land Classification,* 1944-45 (published 1945-46).
    10. *Land Utilisation,* 1943.
    11. *Limestone* [*Limestone : including Chalk* (Sheet 2)], 1955 (published 1957).
    12. *Local Accessibility,* 1955.
    13. *Ministry of Labour local office areas,* 1947.
    14. *Population Changes, 1931-38,* 1944. Sheet 2 only, for official use [▮Ob].
    15. *Population : Changes by Migration 1921-1931,* 1949.
    16. *Population : Changes by Migration 1931-1938/1939,* 1949 (published 1950).
    17. *Population : Changes by Migration 1938/1939-1947,* 1954.

18. *Population Density, 1931,* 1944.
19. *Population of Urban Areas* [1938], 1945.
20. *Population of Urban Areas 1951,* 1954-57 (published 1955-57).
21. *Population : Total Changes 1921-1931,* 1949.
22. *Population : Total Changes 1931-1938/1939,* 1948-49 (published 1949).
23. *Population : Total Changes 1938/1939-1947,* 1954.
24. *Rainfall : Annual Average 1881-1915,* 1949.
25. *Types of Farming,* 1944. Both sheets.
    A strip map of Sheet 1 to complete northern England was also printed in 1944 for the Ministry of Agriculture and Fisheries.
26. *Vegetation : Grasslands of England & Wales,* 1946. Sheet 2.
    Accompanied by a strip of Sheet 1 to complete northern England, 1947.
27. *Vegetation : Reconnaissance Survey of Scotland...,* 1953. Sheet 1.

The outline edition [✣B.1] was intended as a base for a period map:

28. *Monastic Britain,* 1948. Unpublished: a South Sheet proof survives [▮EH].

The outline edition [✣B.1] served as a base for indexes to:

29. *National Grid Index to 1:25,000 Sheets,* 1946.
30. *Maps at Scale of 1:25,000..... on National Grid Sheet Lines,* 1954.
31. *Maps at....Six Inches to the Mile on National Grid Sheet Lines,* 1950 [▮Dtf]; 1954.
32. *Six-inch Air Photo Mosaics,* c.1952. Not found.

The outline edition [✣B.1] also served as a base for Ordnance Survey technical work on the large-scale field programme, Newlyn levelling, retriangulation, etc.

Administrative Areas [✣B.1.1] served as a base for:

33. *Boundary Commissions for Scotland & England / England & Wales : House of Commons (Redistribution of Seats) Acts, 1944 and 1947.*
    Showing parliamentary boundaries (green), administrative areas (red). Variously in *Initial Report of the Boundary Commission for England / Scotland / Wales* (BPP(HC) 1947-48 (Cmd.7260/7270/7274), XV).
34. *Boundary commissions for Scotland & England / Scotland / England & Wales : House of Commons (Redistribution of Seats) Act, 1949.*
    Showing parliamentary constituencies (green), administrative areas (red). Variously in *First Periodical Report of the Boundary Commission for England / Scotland / Wales* (BPP(HC) 1953-54 (Cmd.9311/9312/9313), IX).
35. *Gas Act 1948 : Areas of Gas Boards.* Official issue, 1948; published 1949.
36. *Ministry of Labour local office areas,* 1948 [▮Bg].
37. *National Grid Index to 1:25,000 Sheets,* 1946. Not found.

2. *Topography,* 1944. Outline with layers and water tint.

   Topography [✣B.2] served as a base for Planning Series maps, also period maps:
   1. *Railways,* 1946. Proof copies without hill shading are recorded [▮PC].
   2. *Roads,* 1946 (✣B.6).
   3. *Ancient Britain,* 1951. Also Second Edition, 1964 (published 1965).
   4. *Monastic Britain,* 1950. Also Second Edition, 1954-55.

3. *Geological Map of Scotland and the North of England / England & Wales.*
   Published by the Ordnance Survey. The Irish area is mapped on Sheet 1.
   1. Coloured edition, 1948.
   2. Outline edition, 1951.

4. A *Physical Map,* also named *Physical Features,* reached proof stage in several forms, but was unpublished. See Hellyer (1992).

Military issues

5. GSGS 4676: *Great Britain* (GSGS number allocated 1949). Probably not issued.
   No issue of a topographic map until M325 [**✣90**.A.8] has been recorded.

6. GSGS 4813: *Roads,* Edition 1-GSGS, 1954 (✣B.2.2) [▮Ob].
   For Edition 2-GSGS see M322 [**✣90**.A.7].

90. 1:625,000 Map of Great Britain

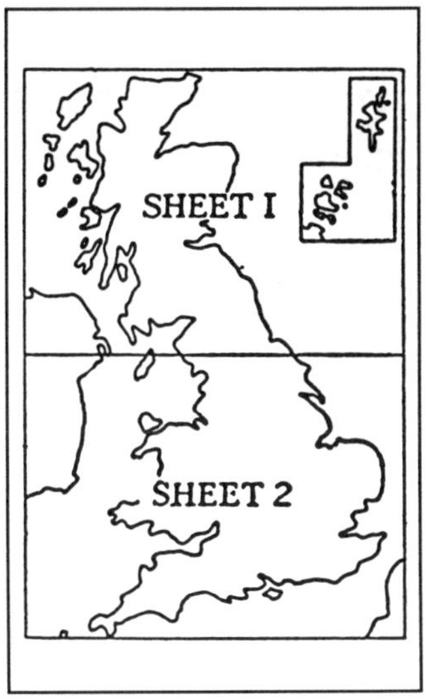

National Grid series. Published in two sheets (sheet co-ordinates 50 km E to 670 km E, 10 km N to 500 km N to 990 km N). Standard sheet coverage 620 by 490 km. Outline and water were transferred from **✚89**, the remainder was newly drawn. Unless noted both sheets were issued, and maps are without contours.

There are insets of Shetland and Orkney Islands, Sule Skerry and Stack Skerry, Sula Sgeir and Rona, St Kilda and Boreray on Sheet 1. There are extrusions on Sheet 2 for the Isle of Man and the Isles of Scilly. There are coastal outlines of France and Ireland.

A. "Ten-Mile" Map

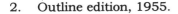

1. Coloured edition, with layers, 1955 (✣A.8).
   Versions with contours were proved [▮PRO (OS 36/6)].

2. Outline edition, 1955.
   Planning Series maps [see **✚89**.B.1] using the outline edition [✣A.2] as a base:
   1. *Gravel including Associated Sands,* 1965. Sheet 2.
      Accompanied by a strip of Sheet 1 to complete northern England, 1969.
   2. *Population Change 1951-1961 : by Wards and Civil Parishes,* 1966.
   3. *Population Density, 1951,* 1960-61.
   4. *Rainfall : Annual Average 1916-1950,* 1967.

   The outline edition [✣A.2] also served as an index to:
   5. *Maps at Scale of 1:10,560.....on National Grid Sheet Lines,* 1957.

   The outline edition [✣A.2] was used for the Ray Society's Publication No.146:
   6. *Watsonian Vice-counties of Great Britain,* 1969.
      With a commentary by J.E. Dandy.

   The outline edition [✣A.2] also served as a base for technical work on the large-scale field programme, metric contouring, continuous revision, six-inch mapping divisions.

3. *Administrative Areas,* 1956.

4. *Roads,* 1956 (✣A.7.1).

5. *Route Planning Map,* edition *A,* 1964 (✣A.7.2).

6. *Geological Map of Great Britain,* 2nd Edition.
   Published by the Ordnance Survey. The Irish area is mapped on Sheet 1.
   1. Coloured edition, 1957.
   2. Coloured edition, overprinted in violet with one-inch sheet lines, published 1964.
   3. Outline edition, 1957.

Military issues

7. M322: *Roads.*
   The First Edition was GSGS 4813 [**✚89**.B.6].
   1. *Roads,* Edition 2-GSGS, 1958 (✣A.4).
   2. *Route Planning Map* [edition *A*], Edition 3-GSGS, 1964 (✣A.5).

8. M325 coloured edition, with layers (✣A.1).
   The number GSGS 4866 was allocated in 1955, but replaced prior to issue.
   1. Edition 1-GSGS, 1957 (issued 1958).
   2. Edition 2-GSGS, 1962.

9. GSGS 4956: *Home Commands Boundary Map,* 1964.

10. GSGS Misc.1636: *Aerodrome and Royal Air Force Non-flying Unit Location Map,* Edition 2-GSGS, 19xx. Not found.

11. GSGS Misc.1820: Edition 1-GSGS, coloured with layers, 1964 [▮Ob].

12. Outline edition, with National Grid (Military System), c.1971 [▮PC].

B. Physical Map

1. Coloured edition, with layers, without contours, 1957.

The *Physical Map* [✣B.1] served as a base for:
1. *Southern Britain in the Iron Age,* 1962. Sheet 2.
2. *River Gauging Stations in Great Britain,* 1972. Sheet 2 recorded [▮NTg]. Compiled by the Water Resources Board.
3. *The Distribution in Scottish Rivers of the Atlantic Salmon,* 1985. Sheet 1. With commentary by R. Gardiner and H. Egglishaw, Edinburgh, Department of Agriculture and Fisheries for Scotland, 1986.

C. Route Planning Map

On some issues the addition of tabular material causes adjustment of the sheet dimensions.

1. *Route Planning Map* (from 1980 (copyright date) *Routeplanner*), editions *B* to *BB* (✣C.16).
   1. Coloured edition, with layers, without contours, 1965 annually to 1971.
   2. Relief edition, 1972 annually to 1984.
   3. Coloured edition, 1985. Further editions, 1986, 1988, 1991.

The *Route Planning Map* [✣C.1], with layers, served as a base to period maps:
4. *Ancient Britain,* Third Edition, 1982. Also Fourth Edition, 1990.
5. *Monastic Britain,* Third Edition, 1976 (published 1978).
6. *Roman Britain,* Fourth Edition revised, 1990.

Repayment service issues based on ✣C.1, put on public sale:
7. *The Camping Club's Camping and Caravan Site Map,* 1978 *et seq* (various titles).
8. *The Where to Fish Map of the important Fishing Rivers, Lochs and Reservoirs of Scotland* (at scale 1:687,500), 1990.

Official issue of the *Route Planning Map* [✣C.1]:
9. *Ministry of Transport Traffic Areas.* 1969 issue recorded.

2. *Outline Style,* 1965, from 1969 *Outline Map.*

The outline editions [✣C.2] served as a base for:
1. *Air Photo Index Map,* 1965 [▮BSg]. Various nominal scales of photography.
2. *Ministry of Labour,* later *Department of Employment and Productivity,* later *Department of Employment Local Office Areas.* Published issues began in 1968.

Department of Employment.....Local Office Areas [✣C.2.2] served as base for:
3. *Local Employment Bill 1969.*
4. *"Travel to Work" Areas,* 1969.

The outline editions [✣C.2] served as a base for indexes to:
5. *1:25 000 Pathfinder Maps and Outdoor Leisure Maps,* 1990-92.
6. *Pathfinder, Outdoor Leisure, Explorer and Landranger Maps,* 1994-95.
7. *Outdoor Leisure, Explorer, Pathfinder, Landranger and Travelmaster,* 1996- .
8. *Maps at 1:10,000 and 1:10,560 on National Grid Sheet Lines,* 1972.

The outline editions [✣C.2] also served as a base for technical work on the 1:50,000 map.

3. District maps.
   Maritime England, 1982.
   Potential Cycleroutes and Disused Railways in England & Wales 1981, 1981.

4. Touring Map (at scale 1:500,000).
   Scotland, 1988.
   National Grid 20 km squares in blue are measured alpha-numerically from the south-west corner. With an inset of the Shetland Islands.

Administrative maps

5. *Administrative Areas,* 1965. A revised base map was issued in 1970.

   These administrative maps [✣C.5] were used as a base for:
   1. *Ministry of Labour,* later *Department of Employment and Productivity,* later *Department of Employment Local Office Areas.* Published issues began in 1968.
   2. *Ministry of Technology Assisted Areas for Industrial Development at 26.2.70.*
   3. *Local Government Act 1972 [& Local Government (Scotland) Act 1973],* 1973.

   Department of Employment.....Local Office Areas [✣C.5.1] served as base for:
   4. *Local Employment Bill 1969.*
   5. *Assisted Areas as defined by the Department of Trade and Industry at 5.8.1971.*

6. *Great Britain (Local Government Areas [& European Constituencies]),* 1976.
   With up to two overprints, showing administrative areas (red), and, beginning 1984 *(North)* and 1983 *(South),* European constituencies (green).

Period maps. With National Grid in blue.

7. *Britain before the Norman Conquest (871 AD to 1066 AD),* 1974.

8. *Roman Britain,* Fourth Edition, 1979.

Geological Survey / Institute of Geological Studies publications by the Ordnance Survey

The Irish area is mapped on Sheet 1.

9. *Aeromagnetic Map of Great Britain,* 1965.
   Sheet 1 (1972) is a non-standard sheet with a northern extension.

10. *Quaternary Map of the United Kingdom,* 1977.

11. *Geological Map of the United Kingdom,* 3rd Edition, Solid, 1979 (published 1980).
    Coloured edition, with index to one-inch and 1:50,000 sheets.

Official maps not published by the Ordnance Survey

12. **Scottish Development Department** and **Scottish Office.** Sheet 1 only.
    1. *Scotland : Sub-regions for Economic Planning (by Administrative Areas),* 1966.
    2. *Reform of Local Government in Scotland : Government Proposals for New Authorities,* 1972.
    3. *Water Resources in Scotland,* 1972.
    4. *National Health Service : Scotland Health Board Boundaries,* 1974.

13. **Geological Survey / Institute of Geological Studies / British Geological Survey**
    1. *Metalliferous Mineral Resources excluding Energy Minerals,* 1974.
    2. *Hydrogeological Map of England and Wales* (1977), *Scotland* (1988).
    3. *Bouguer Anomaly Map of the British Isles,* 1981-86.
    4. *Regional Gravity Map of the British Isles,* 1983. Sheet 1.
    5. *Groundwater Vulnerability Map of Scotland,* 1995. Sheet 1.
    Sheet 1 in ✣13.3, 13.4 were printed by J. Bartholomew. They were published in R.G. Hipkin and A. Hussain *Northern Britain* (Regional Gravity Anomalies 1), London, HMSO, 1983; BGS (IGS) Report 82/10.

14. **Soil Survey of Scotland** [Sheet 1 only]: *Assessment of Climatic Conditions in Scotland* :
    1. *Based on Accumulated Temperature above 5·6°C and Potential Deficit,* 1969.
    2. *Based on Exposure and Accumulated Frost,* 1970.
    3. *The Bioclimatic Sub-regions,* 1971.
    4. *Land Capability for Agriculture in Scotland,* 1982.

15. *Average Annual Rainfall (in Millimetres) International standard period 1941-70,* 1977.
    Published by the Meteorological Office. With an inset of the Channel Islands. With Universal Transverse Mercator Grid.

Military issues

16. M322: *Route Planning Map* [from edition *B*], 1965 (✣C.1).
    M322 was reissued each year from Edition 4-GSGS, 1965, at least as far as Edition 25-GSGS on Edition *Y*.

17. GSGS 5033: *UK Landforces Boundary Map,* ?1968.

18. GSGS 5038: *Aerodrome and Royal Air Force Non-flying Unit Location Map,* 1969.
    With a graticule at 1° intervals.

19. GSGS 5288: *Home Defence Boundary Map.*
    Overprinted with defence (black) and local government (blue) boundaries.
    1. Edition 1-GSGS, 1979 (on *Local Government Areas* [✣C.6]) [▮Wc].
    2. Edition 2-GSGS, 1984 (on *Routeplanner,* edition *W* [✣C.1.2]) [▮Wc].

Special maps of England and Wales on extended sheet lines were issued for official uses. For further information on ten-mile maps not listed here see Hellyer (1992).

91. 1:625,000 Travelmaster Series Map of Great Britain

National Grid series. Published in two sheets. On coloured issues the National Grid is blue, numbered in magenta. The coloured edition is usually printed back to back as Sheet 1 of the *Travelmaster Series.* Sheets 2-9 are at 1:250,000 [**✣65**]. Revised to November 1992, and produced from digital data. Heading: *Ordnance Survey* : *Great Britain Routeplanner North / South* : *Travelmaster Series of Great Britain.*

There is an inset of Shetland Islands with Foula and Fair Isle on the North Sheet. There is an extrusion for the Isles of Scilly on the South Sheet, and another from the North Sheet to complete the Isle of Man. There are coastal outlines of France and Ireland.

For a sheet line diagram see **✣65**.

1. Coloured edition, without contours, 1993. Both sheets.

2. *Outline* edition, 1993. Both sheets.

3. *Index to show Ordnance Survey 1:10 000 and 1:10 560 Scale Maps on National Grid Sheet Lines,* 1994. Both sheets, printed back to back.

4. *European and Westminster Parliamentary Constituency Boundaries,* 1996. Both sheets, numbered 1A, 1B.
    Showing National Boundary (blue), European Constituency Boundary (green), Westminster Constituency Boundary (red). Both sheets are extended to incorporate larger scale town plans.

92. Ten-mile Map of Ireland (1)

Prepared under the aegis of the Railway Commissioners, constructed by Thomas Larcom in 1837, and engraved and published by the Ordnance Survey at Phoenix Park, Dublin (though this is not acknowledged on the maps). With a coastal outline of Great Britain.

1. *Map of Ireland To accompany the Report of the Railway Commissioners 1838,* 1838.
   With a graticule offshore at 1° intervals. The subtitle continues: *Shewing the different lines laid down Under the Direction of the Commissioners and those proposed by Private Parties.* In the atlas of six maps *Irish Railway Commission. Maps* [titles] *Presented to both Houses of Parliament by Command of Her Majesty. 1838,* which accompanied the second report of the railway commissioners (BPP(HL) 1838, XLVII part II, 32-37). Larcom's map was used as the base for the other ten-mile maps in the atlas (three by Henry D. Harness, and Richard Griffith's geological map), which were engraved by Gardner. A *Map of England & Ireland Explanatory of that part of the Report of the Railway Commissioners, which relates to the communication between London and Dublin, and other parts of Ireland,* prepared and engraved at the twenty-mile scale under Larcom's direction in 1837, completed the atlas.

2. *Map of Ireland To accompany the Report of the Land Tenure Commissioners 1845,* 1845.
   Without graticule. The subtitle continues: *Shewing the Places visited by the Commissioners and the relative proportion of the Surface of each County lying between certain lines of Altitude.* Transferred by electrotype from the Railway Commissioners' map [✣1]. In *Index to the minutes of evidence taken before Her Majesty's commissioners of inquiry into the state of the law and practice in respect of the occupation of land in Ireland : part V* (BPP(HC) 1845 [673], XXII, 725). Later it was on public sale.

Other official maps were derived from this map base.

93. Ten-mile Map of Ireland (2)

One of Sir Henry James's more ambitious schemes was the creation of a ten-mile map of the World using what he entitled the Rectangular Tangential Projection. Graticule sheet lines were employed, the centre line of each sheet forming the central meridian of its projection. The greater part of Ireland was engraved in three plates in 1867: *Dublin* (sheet co-ordinates 50°N to 55°N, 12°W to 6°W), and untitled plates to the east (50°N to 55°N, 6°W to 0°Long) and north (55°N to 60°N, 12°W to 6°W) [▮Dna]. The present map was formed by butting together these three plates, the completion of the north-east corner being undertaken separately. Usually with a graticule at 1° intervals. With a coastal outline of Great Britain. Heading: *Ordnance Survey of Ireland.* NB Some of the derived maps listed below may not extend to the original neat line, or may have borders rearranged to the requirements of tabular material.

1. Outline edition, 1868. By engraving.

2. *Index to the* [one-inch] *General Map.* By engraving.
   1. Without graticule, 1868 (published 1871).
   2. With graticule, 1868 (published c.1890).

3. *Poor Law Unions,* 1881. By lithography.
   Early issues are on the Index base [✣2], overprinted in black or red.

4. *Rail and Tramways, Fishery Piers and Harbours &c.,* 1887.
   On the Index base [✣2]. In *Second Report of the Royal Commission on Irish Public Works* (BPP(HC) 1888 [C.5264], XLVIII, 201).

5. *Resident Magistrates,* 1888 [▮Dn].
   Also editions updated to December 1889 and June 1899 [▮Dn]. See also **+94**.12.

6. *Locality of and Expenditure on Works &c. connected with Fisheries,* 1891.
   In *Report of the Inspectors of Irish Fisheries on the Sea and Inland Fisheries of Ireland for 1890* (BPP(HC) 1890-91 [C.6403], XX, 329). See **+94**.7 for updated editions.

7. *Relief of Distress Report,* c.1894 [▮Dn].

8. *Report on Loan Fund Societies,* c.1897.
   In *Report of the Committee appointed to inquire into the Proceedings of Charitable Loan Societies in Ireland.....* (BPP(HC) 1897 [C.8381], XXIII, 417).

9. Index to Six Inch Sheets, 1922 [▮Dtf]. With updated reprints.

10. *Railways,* 1944. Issued without a topographical base.

11. *Rivers and their Catchment Basins.*
    A map with reduced topography and on different sheet lines, primarily in order to accommodate extensive tabular material. British mapping is lacking.
    1. Outline edition, 1868. By engraving.
       Also offered hand coloured.
    2. Colour printed edition, 1923.
       In *Coimisiún na gCanálach agus na mBóthar Uisce Intíre (Canals and Inland Waterways Commission) : Report : July 1923* (IPP 1923, III, 611). Put on public sale from 1927 without the canal commission overprint. Reprinted uncoloured in 1945.
    3. Revised edition with new marginalia.
       1. Colour printed edition, 1958.
       2. Outline edition, 1958 (publication date uncertain).

    The following dependent issues are recorded:
    4. *Drainage Districts...Rivers and Main Streams,* 1886.
       In *Appendix to First Report of the Royal Commission on Irish Public Works.....* (BPP(HC) 1887 [C.5038-I], XXV, 815).
    5. *Rainfall Distribution and Rainfall Stations,* 1921.
       1. Overprinted with rainfall stations in blue.
          In *Board of Trade : Report of the Water Power Resources of Ireland Sub-committee,* Dublin, HMSO, 1921.
       2. Issued with this subtitle but without the overprint [▮NTg].
    6. *Water-Power Sites in Ireland : Index Map,* 1922.
       In *Report on Water Power,* Dublin, Coimisiún Fhiafruighthe maoin is tionnscal éireann (Commission of inquiry into the resources and industries of Ireland), 1922. The tables at the foot of the sheet are cleared.
    7. *Rivers and their Catchment Basins,* later *Rivers, Lakes and Fishery Districts,* 1924.
       In *The Angler's Guide to the Irish Free State* (Dublin, Stationery Office, 1924). The map was revised in the later editions of 1930, 1937 and 1948.
    8. *Fishery Districts,* 1934 [▮Dna]. Not in Hellyer (1992).

British military issues

12. IDWO 1320: *Map of Ireland prepared for the War Department,* 1898. Sheet 4 [▮DGI].
    Engraved and transferred to zinc at the Ordnance Survey Office, Southampton. Sheets 1 to 3 cover Great Britain (see the footnote to **+84**).

13. *Ireland* : [showing Districts of Army Corps], 1900 [▮PRO (MPGG 22), mislaid]. Not found.
    Printed by the Ordnance Survey. Sheet lines are uncertain.

See Hellyer (1992) for fuller details. The War Office sometimes employed the topographical map direct, but mostly constructed its own maps to its own specification.

94. Ten-mile Map of Ireland (3)

Constructed on Bonne's Projection on the origin of 53°30'N,8°W. Laid out in two sheets, and published as a single map of the island following the fusion of the two plates. Reduced from the quarter-inch map [✢**69**]. With a graticule at 1° intervals, unless noted otherwise. With a coastal outline of Great Britain, though this was occasionally cleared. Heading: *Ordnance Survey of Ireland.* NB Some of the derived maps listed below may not extend to the original neat line, or may have borders rearranged to the requirements of tabular material.

A. Topographical maps

1. Outline edition, 1904 (published 1905). By engraving.
   Maintained in print by the Ordnance Survey of Ireland until at least 1949. The Ordnance Survey of Northern Ireland also printed the map at least once, in 1930.

2. Coloured edition, with hill shading, 1905.
   Maintained in print by the Ordnance Survey of Ireland until at least 1949.

3. *Index to the* [one-inch] *General Map,* 1905. By engraving.
   See also ✢A.16, A.17.

4. *Chart showing Positions of Lighthouses, Fog Signals and Other Sea Marks, under the Jurisdiction of the Commissioners of Irish lights,* 1905 [▮Dn].
   Other editions, 1911 (not found), 1926 [▮Lnm]. With sheet lines extended to accommodate tabular material.

5. *Royal Commission on Congestion in Ireland : ABC Map....,* 1907.
   In *Royal Commission on Congestion in Ireland* (BPP(HC) 1906 [Cd.3267], XXXII, 959).

6. *Viceregal Commission on Arterial Drainage,* 1907.
   In *Vice-Regal Commission on Arterial Drainage (Ireland) : Appendix to the Report of the Arterial Drainage Commission (Ireland), 1905* (BPP(HC) 1907 [Cd.3467], XXXII, 489).

7. *Locality of and Expenditure on Works, etc., connected with Fisheries,* 1891.
   For the first issue see ✢**93**.6. In *Royal Commission on Congestion in Ireland* (BPP(HC) 1907 [Cd.3509], XXXVI, 171). Another issue, 1910 [▮Dna] (not in Hellyer (1992)).

8. *Canals and Navigable Rivers of Ireland,* 1907.
   Plate No.2 in *Royal Commission on Canals and Waterways, Volume II Part II : Ireland* (BPP(HC) 1907 [Cd.3717], XXXIII part I, 403).

9. *Electoral Divisions scheduled as Congested,* 1907 [▮Dn].

10. *Royal Commission on Congestion in Ireland....Showing the Travelling, the principal Tours of Inspection, and the Country Sittings of the Commission,* 1908.
    In *Royal Commission on Congestion in Ireland....*(BPP(HC) 1908 [Cd.4097], XLII, 857).

11. *County Boundaries, Rural Districts,* 1908 [▮Dn, Dna].

12. *Resident Magistrates September 1909,* 1909 [▮Dn].
    For earlier issues see ✢**93**.5.

13. *Controlled Canals in Ireland,* 1918.
    In *Canal Control Committee (Board of Trade) Handbook on Canals,* Second Edition, London, HMSO, 1918.

14. [Murders in Ireland].
The Ordnance Survey made three copies of each map for the Lord Lieutenant.
1. *The numbers murdered in each county up to 1st December 1920,* 1920. Not found.
2. *Places where police, military, civilians have been murdered up to 1st December 1920,* 1920 [▮Do].

15. District maps.
1. Province maps, showing county boundaries, rural districts.
Connaught, 1908 (✣B.7).
Leinster, 1908 (✣B.7).
Munster, 1908 (✣B.7).
Ulster, 1908 (✣B.7).
All four maps were reprinted by the Ordnance Survey of Ireland.

2. *Northern Ireland,* 1926.
The province only is coloured, with layers but without contours. Usually found in *[The] Ulster Year Book* (first, third and fifth editions), 1926, 1932, 1938. This map was also enlarged to the quarter-inch scale [**✣74**.A].

Geological Survey of Ireland

The following maps use the *Index* [✣A.3] as a base:

16. *The distribution of Peat-bogs and Coalfields in Ireland,* 1920.

17. *The distribution of Peat-bogs and Coalfields in Ireland : Also the principal localities of Minerals of economic importance.*
1. With the minerals overprint in green, 1920.
On sale, and in *Coimisiún na gCanálach agus na mBóthar Uisce Intíre (Canals and Inland Waterways Commission) : Report : July 1923* (IPP 1923, III, 609).
2. With the minerals overprint in carmine, 1920.
In G.A.J. Cole *Memoir and Map of Localities of Minerals of Economic Importance and Metalliferous Mines in Ireland,* Dublin, Stationery Office, 1922. Reprinted by the Ordnance Survey of Ireland in 1956 to accompany the reprint of the memoir.

Ordnance Survey of Ireland

18. *Ireland,* coloured by county, 1923.
In *Handbook of the Ulster Question,* Dublin, Stationery Office, 1923.

19. *Inland Navigations and Railways,* 1923.
In *Coimisiún na gCanálach agus na mBóthar Uisce Intíre (Canals and Inland Waterways Commission) : Report : July 1923* (IPP 1923, III, 605).

20. *Bogs in Ireland,* 1923.
In *Coimisiún na gCanálach agus na mBóthar Uisce Intíre (Canals and Inland Waterways Commission) : Report : July 1923* (IPP 1923, III, 607).

21. *District Justices July 1923,* 1923 [▮Dna]. Not in Hellyer (1992).

22. *Irish speaking districts and the partly Irish speaking districts....,* 1926.
In *Coimisiún na Gaeltachta : Report,* Dublin, Stationery Office, 1926.

23. *Ireland* : [shewing areas where trawling is prohibited], 1930 [▮Dna]. Not in Hellyer (1992).

24. *Map for the Official Handbook of Saorstát Eireann,* 1931.
With a one-inch alpha-numeric squaring system overprinted in red. In *Saorstát Eireann : Irish Free State : Official Handbook,* Dublin, Talbot Press and London, Ernest Benn, 1932.

25. *Biological Subdivisions,* 1949.

British military issues

26. TSGS 2028: Untitled: [Telegraph and telephone systems], 1906 [■BL].

27. TSGS 2360: *Irish Command Scheme,* 1908. Another edition, as GSGS 2360a, 1913.
    The 1908 edition is in *Irish Command Scheme,* London, War Office A.1287 [■PRO (WO 33/459)].

28. Untitled: [Divisional and brigade boundaries], 1920 [■PRO (Air 5/769)].
    The same source includes another issue, 1921.

Irish military issues

The Irish Free State's Department of Defence made use of the two plates of the 1904 outline map [✣A.1], as originally made prior to their copying and fusion into one. Two issues of the original Sheet 2 have been recorded [■Dm]. The sheet number was cleared, but the publication date was left incomplete as 190 . Both are classified *Secret.*

B. Skeleton maps

For military and administrative purposes. Without graticule.

1. *Military Districts,* 1904.

2. *Viceregal Commission on Irish Railways including Light Railways,* 1906.
   In *Vice-regal Commission on Irish Railways, including Light Railways* : *Appendix to the First Report* (BPP(HC) 1907 [Cd.3633], XXXVII, 575).

3. *County Boundaries and Rural Districts.*
   1. For official use, 1908.
   2. First public issue, 1921.
   3. Renamed *County boundaries, rural districts (former),* 1957.
   4. *County boundaries, rural districts (former),* 1957 (at scale 1:1,013,760) [■Dtf].

4. *County boundaries, national boundaries,* 1928.

5. *County boundaries, barony boundaries,* 1938.

6. *County boundaries,* 1956.

7. Province maps, showing county boundaries, rural districts.
   Connaught, 1908 (✣A.15.1).
   Leinster, 1908 (✣A.15.1).
   Munster, 1908 (✣A.15.1).
   Ulster, 1908 (✣A.15.1).
   All four maps were reprinted by the Ordnance Survey of Ireland.

95. 1:500,000 Map of Éire

With a graticule at 1° intervals. Published by the Ordnance Survey of Ireland. The Scottish area is not mapped.

1. Outline edition, with water in blue, roads in red, 1938.
   In Irish. Produced in collaboration with the Department of Education.

---

96. 1:500,000 Map of Ireland

With a graticule at 1° intervals. Published by the Ordnance Survey of Ireland. With an inset of the Blasket Islands and Bray Head and a coastal outline of Scotland.

1. Coloured edition, with layers, 1953. With updated reprints.

2. Outline edition, with water in blue, 1953. With updated reprints.

3. Administrative edition, 1953. In three colours. Not found.
   Listed in the Supplement No.10 (July-December 1953) to the 1949 catalogue.

---

97. 1:575,000 Map of Ireland

Constructed on Irish National Grid sheet lines. With a graticule at 1° intervals, and Irish National Grid at 10 km intervals in the border. See also **+99**. Published by the Ordnance Survey of Ireland. With an outline of Scotland, which was sometimes cleared.

1. Coloured edition, with layers, 1963. With updated reprints.

2. Outline edition, 1963. With updated reprints.

3. *Éire,* coloured edition, with layers, 1970. In Irish.

4. *Catholic Diocesan Boundaries and Names,* 1963.

5. *Chart showing Positions of Lighthouses, Lightfloats, Fog Signal Stations and Sea Marks under the Jurisdiction of the Commissioners of Irish Lights,* 1985 [■Dtf].
   The sheet width was extended for tabular material.

6. *Electoral (Amendment) Act,* 1995.
   Overprinted in red with parliamentary constituency boundaries.

Published by the National Soil Survey, and printed by the Ordnance Survey of Ireland

7. *General Soil Map,* First Edition, 1969.
   With an *Explanation of the Legend* by M.J. Gardiner.

8. *Land Drainage Problems,* First Edition, 1971.

9. *Peatland Map,* 1978.
   In R.F. Hammond *The Peatlands of Ireland* (Soil Survey Bulletin 35), Dublin, 1978.

98. 1:625,000 Map of Ireland

Irish National Grid map (sheet co-ordinates 10 km E to 370 km E, 10 km N to 470 km N), though the grid co-ordinates do not appear on the map. Published by the Ordnance Survey of Ireland. With a coastal outline of Scotland.

1. *Monastic Ireland,* 1960. Also Second Edition, 1965.

2. Outline plate only, with no publication information.

3. District map. Coloured with layers.
   North of Ireland : Average Annual Rainfall (in Millimetres) : International standard period 1941-70, 1976.
   Published by Her Majesty's Stationery Office for the Meteorological Office.

---

99. 1:750,000 Geological Map of Ireland

Constructed on Irish National Grid sheet lines. With a graticule at 1° intervals, and Irish National Grid at 10 km intervals in the border. Mapping is common with that of the 1:575,000 Map of Ireland [✢**97**] which was in preparation at the same time, though it extends some 15 km further west. Both maps presumably derive from the 1:500,000 map of Ireland [✢**96**]. Published by the Ordnance Survey of Ireland. With a coastal outline of Scotland.

1. *Geological Map,* 3rd Edition, 1962. Another issue, 1972.
   See ✢**113**.4, **113**.5 for earlier editions, at scale 1:1,000,000.

---

100. 1:500,000 Map of Northern Ireland

Irish National Grid map (sheet co-ordinates 180 km E to 370 km E, 310 km N to 460 km N). Published by the Ordnance Survey of Northern Ireland. Only the province is mapped.

1. Coloured edition, with layers, 1959. With updated reprints.
   Also in R. Common (ed.) *Northern Ireland from the air,* Belfast, The Queen's University, 1964, and *The Ulster Year Book* from the 1966-68 (thirteenth) edition.

2. Coloured edition, coloured by county, 1959. With updated reprints.
   Known as the *Communications Edition.* Also found in *The Ulster Year Book* (tenth, eleventh and twelfth editions), 1957-59, 1960-62, 1963-65.

3. Outline edition, with water in blue, 1959. With updated reprints.

4. *Land Classification Map* (at scale 1:375,000), 1963.
   Prepared for the Land Utilisation Survey of Northern Ireland and published by the University of London Press; The Queen's University, Belfast, copyright.

- For the 1947 map of Northern Ireland at approximately 5½ miles to 1 inch see ✢**74**.B.

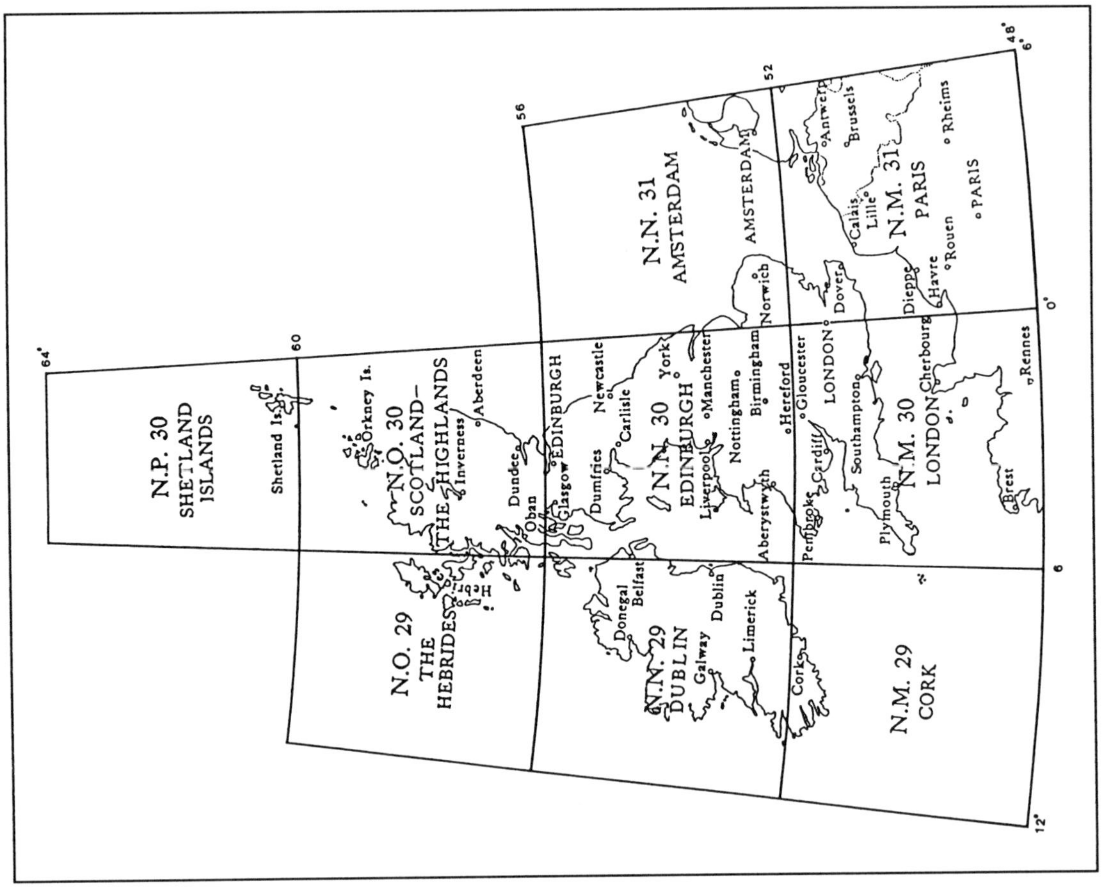

101. 1:1,000,000 International Map of the World (1)

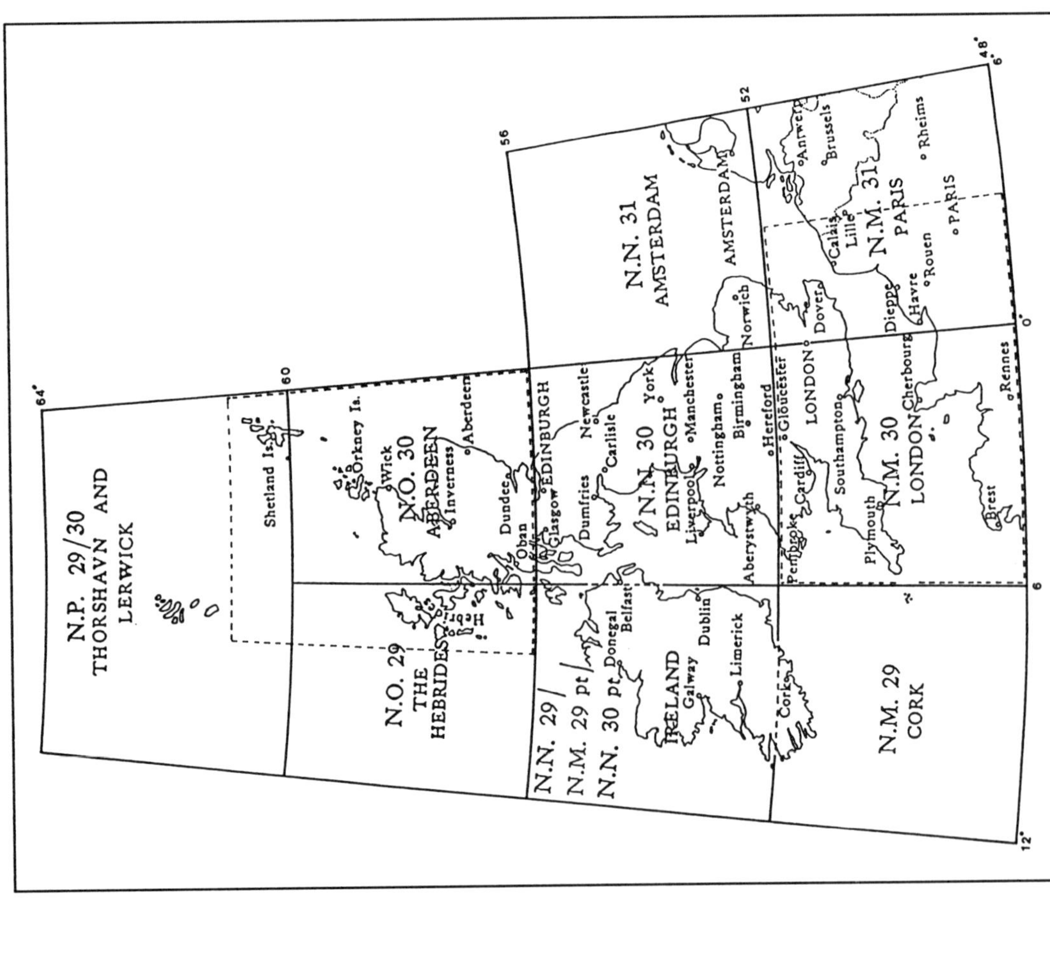

Aberdeen as enlarged and *London* - *Paris* are shown by pecked lines

102. 1:1,000,000 Map of Europe

101. 1:1,000,000 International Map of the World (1)

Constructed on the IMW Projection. Laid out on graticule sheet lines in sheets of 4° in latitude by 6° in longitude. Nine sheets cover the British Isles: NM29 *Cork*, NM30 *London*, NM31 *Paris*, NN29 *Dublin*, NN30 *Edinburgh*, NN31 *Amsterdam*, NO29 *The Hebrides*, NO30 *Scotland - The Highlands*, NP30 *Shetland Islands*. Sheet NN30 is named *Central Britain* or *Great Britain (Central)* on some indexes. The sheet lines of several sheets in **✢102** are identical. The Isles of Scilly are on Sheet NM29, Channel Islands on NM30. There is an extrusion covering London on Sheet NM31. With a graticule at 1° intervals and an associated alpha-numeric border. Maps in ✢3, 4, 5 have additional values printed outside the border to the east and north (✢5 all round) measuring degrees latitude northwards from the South Pole and degrees longitude eastwards from the 180° meridian. Coloured editions, with brown layers, unless noted.

1. *Carte de la Terre.*
   Published by Le Service Géographique de l'Armée.
   1. Coloured edition, with brown layers, 1911. Sheet NM31 [▮RGS].
   2. Coloured edition, 1911. Sheet NM31 [▮Wc].

2. *International Map Europe.*
   1. Coloured edition, with brown layers, 1912. 2 sheets: NO29, NO30 [▮RGS].
      Unrevised proof copies of both sheets dated 1911 survive [▮RGS].
   2. Coloured edition [headed *Outline Edition*], 1912. ?2 sheets: NO29 [▮Sg], ?NO30.
      The colours are black outline, red roads, brown contours and blue water.

3. *International Map of the World / Carte internationale du Monde.*
   1. Ordnance Survey publications, 1922-24. 6 sheets: NM30, NN30, NN31, NO29, NO30, renamed *Aberdeen*, NP30.
   2. Le Service Géographique de l'Armée publications. 2 sheets: NM31 (1923), NM30, renamed *Rennes* (1926) with England and Wales mapped in outline only [▮BL].
   3. Ordnance Survey of Ireland publications.
      Sheet NN29 was reported to the Central Bureau in 1948, NM29 (the English version only) by 1956.
      1. In English, 1940. 2 sheets: NM29, NN29.
      2. In Irish, 1940. 2 sheets: NM29 *Corcaigh*, NN29 *Baile átha cliath.*

   Also on sale in Great Britain was the derived map **✢104**. Modern editions of the international map employ combined sheet lines. Sheet NM30/31 *London - Paris* was published in Paris by L'Institut Géographique National in 1968. The British Isles sheets were redesigned in rectangular formats [**✢106**].

4. *International Map of the Roman Empire / Carte internationale de l'Empire Romain.*
   1. [Provisional edition], with contours, 1931. Sheet NN30.
   2. [Provisional edition], without contours, 1934. Sheet NO30 *Aberdeen.*

   The series was later entitled *Tabula Imperii Romani.* Sheet NM31 was published in Paris in 1975. Final versions of two sheets covering the whole of Great Britain were published by Oxford University Press using GSGS 4646 mapping [**✢103**.3].

5. *International Local Aeronautical Map / Carte normale aéronautique internationale.*
   Planned in nine sheets of which four were published. With air information overprinted in black.
   1. Le Service Géographique de l'Armée publication, ?1936. Sheet NM31 [▮BL].
      Publication and revision dates given (1923 and 1930) are those of the parent sheet in ✢3.2. 1936 is the earliest recorded air information date.
   2. Ordnance Survey publications. 3 sheets: NM30, NN30 (both 1939), NN31 (1937).
      There is an extrusion on NM30 for the Isles of Scilly. For NM30 in GSGS 3965 see **✢102**.5. Sheets NO29, NO30, NP30 were unpublished.

   Sheets NM29 and NN29 would have been Ordnance Survey of Ireland publications, but they were never issued.

102. 1:1,000,000 Map of Europe

Constructed on the IMW Projection. Laid out on graticule sheet lines, numbered in sectors 4° in latitude by 6° in longitude. Ten sheets in nine cover the British Isles: NM29 *Cork*, NM30 *London*, NM31 *Paris*, NN29/NM29pt/NN30pt *Ireland*, NN30 *Edinburgh*, NN31 *Amsterdam*, NO29 *Stornoway*, NO30 *Aberdeen*, NP29/30 *Thorshavn and Lerwick*. The sheet lines of several sheets in **✣101** are identical. The Isles of Scilly appear also as an extrusion on Sheet NM30. The extensions added to Sheet NN29 from neighbouring sheets provide complete coverage of Ireland. With a graticule at 1° intervals and an associated alpha-numeric border unless noted otherwise. All sheets were initially drawn and printed by the Ordnance Survey. For the derived map of Great Britain, GSGS 3787, see **✣105**.

1. GSGS 2758: *Provisional Edition*.
   1. Coloured edition, with brown layers, 1917. 2 sheets: NO29, NO30 [▮RGS].
   2. Coloured edition, 1916-18. All 10 sheets in 9: NM29, NM30, NM31, NN29/NM29pt/NN30pt, NN30, NN31, NO29, NO30, NP29/30.

      Sheet NM31 is also recorded as Map 2 from an as yet unidentified report [▮DGI]. Sheet NP29/30 did not appear in Second Edition [✣3], and was last reprinted in 1941.

2. GSGS 2758: [Provisional Edition], revised 1932.
   1. Coloured edition, with brown layers, 1932. Sheet NM31.
   2. Coloured edition, with brown layers, with air information overprinted in blue, 1932 (issued 1935). Sheet NM31.
   3. Coloured edition, 1932. Sheet NM31 [▮DGI].

3. GSGS 2758: Second Edition.

   Sheet NO30/29pt/NP29pt/30pt *Aberdeen* was extended to 61°N and 8°W to cover the Western and Shetland Islands. Sheets NM29 and NO29 were discontinued.
   1. Coloured edition, with brown layers, 1934-39. 10 sheets in 6: NM30, NM31, NN29/NM29pt/NN30pt, NN30, NN31, NO30/29pt/NP29pt/30pt.
   2. Coloured edition, with brown layers, with air information overprinted in blue, 1934-39. ?10 sheets in 6: NM30, NM31, NN29/NM29pt/NN30pt, ?NN30, ?NN31, NO30/29pt/NP29pt/30pt [▮DGI, RGS, Wc].
   3. Coloured edition, 1936-44. 8 sheets in 3 recorded: NM30, NN29/NM29pt/NN30pt, NO30/29pt/NP29pt/30pt [▮DGI, RGS].

   The following dependent issues of Sheet NN29/NM29pt/NN30pt are recorded:

   4. GSGS 2758, overprinted in red with secret air information, 1943 [▮DGI].

      Showing landing sites, anchorages, look-out posts, isogonals.
   5. GSGS 2758A, overprinted in blue with confidential air information, 1944 [▮RGS].

      Showing landing sites, anchorages, look-out posts, isogonals.

4. Outline edition (black plate only). Sheet NN29/NM29pt/NN30pt.
   1. With War Office Irish Grid at 10,000 metre intervals in black, 1919.
   2. With *Index to ½" Sheets of Ireland* overprinted in addition in red [▮DGI].

      It is not yet confirmed whether ✣4.1 was issued without the ✣4.2 overprint.

5. GSGS 3965: *International Local Aeronautical Map / Carte normale aéronautique internationale*, 1934. Sheet NM30.

   Coloured edition, with brown layers, with air information overprinted in black.

   For other *International Local Aeronautical Maps* see **✣101**.5.

6. District map. Coloured with brown layers.

   GSGS 3024: *Western Theatre of War*, 1915.

   Showing England south-east of 52°N,0°Long.

GSGS 2758 was revised in 1942. Coverage of Great Britain was transferred to a two-sheet map GSGS 4370 [✣**104**.A.6], using as a base a map that had been published in 1933. Sheets NN30, NN31, NO30/29pt/NP29pt/30pt were thus discontinued. Coverage of peripheral areas was achieved by three combined sheets in GSGS 2758. Sheets NM30 and NM31 were combined as NM30/31pt *London - Paris* (sheet co-ordinates 48°N to 52°N, 6°W to 3°E, with an extrusion for the Isles of Scilly). *Ireland,* renumbered "N29 and parts of M29 & GSGS 4370 Sheet 2", and Sheet NP29/30 *Thorshavn and Lerwick* completed the trio. Isogonals were added, alpha-numeric systems cleared from borders, and marginalia was usually revised. Sheet edition numbers begin anew and continue sequentially into GSGS 4646 [✣**103**].

7. GSGS 2758 coloured edition, with purple layers.
   1. First Edition, *Ground/Air,* 1942. Sheet NM30/31pt recorded [▮Wc].
      Layers above 200 metres are brown.
   2. First Edition, *Army/Air Style,* 1942. All sheets.
   3. Second Edition, *Army/Air Style,* 1942-44. All sheets.
   4. Third Edition, *Army/Air Style,* 1948-50. Sheets NM30/31pt, [N]N29 etc.
   5. Fourth Edition, *Army/Air Style,* with air information, 1950. Sheet [N]N29 etc.

8. GSGS 2758 coloured edition.
   Army/Air Style headings may survive, even though there are no layer colours.
   1. First Edition, 1943-44. Sheets NM30/31pt, NP29/30 recorded [▮DGI, Wc].
   2. Second Edition, 1944 (issued 1945). Sheet NM30/31pt recorded [▮Ob].

United States Army Map Service issues

Many Army Map Service issues are derived from GSGS 2758, but the organisation of any listing proved complex to the point that to have attempted integration with the list of British issued maps would have rendered the entire section virtually unusable. They thus appear separately here, with cross references to the British editions from which they were derived. This is a list of states recorded, by no means all those which were made. The information offered here is essentially related to the American editions; most of the surviving GSGS marginalia has not been quoted. Unless noted, the copies recorded are in ▮Wc or ▮Wn.

9. The first Army Map Service editions were monochrome copies, usually classified *Advance edition.* Some have no heading. The sheets recorded are NM30, NN29/NM29pt/NN30pt, NN30, NN31, NO29, NP29/30 on ✣1.2, 3.1, 3.3 base maps, dated 1941-42. Another *Advance edition* of Sheet NO29 used a ✣**101**.3 base map, and there is even an AMS 1 edition, 1943. This was classified *Provisional GSGS 2758.*

10. [AMS 1301], later AMS 1301 (GSGS 2758), coloured edition, with brown layers.
    1. AMS "Reprint 1942". Sheet NN29/NM29pt/NN30pt [✣3.1].
    2. AMS 2, 1943. Sheets NN30, NN31, NO30/29pt/NP29pt/30pt [✣3.1].
    3. AMS 2, 1950. Sheet NO30/29pt/NP29pt/30pt [✣3.1].
       With green layers to 200 metres; the upper layer tints are deleted.

11. [AMS 1301] coloured edition, "Reprint October 1942". Sheet NP29/30 [✣1.2].

12. [AMS 1301], later AMS 1301, coloured edition, usually with purple layers.
    1. AMS 1, *Ground/Air,* 1943. Sheet NM30/31pt [✣7.1].
       Layer colours are green to 200 metres, then brown.
    2. AMS 1, *Army/Air Style,* 1943. Sheets NM30/31pt [▮Ob] [✣7.2].
    3. AMS 2, *Army/Air Style,* 1943. Sheets NM30/31pt, [N]N29 etc [✣7.2].

13. AMS 1301 (GSGS 2758) coloured edition.
    Originals that were layered had *gradient tints deleted by AMS.*
    1. AMS 1, 1948. Sheet NN29/NM29pt/NN30pt [✣3.1].
    2. AMS 2, 1949-51. Sheets [N]N29 etc [✣8.3], NN30 [✣3.1], NP29/30 [✣7.3].
    3. AMS 3, 1947. Sheet NM30/31pt [▮Ob] [✣8.2].

14. AMS 1301 (GSGS 2758) coloured edition, 1953. Sheet NM 30/31pt recorded.
    The map claims Edition 2-GSGS derivation, but carries both National and Universal Transverse Mercator Grids.

103. 1:1,000,000 Map of the World

Numbered in IMW graticule sectors 4° in latitude by 6° in longitude, but laid out across the British Isles in combined sheets 4° in latitude by 11° in longitude. Eleven sheets in five cover the British Isles: NM30/29pt/31pt *London*, NN29/30pt/NM29pt/30pt *Dublin*, NN30/29pt/31pt *Edinburgh*, NO30/29pt/31pt *Aberdeen* (with an extrusion for St Kilda), NP30/29pt/31pt *Lerwick*. With a graticule at 1° intervals. Compiled from GSGS 2758 [✢**102**] and GSGS 4370 [✢**104**.A.6] mapping. Superseding both GSGS 2758 and 4370.

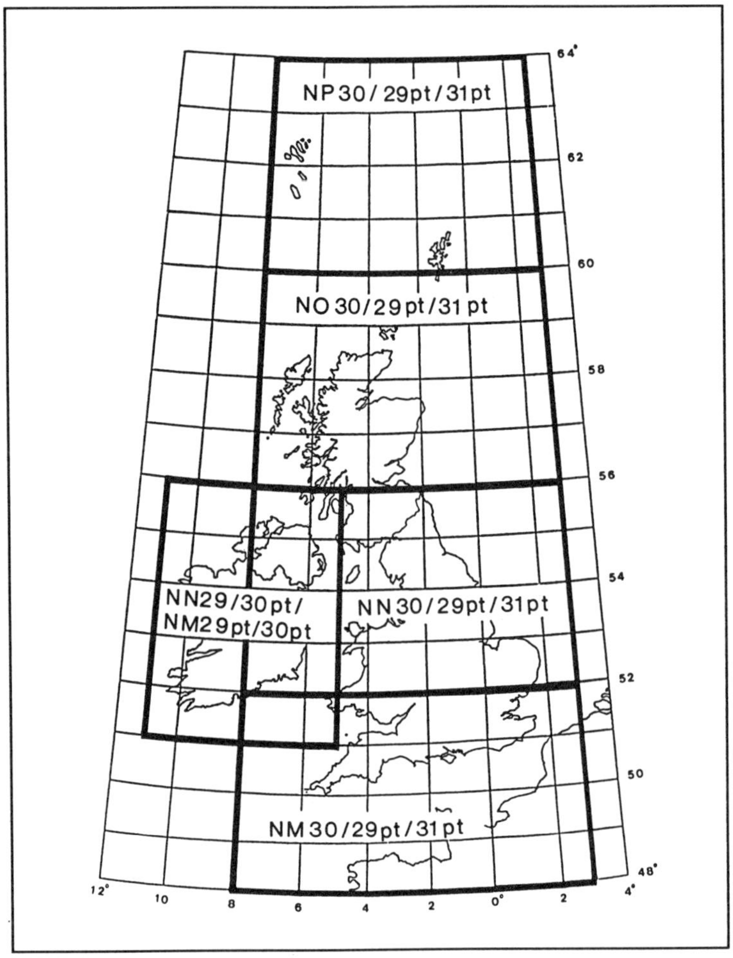

1. GSGS 4646, later Series 1301, coloured edition, with brown layers. All sheets.
   Overprinted in blue with British and Irish National and Universal Transverse Mercator Grids. Sheet edition numbers continue sequentially from those in GSGS 2758 [✢**102**].
   1. Printed by the Ordnance Survey, 1954-56 (issued 1955-56). Sheets NN30/29pt/31pt, NO30/29pt/31pt, NP30/29pt/31pt (Edition 3-GSGS); NM30/29pt/31pt (Edition 4-GSGS); NN29/30pt/NM29pt/30pt (Edition 5-GSGS).
   2. Printed by the Army Map Service, 1956-58. Sheets NN30/29pt/31pt, NO30/29pt/31pt, NP30/29pt/31pt (Edition 3-GSGS); NM30/29pt/31pt (Edition 4-GSGS); NN29/30pt/NM29pt/30pt (Edition 5-GSGS) [▮Wc, Wn].
      The series number of the Army Map Service edition is 1301 (GSGS 4646). The grids are coloured purple.

2. GSGS 4646 without grids, 1956. Sheet NN29/30pt/NM29pt/30pt recorded.

3. *Tabula Imperii Romani.* 2 combined sheets: NM30/[31pt] *Condate - Glevum - Londinium - Lutetia* (1983), NN30/NO30/[NN31pt] *Britannia Septentrionalis* (1987).
   Published by Oxford University Press. These are final versions of the two British sheets in *Tabula Imperii Romani* [see ✢**101**.4], using GSGS 4646 mapping.

104. 1:1,000,000 Map of Great Britain (1)

Constructed on the IMW Projection. Laid out on graticule sheet lines and published in two sheets (sheet co-ordinates 50°N to 56°N (Sheet 2), 54°N to 60°N (Sheet 1), 8°W to 2°E). Drawn *in the style of the International 1/M. Map.* Heading, where present: *Ordnance Survey of Great Britain.* Inset on Sheet 1 are the Shetland Islands; there are extrusions for Lizard Point and Isles of Scilly on Sheet 2. With contours on topographical issues unless noted. With coastal outlines of France and usually of Ireland. Both sheets were issued unless noted otherwise.

A. With a graticule at 1° intervals

Some pre-war issues have additional values outside the border to the north and east measuring degrees latitude northwards from the South Pole and degrees longitude eastwards from the 180° meridian. With an alpha-numeric border unless noted.

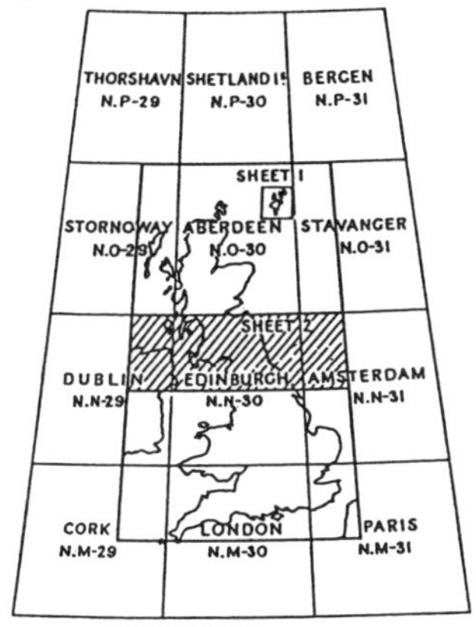

1. Coloured edition, with layers, 1933.

2. Outline edition, with water in blue, 1933 (published 1937-38).

3. *Population of Great Britain 1931,* 1933-34 (published 1934).
   Compiled from the 1931 Census. Prepared by A.C. O'Dell.

4. *RAF Edition,* coloured with brown layers, 1933 (issued 1938).
   With air information overprinted in blue. See also ✣A.6.

Geological Survey of Great Britain

5. District maps. With a simple border. Published by the Ordnance Survey.
   The Chief Limestones of England and Wales, 1937.
   The Coalfields of England and Wales, 1935.
   The Iron Ores of England and Wales, 1935.
   Outline edition, with water in blue, 1937 [▮Og].

Military issues

With mapping of Ireland. Related maps may be found in GSGS 2758 *Europe* [**✣102**]. The border is cleared of the alpha-numeric system. Army Map Service *Advance editions* were monochrome copies of ✣A.1 issues; AMS 2 issues, unusually, were redrawn to new specifications.

6. GSGS 4370: *Europe* : *Great Britain,* Second Edition.
   The First Edition of this map may *de facto* have been the *RAF Edition* [✣A.4].
   1. *Ground/Air* edition, coloured with purple and brown layers, 1942 [▮PRO*].
   2. *Army/Air Style,* coloured with purple layers, 1942 (issued 1943).
   3. *Army/Air Style,* coloured, 1942 (issued 1946) [▮PRO*].
   4. *Army/Air Style,* outline, dated 1942.

7. GSGS Misc.509: *Topographical Consol Chart,* 1947 [▮PRO*].

8. District map. Outline, overprinted with War Office Cassini and adjacent grids in blue.
   Great Britain, 1945 [▮Ob].
   Issued by SHAEF Air Staff, Maps No.120. Two smaller sheets, derived from ✣A.6.

B. With National Grid at 100 km intervals

1. Coloured edition, with layers, without contours, 1933 (published 1946).

2. *National Parks in England and Wales,* 1958. Sheet 2 [▮RML].

105. 1:1,000,000 Military Map of Great Britain

Issued in one sheet. A rectangular sheet created from the outline and water plates of GSGS 2758 [**✚102**], covering in addition the greater part of Ireland. With a graticule at 1° intervals. The French area is mapped. With an inset at scale 1:1,666,667 of Shetland and Orkney Islands. The base map is untitled.

1. GSGS 3787 outline edition in black, 1936 [▮Bg]. Reprinted in grey, 1946 [▮DGI].

   The following dependent issues are recorded or documented; titles may be descriptive of the map's content rather than actual. Suffix letters relate to overprint plates:

   1. GSGS 3787a: *RAF stations in the British Isles,* 1936. Another edition, 1938. See also ✢1.20.
   2. GSGS 3787b: *RAF stations and civil aerodromes,* 1937.
   3. GSGS 3787ab: *RAF stations and civil aerodromes and landing grounds in the British Isles,* 1939. Another edition, 1940.
   4. GSGS 3787c: *Essential railways,* 1940 [▮Ob].
   5. GSGS 3787d: *RAF stations and additional information,* 1937.
   6. GSGS 3787ad: *RAF stations and low flying areas,* 1938.
   7. GSGS 3787e: *Eastern Command exercise, No.2, situation 1st September 1938.*
   8. GSGS 3787f: *RAF fuel depots etc,* 1939.
   9. GSGS 3787k: *Areas dangerous to flight of civil aircraft,* 19xx. Also ?second and ?third editions; fourth edition, 1947.
   10. GSGS 3787l: *Explosive areas,* 19xx. Also second edition, 1946.
   11. GSGS 3787m: *Scheduled air services operating within, to and across the United Kingdom as at 31st December 1947,* 1948 [▮Og].
   12. GSGS 3787km: *Danger areas overprinted with scheduled air services,* 1947.
   13. GSGS 3787nop: *Areas hazardous to aviation,* 1947.
   14. GSGS 3787q: *Aerodromes available to civil aircraft,* 1947.
   15. GSGS 3787s: *Conveyance by rail......of......tanks,* no date.
   16. GSGS 3787t: *Commands, areas and county divisions,* 1941 [▮DGI].
   17. GSGS 3787u: *Movement control boundaries,* 1941.
   18. GSGS 3787tu: *Commands, areas and county divisions, movement control boundaries,* 1941 [▮DGI].
   19. GSGS 3787vw: *High ground accidents, 1st June 1944 to 31st December 1944.*
   20. ADI (Maps) AM 7528: *RAF stations in the British Isles,* 1941.
       Another edition of GSGS 3787a in *Aerodromes and RAF Stations in the British Isles,* London, Air Ministry SD 229 [▮PRO (MPI 570)].

2. GSGS 4653: First Edition, 1948 [▮RGS].
   An outline diagram lacking topography, with towns and location markers, completely relettered. With an additional inset of the Channel Islands.

   The following dependent issue is recorded:

   1. GSGS 4653abcd: *Areas hazardous to aviation,* 1948.

   This diagram was superseded by a succession of others, on a variety of sheet lines, many of which carry overprints. These are not listed here, but see, for instance, GSGS Misc.412, GSGS Misc.1598, GSGS Misc.1788, GSGS 4970, GSGS 4971, GSGS 4993, GSGS 5201.

106. 1:1,000,000 International Map of the World (2)

Constructed on the Lambert Conformal Conical Projection and laid out on rectangular sheet lines. Three sheets were made to cover the British Isles: NN30 *England and Wales,* NO30 *Scotland,* extended to cover outliers, and NN29 *Ireland,* extended to cover the entire island. Even though the map is not on the IMW Projection the system of sheet numbering is in accordance with that of the International Map of the World. Because of its derivation the sheet lines of the Ireland sheet are at an angle to those of the British. With a graticule at 1° intervals. For Great Britain this edition supersedes **+104**.B.1.

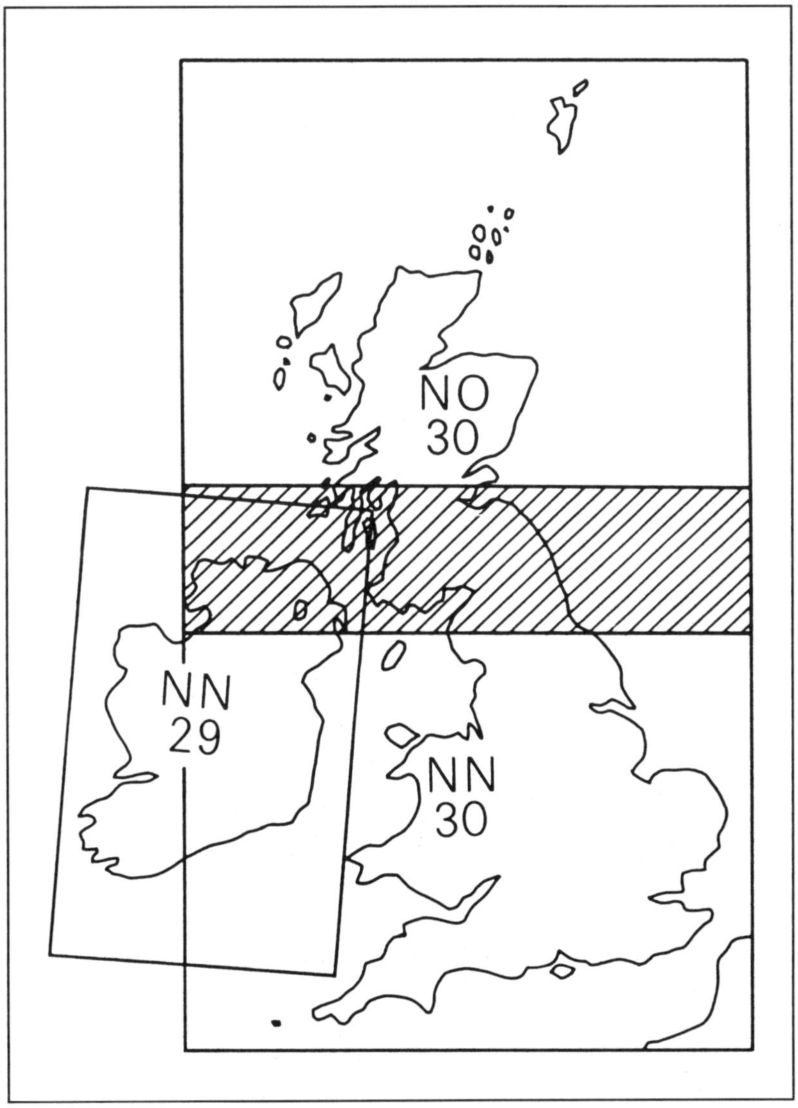

1. Coloured edition, with layers and hill shading.
   1. Ordnance Survey of Great Britain publications, 1965. 2 sheets: NN30, NO30.
   2. Ordnance Survey of Ireland publication, 1968. Sheet NN29.

2. *National Parks,* 1966. Sheet NN30.

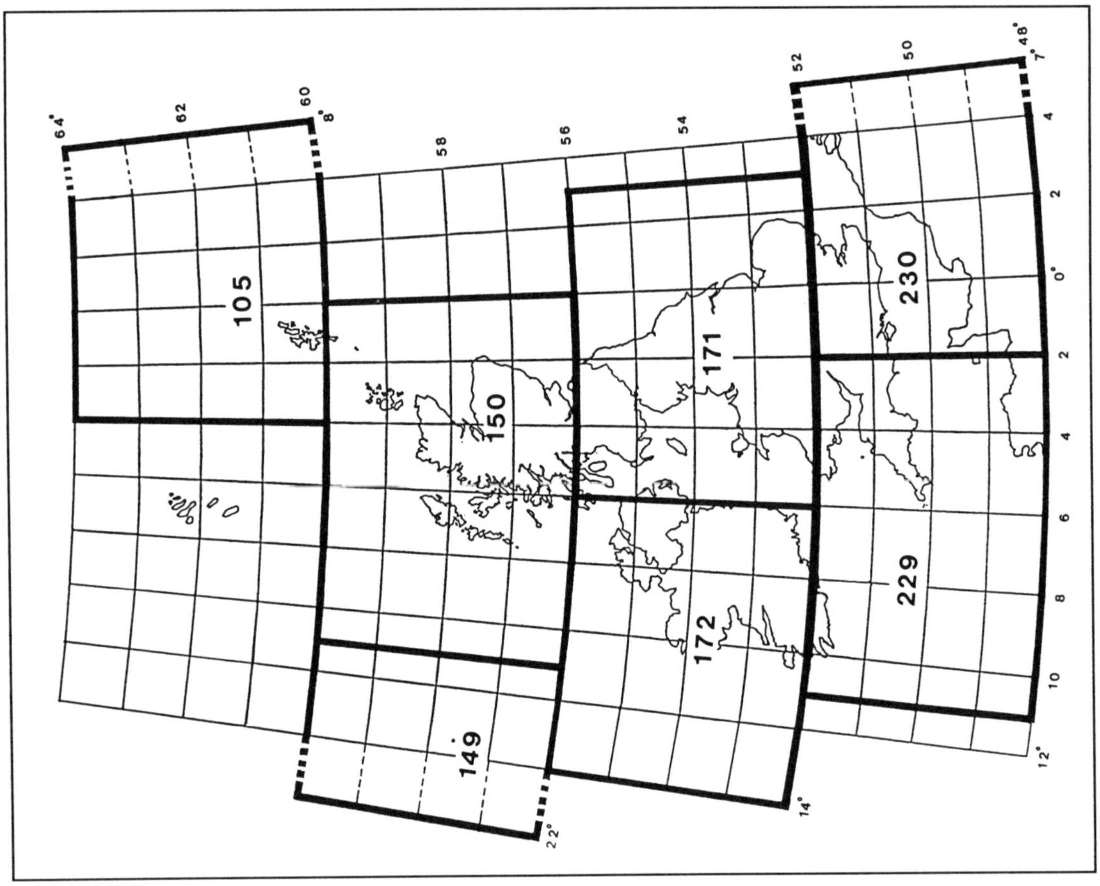

107. 1:1,000,000 RAF Aeronautical Chart

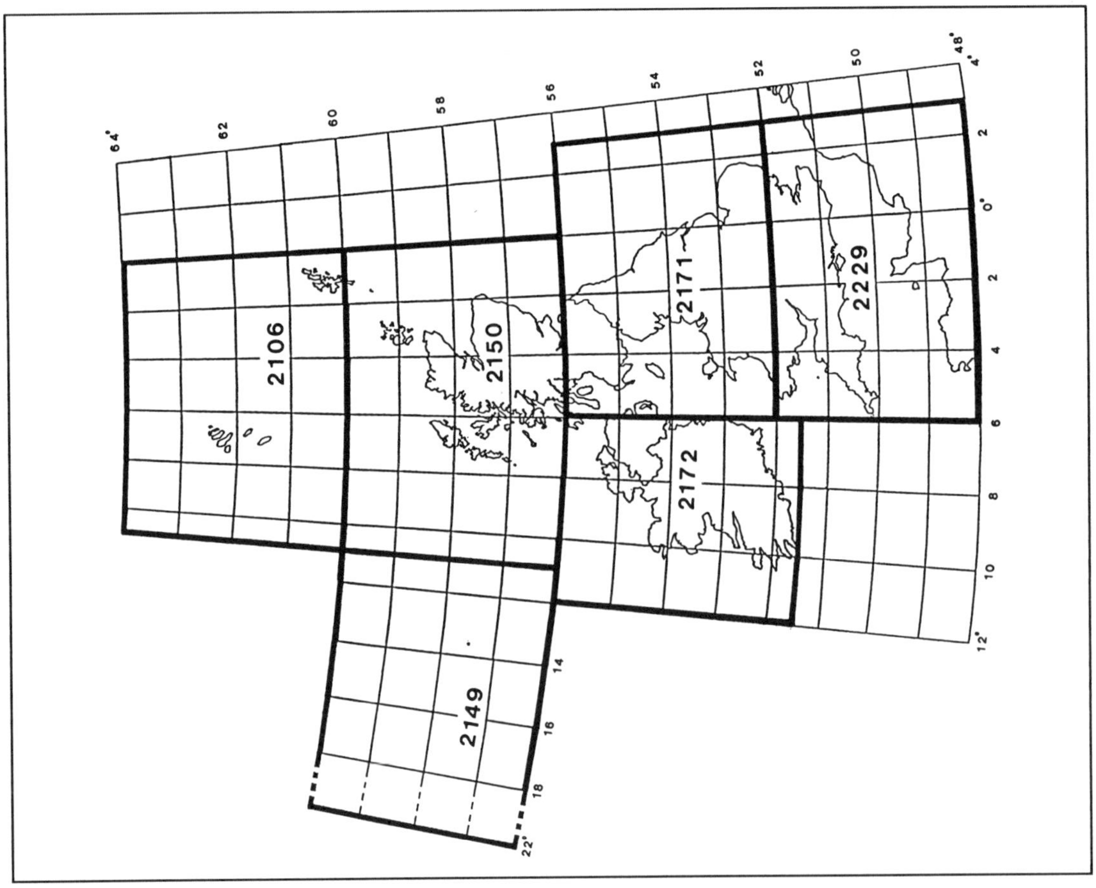

108. 1:1,000,000 World Aeronautical Chart

107. 1:1,000,000 RAF Aeronautical Chart

Constructed on the Lambert Conformal Conical Projection. Laid out over the British Isles on graticule sheet lines in sheets of 4° in latitude by 8° or 9° in longitude south of 56°N and 11° or 12° in longitude north thereof, later issues having edges bled off north and east. Seven sheets cover the British Isles: 105 *Shetland Islands,* 149 *Rockall,* 150 *The Grampians,* 171 *Pennine Chain,* 172 *Ireland,* 229 *Lands End,* 230 *Strait of Dover.* With a graticule at 30' intervals. Heading: *RAF 1:1,000,000 Aeronautical Chart (based on USAF World Aeronautical Chart).* All sheets were initially drawn and issued in American editions, but these are disregarded. Only British issues are noted here. All known issues are coloured, with purple layers, and with air information and Georef overprinted in blue.

1. GSGS 4695: First Edition-GSGS, 1951-61. All the above sheets [▮Ob].

2. GSGS 4695: Edition 2-GSGS. 2 sheets recorded: 105 (1959), 230 (1955) [▮Ob].

3. GSGS 4695: Edition 3-GSGS.
    1. With grey town infill, 1957 (issued 1958). Sheet 230 [▮Ob].
    2. With yellow town infill, 1959. Sheet 230 [▮RGS].

---

108. 1:1,000,000 World Aeronautical Chart

Constructed on the Lambert Conformal Conical Projection. Laid out over the British Isles on graticule sheet lines in sheets of 4° in latitude but of varying widths, with edges bled off north and east. Five sheets cover the British Isles: 2106 *Faeröe Islands,* 2150 *The Grampians,* 2171 *Pennine Chain,* 2172 *Ireland,* 2229 *English Channel;* in addition Sheet 2149 *Rockall* appears on some indexes, but there is no evidence that it was issued. With a graticule at 30' intervals. Compiled by the Ordnance Survey, in part from GSGS 2758 [✚**102**] and GSGS 4370 [✚**104**.A.6] mapping. Pre-publication versions of Sheet 2171 (carrying the sheet number 171 first allocated to it), in both GSGS 4622 and GSGS 4648, are recorded [▮DGI].

With an extrusion on Sheet 2229 for the Isles of Scilly.

1. GSGS 4622: *RAF 1:1,000,000,* coloured with purple layers. 5 sheets.
    With air information overprinted in blue.
    1. First Edition-GSGS, 1951 (issued 1951-52). 5 sheets: 2106, 2150, 2171, 2172, 2229.
    2. Second Edition-GSGS. 2 sheets recorded: 2150 (1955), 2172 (1953).

2. *ICAO 1:1,000,000,* coloured with brown layers. 5 sheets.
    With air information overprinted in magenta.
    1. GSGS 4648: First Edition, 1948-49 (issued 1948-50). 3 sheets: 2150, 2171, 2229.
    2. L'Institut Géographique National publication, 1951. Sheet 2229 *La Manche.* Copy ▮RGS. The heading is *Carte Aéronautique du Monde* : *OACI 1:1,000,000.*
    3. Ordnance Survey of Ireland publication, 1953. Sheet 2172.
    4. Directorate of Civil Aviation Copenhagen publication, 1954. Sheet 2106.

    From Edition 2-GSGS in 1957 British coverage was reorganised in two combined sheets: 2150/2106pt/2171pt/2172pt *British Isles (North)* (sheet co-ordinates 55°N to 61°N, 9°W to 2°E, so including the Shetland Islands), 2171/2172pt/2229pt *British Isles (South)* (sheet co-ordinates 50°N to 56°N, 7°30'W to 3°E, with extrusions for the Isles of Scilly and the Channel Islands). Both British and Irish sheets were updated several times in numbered editions, not listed here.

109. 1:1,000,000 Map of Great Britain and Ireland

Constructed on a Minimum Error Conical Projection and published in two sheets. With a graticule at 1° intervals. With a title on Sheet 1: *Ordnance Survey of Great Britain and Ireland.* Both sheets were issued unless stated otherwise.

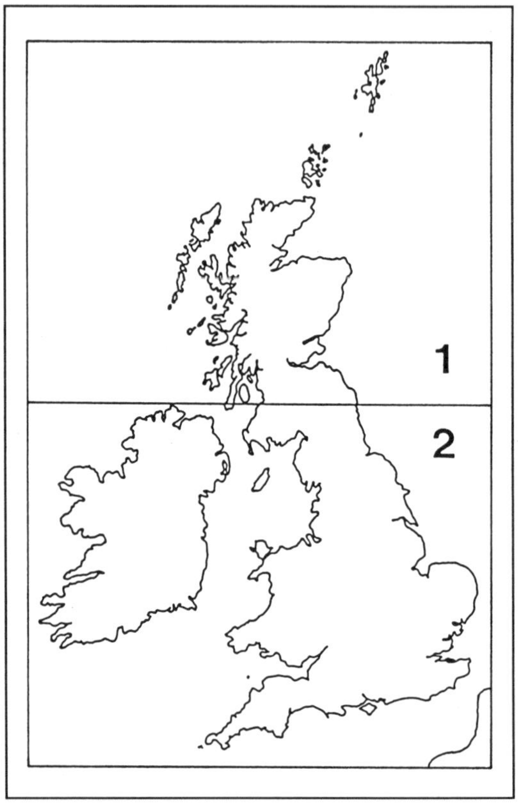

1. Outline edition, 1904 (published 1905). By engraving.

2. Coloured edition, with hachures, 1905.

3. Coloured edition, with hill shading, 1909.
   The publication date appears as 1904 on some reprints.

Produced from 1926 revision of Great Britain

4. Outline edition, 1927. By engraving or lithography.

5. Coloured edition, with hill shading, 1927.

6. *The Transverse Mercator National Grid (Origin Lat: 49°N Long: 2°W),* ?1933 [▮RGS].
   The title and National Yard Grid at 50,000 yard intervals are overprinted in red. Probably issued for use at a discussion at the Royal Geographical Society on the new "national grid" in April 1933.

Aeronautical and military issues

The source for ✣9, 11, 12 is the *Register of GSGS Maps* and their base maps are unconfirmed.

7. Coloured edition, with hachures, overprinted for a military exercise, no date. Sheet 2.

8. *Map Showing Naval & Military Aircraft Stations & Depôts to date 30th April 1916,* 1916.
   Coloured by command area (Ireland is uncoloured). Accompanying AWS (CB 1235) Air Packet No.65 [▮PRO (Air 1/345/15/226/294)]. For Air Packets see **✣53**.8.

9. GSGS 2838: *Military and Police Map of Great Britain and Ireland,* 1917. Not found.

10. *Map showing Areas, Groups & RAF Stations,* 1918.
    1. *Corrected to the 10th May, 1918* [▮BL].
    2. IDAM 1A, *Corrected to the 15th July, 1918* [▮BL].
    3. IDAM 1B, *Corrected to the 16th Nov, 1918* [▮BL, PRO (Air 1/2107/207/43/2)].

11. GSGS 2935: *Military Commands,* 1919. Not found.

12. GSGS 3900: *Index Diagrams to Lists of Trigonometrical Points,* 1930. Not found.

13. District maps. Outline.
    Part of the British Isles.
    The area covered includes part of the Isles of Scilly and Ireland, and extends north to Stonehaven. The European coastline is present.
    1. GSGS 3710: *Part of the British Isles,* 1919 [▮DGI]. Another issue, 1931 [▮Bg].
       Issued by the Ordnance Survey (1919), by the War Office (1931).
    2. GSGS 3788: *Weather Forecast Areas,* 1926 [▮PRO*].
       Boundaries are overprinted in purple, aerodromes in red.

The following issues dependent upon GSGS 3710 are recorded or documented. Titles may be descriptive of the map's content rather than actual. Suffix letters relate to overprint plates:

3. GSGS 3710a: *Commands and areas,* 1919. Another edition, 1940 [▮DGI].
4. GSGS 3710b: *Proposed MT workshops.*
5. GSGS 3710ab: *Commands, areas & AA divisions,* 1939.
6. GSGS 3710c: *Aerodromes, routes, etc,* 1930 [▮Ob].
7. GSGS 3710d: *Appendix X* in *Instructions for Air Exercises,* 1930 [▮Ob].
8. GSGS 3710ad: *Situation of troops.*
9. GSGS 3710e: *Cloud flying areas of British Isles,* ?1934.
10. GSGS 3710f: *Batteries & units for AA defences,* 1936 [▮DGI].
11. GSGS 3710g: *Emergency deployment light AA gun defences,* 1938 [▮DGI].
12. GSGS 3710h: *AA divisions,* 1938.
13. GSGS 3710ij: *Estimated scale of air attack on Great Britain.*
14. GSGS 3710k: *Night flying sub-areas,* 1939.
15. GSGS 3710k: *Regional areas, boundaries and headquarters,* [1940] [▮DGI].
16. GSGS 3710al: *Movement control district HQ and boundaries,* 1940 [▮DGI].
17. GSGS 3710s: *Air and road routes,* 1927.
18. GSGS 3710s: *Air mail scheme - map of air and road routes,* 1931; 1933 [▮PRO*].
19. GSGS 3710t: *Air mail scheme - map of air and road routes,* 1933 [▮Ob].

Great Britain. In two sheets, *(North)* and *(South).*

North and south sheet limits and to the east of the south sheet are as the original map. Mapping of Ireland is omitted.

1. *Index Diagram to Sheets of the Map of Great Britain on the 1:20,000 Scale.*

   Consisting of 103 rectangles over land areas, each 75 km by 50 km, overprinted in red on War Office Cassini Grid (British System) co-ordinates. The system originates off Land's End at 170 km E, 30 km N, thus the Isles of Scilly fall outside the indexed area. The rectangles, numbered south-west to north-east in the range I to CIII, are each divided into 25 rectangles of 15 km by 10 km lettered A to H, J to Z north-west to south-east. These rectangles form the sheet lines of 1:20,000 GSGS 2748. A Roman numeral and a letter constitute each sheet number.

   1. First issue, 1918 [▮CCS]. Another edition, 1924 [▮CCS: South].
   2. OR 209 (south sheet), OR 209a (north sheet), 1929 [▮CCS].

2. GSGS 3912: *Index Diagram to Sheets of the Map of Great Britain on the 1:25,000 Scale GSGS No.3906,* 1931. Also editions updated to 1939 [▮CCS].

   Overprinted in red. The system is described in **✛116**. The sheet lines of GSGS 3036 1:25,344 *East Anglia* are overprinted in blue (not 1939).

The following issue dependent upon GSGS 3912 is recorded:

3. GSGS 3901: *Lists of Trigonometrical Points,* 1931 [▮CCS: North].

England and Wales.

The Scottish and Irish areas are filled. With the coastline of France. The Isles of Scilly are lacking except where noted.

1. *The United Kingdom, Portion of Sheet 2, England,* 1913 [▮PRO (OS 5/60)].
2. *England & Wales,* 1913. Another edition, 1916 [▮PRO (WO 153/425, MPII 74)].
3. GSGS 3721, 1919. Probably this map, issued for the Staff College. Not found.

The following dependent issue is recorded:

4. *England and Wales, showing Prohibited Areas Under the "Aliens Restriction Order, January, 1916",* no date [▮PRO (FO 925/30137)].

   Northumberland breaks the northern neat line. The Isles of Scilly are inset.

Scotland.

England, Ireland and Shetland Islands are not mapped.

1. Untitled outline issue, 1908 [▮PRO (OS 5/62)].

The following dependent issue is recorded:

2. *Scotland, showing Prohibited Areas Under the "Aliens Restriction Order, January, 1916",* 1916 [▮PRO (FO 925/30138)].

- For Ireland see **✛113**.

110. 1:1,000,000 Maps of England and Wales, and Scotland

Constructed on a Minimum Error Conical Projection. Usually with a graticule at 1° intervals. 1922-24 issues were coloured with layers, and with contours, thereafter without contours unless noted. With extrusions for Jersey, and the Dublin and Edinburgh hinterlands on England and Wales. The Isles of Scilly are not covered. French and Irish areas are mapped.

A. Physical Map

Heading: *Ordnance Survey Physical Map of England and Wales / Scotland.*

1. England and Wales, 1922. With an alpha-numeric border.

2. Physical issue, without black plate, c.1924. England and Wales.

3. England and Wales, Scotland, 1928.
   Proof copies with contours recorded [▮RML].

4. Relief edition, with contours, 1928, reprinted 1929.
   England and Wales recorded [▮Mg].

5. *Magnetic Edition,* 1928. England and Wales.
   A proof copy with contours is recorded [▮RML].

6. *Magnetic Edition (1933),* 1933 (published 1934).
   Both sheets. Reprinted 1946.

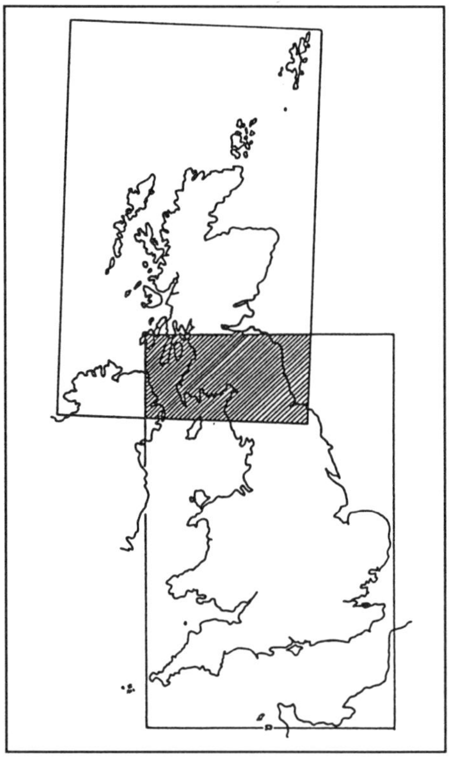

B. Period maps

With an alpha-numeric border, unless noted.

1. *Roman Britain,* 1924. England and Wales.

2. *XVII Century England,* 1930. England and Wales.

3. *Britain in the Dark Ages (South Sheet),* 1935, *(North Sheet),* 1938 (published 1939). Reprinted 1949.

4. Outline edition, with water in blue, contours in brown, 1933.
   Reproduced under the direction of a committee of the British Association, for inclusion in H.A. Wilcox *The Woodlands and Marshlands of England,* University Press of Liverpool, and London, Hodder & Stoughton, 1933. The England and Wales sheet only, without alpha-numeric system, overprinted to show:
   1. *The Woodlands and Marshlands of England (prehistoric).*
   2. *The Woodlands and Marshlands of England (As deduced from early literature).*

C. Period maps with extended sheet lines

1. *Roman Britain,* Second Edition, 1928. Reprinted 1946.
   Sheet lines were shifted north and extended north to cover Roman sites in Scotland.

2. An otherwise unused physical map covering mainland Great Britain formed from the union of the Scotland and England and Wales maps. Shetland and Orkney Islands are inset: there is an extrusion for the Isles of Scilly. The French area covered is mapped, though not the Irish. With National Grid at 100 km intervals.
   1. *Roman Britain,* Third Edition, 1956.
   2. *Britain in the Dark Ages,* Second Edition, 1965 (published 1966).

111. 1:1,000,000 Map of Great Britain (2)

National Grid map (sheet co-ordinates 50 km E to 670 km E, 10 km N to 990 km N). Ireland and France are not mapped. There are insets of Shetland Islands, Orkney Islands, Sule Skerry and Stack Skerry, Sula Sgeir and Rona, St Kilda, Rockall.

1. ?Outline edition, ?1977. Not found, and perhaps not published.
   Probably made primarily for use as the base to ✢2.

2. The map served as an index to:
   1. *1:50 000* [First and Second] *Series,* 1977-83.
   2. *1:25 000 First and Second Series,* 1977-85.
   3. *1:25 000 First and Pathfinder (Second) Series and Outdoor Leisure Maps,* 1985-89.
   4. *1:10 000 and 1:10 560 National Grid Series,* 1977-89.

The map was also used by the Ordnance Survey for technical purposes.

---

112. 1:1,000,000 Wall Maps

Though on uniform paper sizes, the land mass is moved according to the need of tables, coverage of Ireland, etc. With insets of Shetland Islands, Orkney Islands.

A. Narrow sheet width

1. *Discover Britain with Ordnance Survey Landranger Maps,* 1983.

2. *Great Britain* : *Wall Map,* 1988. Another edition, 1989.

3. *Great Britain* : *Communication,* 1993. Outline edition.

B. Broad sheet width

1. *British Isles* : *Communication,* 1993. Another edition, 1995.

2. *Great Britain* : *Physical,* 1994.

3. *United Kingdom* : *Protected Environment,* 1994.

4. *United Kingdom* : *Administrative,* 1996.

5. *United Kingdom* : *Rainfall,* 1996.

6. *United Kingdom* : *Geology,* 1997.
   Published jointly by the Ordnance Survey and the British Geological Survey.

7. *British Isles* : *Political,* 1997.

113. 1:1,000,000 Map of Ireland

Extracted from **✣109**. With a graticule at 1° intervals. The mapping of British areas is usually in place, though sometimes cleared. Both simple and graduated borders were used.

1. Untitled outline issue, 1915 [▮PRO (OS 5/61)].

2. *Ireland, showing Prohibited Areas Under the "Aliens Restriction Order, January, 1916"*, 1916 [▮PRO (FO 925/30139)].
   With prohibited areas overprinted in red.

Ordnance Survey of Ireland

3. *Ireland, showing Prohibited Areas Under the "Prevention of Illicit Distillation Orders, 1925-26"*, 1928 [▮Dna].
   With county boundaries and prohibited areas overprinted in red.

4. *Ireland.*
   These two maps were printed on the same sheet of paper. An intact pair is in ▮Og.
   1. *Topographical Map*, 1928. Coloured with hill shading.
   2. *Geological Map*, [First Edition], 1928.

5. *Geological Map*, 2nd Edition, 1952.
   See **✣99** for the Third Edition, at scale 1:750,000.

Geological Survey of Ireland

6. *Magnetic Intensity.*
   Included here for the sake of completeness, though the sheet lines are more generous on all sides. The two maps were printed on the same sheet of paper. An intact pair is in ▮Og.
   1. *Lines of Equal Vertical Magnetic Intensity*, 1949.
   2. *Lines of Equal Anomaly of Vertical Magnetic Intensity*, 1949.

Symbols **:** a **bold** number prefixed with ✣ is a cross reference to another section of the book; a number prefixed with ✥ is a cross reference within the current section; a reference number in ( ) at a district map identifies the next, or previous, such map listed with the same sheet lines; the ▮ symbol accompanies a source reference for maps rarely encountered (library sigla are listed on page 241); ❍ warns that there are noted exceptions to the information given in headings; ↑ identifies what is referred to here as War Office marginalia (for a description see page xxii); ❂ refers to the exceptional use of the heading *Ordnance Survey of Great Britain*.

114. 1:1,250,000 Map of Great Britain (1)

Issues to edition *D* are reduced from the two 1:625,000 sheets [**✤89**.B]. On National Yard Grid sheet lines (sheet co-ordinates 620,000 yards E to 1,300,000 yards E, 1,120,000 yards N to 2,180,000 yards N). With National [metric] Grid at 10 km intervals, unless noted otherwise. Superseded by edition *E* [**✤115**]. There are insets of Shetland and Orkney Islands, Sule Skerry and Stack Skerry, Sula Sgeir and Rona, St Kilda and Boreray, and an extrusion for the Isles of Scilly. With the coastal outlines of Ireland and France.

1. Outline edition, 1946 (published 1947).

2. *National Parks and Conservation Areas,* 1946 (issued 1947).
   Accompanying two Ministry of Town and Country Planning reports: *Report of the National Parks Committee (England and Wales)* (Cmd.7121) and *Conservation of Nature in England and Wales : Report of the Wild Life Conservation Special Committee* (Cmd.7122). The map was later sold independently.

3. *Land required by Service Departments for Training,* 1947. Unpublished proof [▮OS].
   Prepared by the Ministry of Town and Country Planning for the use of civilian planners. Publication of the map was blocked for security reasons.

4. The map served as an index to:
   1. *New Popular, 5th Edition and Popular Edition One Inch Maps,* issued 1949 [▮RML].
   2. *Popular, New Popular and 7th Series One Inch Maps of Great Britain,* 1952 [▮RML].
   3. *1:50,000 Sheet Lines,* 1970-72.
   4. *1:50 000 Scale Map,* 1974.
   5. *1:50,000 Sheet Lines* : *One Inch Seventh Series Sheet Lines,* 1972-73.
   6. *1:50 000 Scale Map and One-inch Seventh Series Map,* 1974.
   7. *1:25,000 Second Series (20 Km x 15 Km Sheet Lines),* printed c.1960 [▮OS].
      The only sheet to be published, 856, is shown with incorrect sheet lines.
   8. *1:25,000 Second Series,* 1964-66.
   9. *1:25,000 Provisional Edition & 1:25,000 Second Series,* 1967-71.
   10. *1:25 000 First & Second Series,* 1972-74.
   11. *1:25 000 First & Second Series* [and] *Outdoor Leisure Maps,* 1975-76.
   12. *The Second Land Utilisation Survey of Britain* : 1:25,000 Series, 1964.
   13. *Six-inch National Grid Series,* 1956-69.
   14. *1:10,000-1:10,560 National Grid Series,* 1970-76.

5. *Administrative Areas,* 1974. Another issue, 1979.
   Issued by the Department of the Environment.

6. *United Kingdom Atmospheric Corrosivity Values,* 1986.
   Issued by the Ministry of Agriculture, Fisheries and Food.

Military issues

7. ?Outline edition, without grid but with a graticule at 1° intervals. Not found.
   Perhaps prepared solely for use as the base map to ✤8.

8. GSGS Misc.1698: *Adjustment Curves* : *UK 1936 Datum to UK 1955 Datum,* 1956 [▮Ob].
   With a graticule at 1° intervals on the grey base map, and National Grid at 10 km intervals overprinted in blue.

9. GSGS 4990: *Defence Lands* :
   1. *Service Regions and Districts in Great Britain,* Edition 1-GSGS, 1966 [▮DGI].
   2. *Service Regions & Districts in the United Kingdom,* Edition 2-GSGS, 1968 [▮DGI].

The map was used in preparatory work on the one-inch *Seventh Series* and the 1:50,000 map; for official use (as issued and in skeleton form), and at reduced scales in atlas form.

115. 1:1,250,000 Map of Great Britain (2)

National Grid map (sheet co-ordinates 50 km E to 670 km E, 10 km N to 990 km N). Reduced from the 1:625,000 *Routeplanner,* edition *M* [✤**90**.C.1.2]. The map carries the edition letter *E,* in sequence from those in ✤**114**. There are insets of Shetland and Orkney Islands, Sule Skerry and Stack Skerry, Sula Sgeir and Rona, St Kilda and Boreray, and an extrusion for the Isles of Scilly. With coastal outlines of Ireland and France.

1. Outline edition, 1975.
   1. With National Grid at 10 km intervals.
   2. With National Grid at 100 km intervals.

2. *Index to 1:25 000 First & Second Series* [and] *Outdoor Leisure Maps,* 1984.

---

116. 1:1,500,000 Map of Great Britain, Northern Ireland and Eire

On graticule sheet lines (sheet co-ordinates 50°N to 60°N, 11°W to 2°E). With a graticule at 1° intervals. Reduced from the 1:1,000,000 maps GSGS 2758 [✤**102**], GSGS 4370 [✤**104**.A.6].

The Shetland Islands are inset. There is an extrusion for the Isles of Scilly. With a coastal outline of France.

1. ?Outline edition, 1940. Not found.
   Perhaps made solely for use as the base to ✤2.

2. *Index to Sheets on the 1/25,000 Scale, GSGS No.3906,* 1940 [▮CCS].
   Sheet lines and numbers are overprinted in red. In Great Britain the individual 15 km by 10 km sheets of the 1:20,000 GSGS 2748 are retained in the 1:25,000 training map GSGS 3906 introduced in 1931 [see ✤**109**.13:Great Britain], but their numbering is organised in a wholly different way. They are considered geographical quarters of "full" sheets measuring 30 km by 20 km which are numbered according to their distance east and north of the false origin of the War Office Cassini Grid, with the final "0" removed. Sheet numbers thus increase by 3 eastwards and 2 northwards. The sheet including the Tower of London is 56/18NE. A similar system of sheet numbering for Ireland was implemented, measured from the origin of the War Office Irish Grid. The use of odd numbers for the northings ensured that no sheet number was identical with one for Great Britain. An updated index covering only Great Britain was printed by the Survey Production Centre, Hillside, in September 1945 [▮NLS].

Another map reduced from 1:1,000,000 GSGS 2758 mapping is GSGS 3650 *The North Sea,* a 1:2,000,000 outline map with water in blue produced by the Ordnance Survey in 1916 and 1917 (sheet co-ordinates 48°N to 60°N, 6°W to 12°E) [▮PRO*].

117. 25-mile Geological Map of the British Islands (1)

Constructed on a Minimum Error Conical Projection. Without graticule. Published by the Ordnance Survey. With an extrusion for the Shetland Islands. Publication of the map continued in ✣**118**.

1. Coloured edition.
   1. [First Edition], 1906.
   2. 2nd Edition, 1912.
   3. 3rd Edition, 1939. Reprinted 1948.

2. Outline edition.
   1. [First Edition], 1906.
   2. 2nd Edition, 1912.
   3. ?3rd Edition, 1939. Not found.

3. Index to the one-inch and quarter-inch series.
   1. [First Edition], 1906.
   2. 2nd Edition, 1912.

---

118. 25-mile Geological Map of the British Islands (2)

Constructed on a Minimum Error Conical Projection. With a graticule at 2° intervals, and National Grid co-ordinates in the border at 100 km intervals. Published by the Ordnance Survey. Superseding ✣**117** with sheet lines adjusted to include the Channel Islands, so necessitating an extrusion for Unst.

1. Coloured edition.
   1. 4th Edition, 1957.
   2. 5th Edition, 1969.

2. Outline edition.
   1. 4th Edition, 1957.
   2. 5th Edition, 1969.

3. *Tectonic Map of Great Britain and Northern Ireland,* 1st Edition, 1966.

4. *Smoothed Aeromagnetic Map of Great Britain and Northern Ireland,* 1st Edition, 1970.

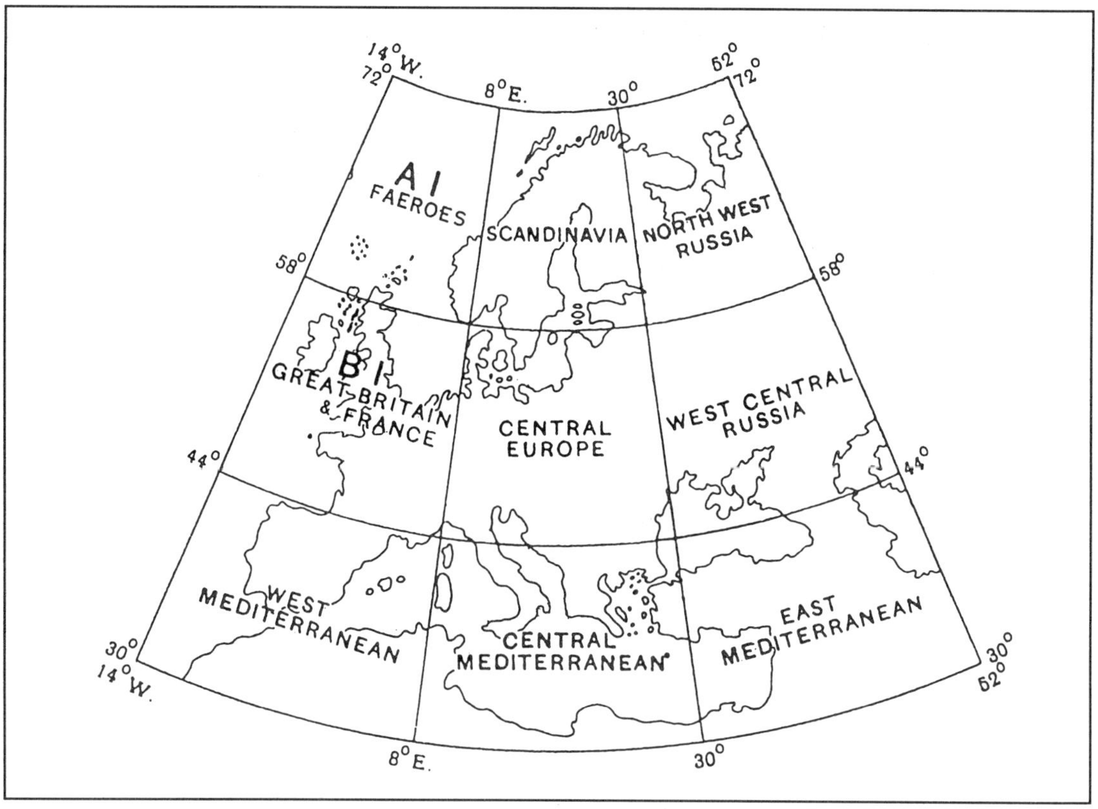

119. 1:2,000,000 Map of Europe

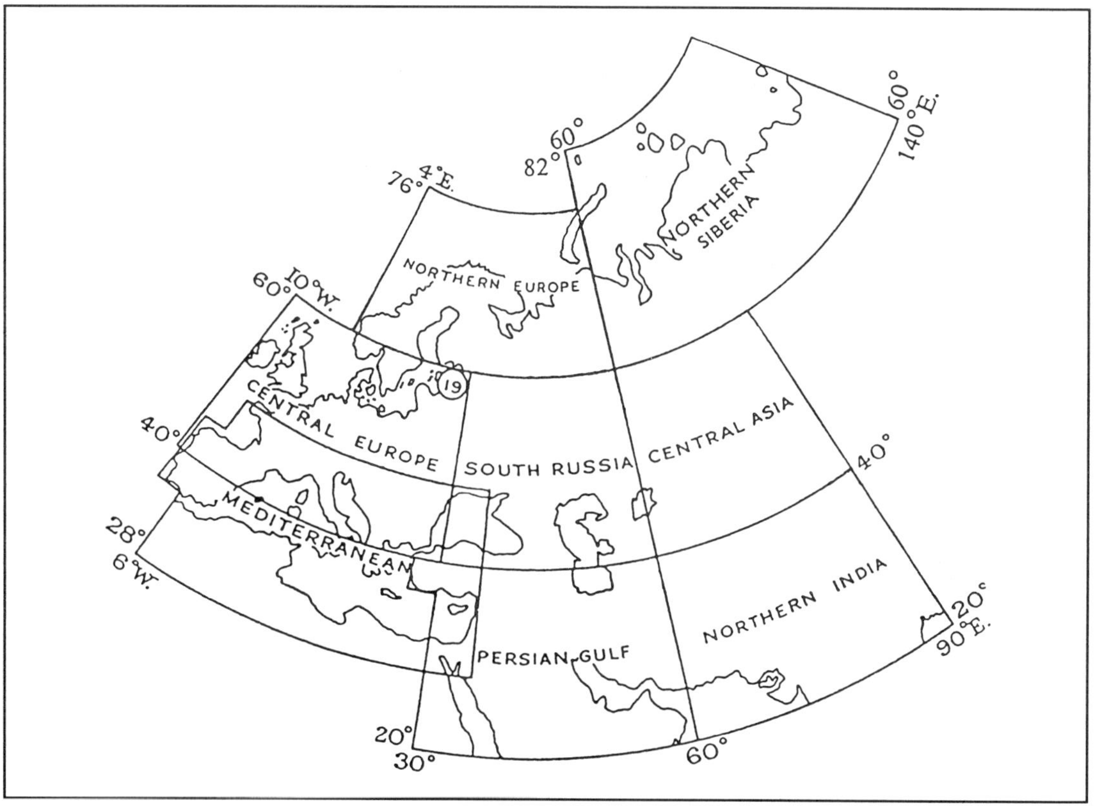

121. 1:4,000,000 Map of Europe, North Africa and Asia

119. 1:2,000,000 Map of Europe

Enlarged from GSGS 2957 1:4,000,000 [**✚121**]. Laid out in nine sheets on graticule sheet lines of 14° in latitude by 22° in longitude, numbered alpha-numerically from the north-west corner at 72°N,14°W. The British Isles are covered by two sheets: A1 *Faeroes,* later *Faeroe Islands,* B1 *Great Britain & France.* With a graticule at 2° intervals. GSGS 4464 issues are coloured, with brown layers. The map was compiled and drawn at the War Office.

1. GSGS 4464: [First Edition].
   1. GSGS issue, 1944. Both sheets.
   2. AMS 6203 (GSGS 4464): AMS 1, 1947. Both sheets.

2. AMS 6203 (GSGS 4464), later 6203 (GSGS 4464): Edition 2-AMS.
   1. Printed by the Army Map Service, 1955. Both sheets.
   2. Printed by the Ordnance Survey, 1958. Both sheets.

3. GSGS 4626: *Civil Aviation Consol Chart,* 1947. Sheet B1 only [▮PRO*].
   Superseded by GSGS 4697 *Consol* and *Decca Navigation Charts (Civil)* (not listed here). This number was allocated in 1950.

---

120. 1:2,186,607 Map of the British Isles

Constructed on Mercator's Projection. The scale is correct at 54°N. With a graticule at 1° intervals. Sheet co-ordinates are 47°N to 61°N, 14°W to 2°E. Additional values measure degrees latitude northwards from the South Pole and degrees longitude eastwards from the 180° meridian (here called the Antimeridian of Greenwich). International Map of the World zones and sectors are identified. One of a series of sheets issued by the Air Ministry entitled *International General Aeronautical Map.* Produced by the War Office, with air information in black, woods in green, towns in red. The French area is mapped.

1. GSGS (Air) 113: *Britain, Provisional* [edition], coloured with black layer, 1924 [▮RGS].

2. GSGS 3803: *Britain, Provisional* [edition], outline with brown layer, 1924 [▮PRO*].

121. 1:4,000,000 Map of Europe, North Africa and Asia

Constructed on the Lambert Conformal Conical Projection, and laid out on graticule sheet lines. Sheet 19 *Central Europe* (sheet co-ordinates 40°N to 60°N, 10°W to 30°E) shows the British Isles, though extrusions north and west are required. With a graticule at 2° intervals and an associated alpha-numeric border. The maps was compiled and drawn at the War Office. The series title occurs irregularly as a map heading.

1. GSGS 2957: First Edition, coloured with brown layers.
   Some issues lack reference to *First Edition.*
   1. GSGS issue, 1936. Sheet 19.
   2. The first AMS edition was a monochrome copy dated 1941 [■Wc].
   3. [Series 1202]: AMS 2, 1943. Sheet 19 [■Wc].
   4. Middle East Drawing and Reproduction issues.
      1. MDR 533/769, 1941. Sheet 19 [■PC].
      2. MDR 533/6662, 1943. Sheet 19 [■Wc].
         Reproduced by 512 Field Survey Company, Royal Engineers.
      3. MDR 533/12052, 1945. Sheet 19 [■Wc].
         Reproduced by 17 Map Reproduction Section, Royal Engineers.
   5. Allied Forces issue: AF 5467, 1944. Sheet 19 [■Wc].
      Reproduced by 11 Map Reproduction Section, Royal Engineers.
   6. Land Forces Headquarters issue: LHQ Misc.6308. Sheet 19 [■Wc].

2. GSGS 2957: [First Edition], coloured.
   1. GSGS issue, 1936. Sheet 19.
   2. AMS 1202 (GSGS 2957): First GSGS Edition, AMS 2, 1952. Sheet 19 [■Wn].
      The map carries a note: *Gradient tints deleted by AMS, 1949.* There may therefore be an earlier issue.

3. GSGS 2957: Edition 2-GSGS, coloured with brown layers, 1954 (issued 1955). Sheet 19.

4. GSGS 2957: Edition 3-GSGS, coloured with brown layers.
   1. Printed by the Ordnance Survey, 1957. Sheet 19.
   2. Printed by the Army Map Service, 1958. Sheet 19 [■Wc].
      The series number of the Army Map Service edition is 1202 (GSGS 2957). The usual green layer at sea level is replaced by yellow.

5. Series 1202: Edition 4-GSGS, coloured with brown layers.
   1. Printed by the Ordnance Survey, 1958. Sheet 19.
   2. Printed by the Army Map Service, 1961. Sheet 19 [■Wc].
      The series number of the Army Map Service edition is 1202 (GSGS 2957).

6. Physical issue, without black plate. Sheet [19] [■NTg].

GSGS 3984 *Europe and the Mediterranean* is a 1:6,000,000 map derived from GSGS 2957 issued in 1939, with sheet lines extended south and east beyond those of Sheet 19. It was also used for index purposes, one version showing the sheet lines of the 1:250,000 and 1:500,000 air series GSGS 3982, 4042 and 4043.

122. Two-inch Map of War Department Land on Salisbury Plain (1)

Enlarged by heliozincography from the contemporary one-inch map, constructed on Cassini's Projection on the origin of Delamere. The War Department property boundary is overprinted. The map was allocated the number IDWO 1471 by the War Office in 1900 (Jewitt 1992).

1. Coloured edition, with contours and horizontal hachures.
   1. With overprint in purple, 1898 [▮PC].
   2. With overprint in red, and revised with additional information, ?1899 [▮PC].
   3. IDWO 1471, 1900. Not found.

---

123. Two-inch Map of War Department Land on Salisbury Plain (2)

Reduced by heliozincography from the 1:2500 map, constructed on Cassini's Projection on the origin of Dunnose. Sheet lines are thus at an angle to those of the preceding map [✣**122**]. The War Department property boundary is overprinted.

1. Coloured edition, with contours and horizontal hachures.
   1. First issue, 1903 [▮BL].
   2. Another edition, revised with additional information, 1905 [▮PC].
   3. Another edition, revised with additional information, 1906 [▮PC].

2. As ✣1, with yellow ground colour outside the War Department area, 1906 (issued 1908). Copy ▮BL. The War Department property is revised to 1908.

---

124. Two-inch Map of War Department Land on Salisbury Plain (3)

Reduced by heliozincography from the 1:2500 map, constructed on Cassini's Projection on the origin of Dunnose. Sheet lines are as ✣**123** with an extension 4½ miles west.

1. Coloured edition, with contours and horizontal hachures. With a 1906 publication date.
   1. With the War Department property revised to 1911 [▮BL].
   2. With the War Department property revised to 1914 [▮PRO (OS 5/55)].

2. As ✣1.1, with yellow ground colour outside the War Department area, 1906 (issued 1911) [▮PC].
   The War Department property is revised to 1911.

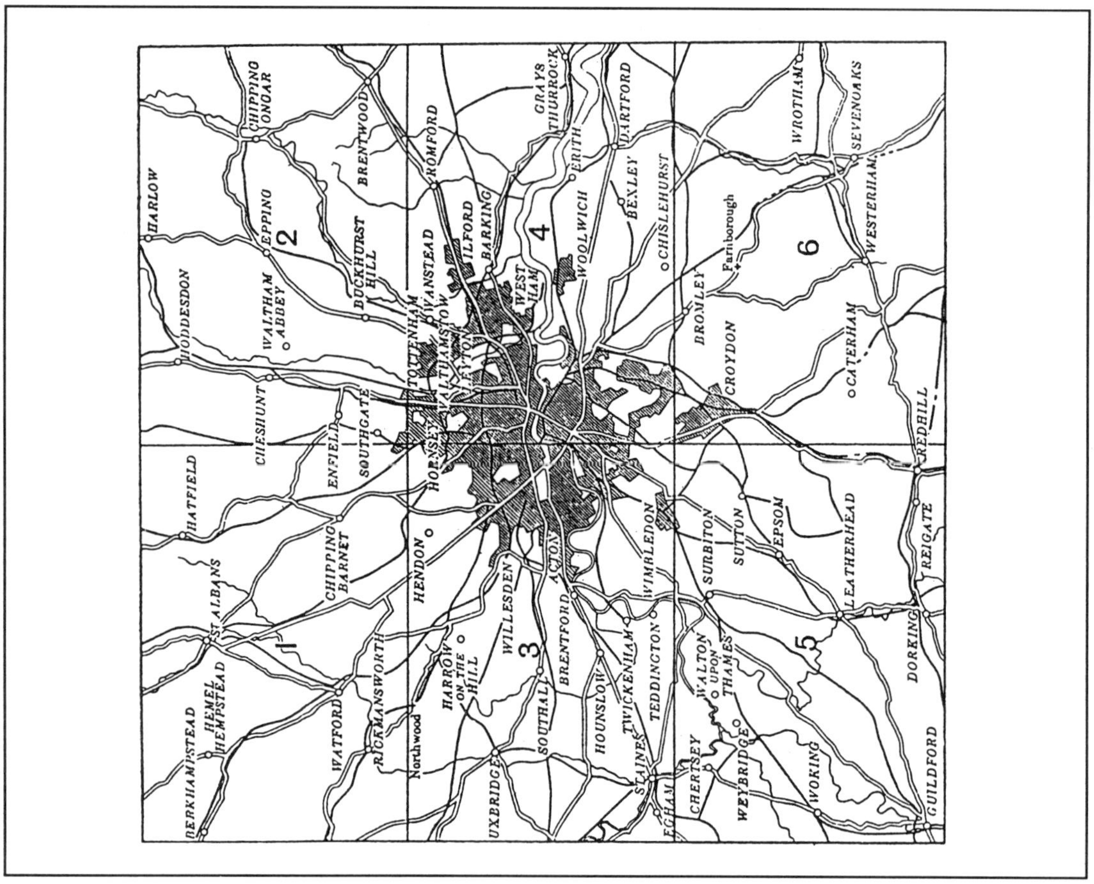

125. Two-inch Map of London (1)

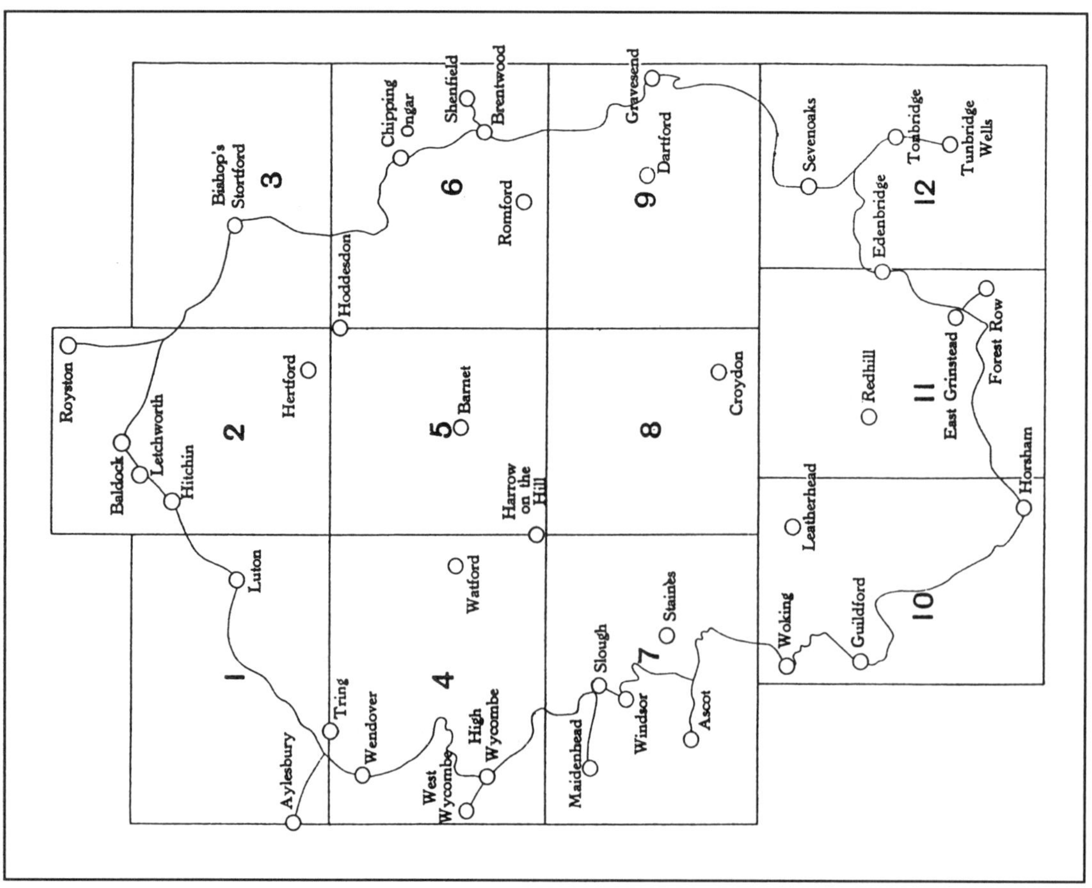

126. Two-inch Map of London (2)

125. Two-inch Map of London (1)

Enlarged from the one-inch *Popular Edition* [**✚10**], and published in six sheets.

1. Outline edition, with water in blue, contours in brown, 1920. All sheets [▮PC].
   Not for public issue, but the official use is not disclosed. Without reference system.

2. *Ministry of Transport Road Map,* 1923. All sheets.
   Base map as ✣1, without contours. With first class roads in red, second class green.

---

126. Two-inch Map of London (2)

Reproduced from the two-inch drawings of the one-inch *Fifth Edition* [**✚11**], and published in twelve sheets. Without reference system. Heading: *Ordnance Survey of Great Britain.*

1. Outline edition, with water in blue, 1935. All sheets.
   Showing the London Passenger Transport Board boundary in blue. All sheets were reprinted in 1941 (Sheet 7 again in 1946), and were still on sale after the war.
   1. With the outline in black. All sheets.
   2. With the outline in grey. All sheets.

---

127. 1:20,000 Map of the County of London

Constructed on Cassini's Projection on the origin of Dunnose. Issued in two sheets (sheet co-ordinates 562 km E to 577 km E to 592 km E, 188 km N to 208 km N). Mapping was transferred from the 1:20,000 Map of Great Britain, GSGS 2748. With War Office Cassini Grid (British System) in purple at 1 km intervals. The map was issued with a gazetteer.

1. GSGS 3786 coloured edition, 1926 [▮BL].

2. GSGS 3786A coloured edition, showing secret information, 1926 [▮BL].
   The locations of police, power and fire stations and military boundaries and installations were overprinted for government use during the General Strike.

---

128. Three-inch Map of London

Constructed on the national Transverse Mercator Projection on the origin of 49°N,2°W, and published in four sections entitled *London NW, London NE, London SW, London SE.* Overall co-ordinates are 1,128,900 yards E to 1,161,300 yards E, 1,294,400 yards N to 1,315,800 yards N. With National Yard Grid at 1000 yard intervals in red. Mapping was reduced and transferred from the 1:20,000 map on Cassini's Projection [**✚127**]. With a border applied only to the outer edges to facilitate the mounting of the map whole.

1. Coloured edition, 1933. All sheets. Issued with a gazetteer.

2. District map.
   Central London, 1934 [▮PC].
   For the fifth international congress of the International Federation of Surveyors.

129. Two-inch Map of the Isles of Scilly

Constructed on the national Transverse Mercator Projection on the origin of 49°N,2°W. On National Yard Grid sheet lines (sheet co-ordinates 650,000 yards E to 670,000 yards E, 1,115,000 yards N to 1,130,000 yards N). With National Yard Grid at 5000 yard intervals. Newly drawn, and produced from 1932 revision. Considered an unnumbered member of the One-inch *Fifth (Relief) Edition* [**✢11**.1]. Heading: *Ordnance Survey of Great Britain.*

1. Special District (Relief) Map, 1933.

2. Special District (Relief) Map, 1933 (reissued 1945).
   The National Yard Grid co-ordinates are cleared and replaced by an alpha-numeric system. Superseded by 1:25,000 maps, 1964, 1982, 1996 (not listed here).

Channel Islands

There is no Ordnance Survey mapping of the Channel Islands as a group except in French, European or World series. See **✢44** (GSGS 4249 1:100,000 France), **✢45** (GSGS 2738 1:250,000 France), **✢46** (GSGS 3982 1:250,000 Europe (Air)), **✢80**, **81** (GSGS 4072 1:500,000 Europe (Air) and GSGS 4649 1:500,000 Europe ICAO), **✢101** (1:1,000,000 International Map of the World), **✢102** (GSGS 2758 1:1,000,000 Europe).

Mapping of Alderney, Sark and the smaller islands is on scales too large to be considered here. Also disregarded is 1:25,000 mapping of Jersey, and all mapping larger than the four-inch scale.

---

130. Two-inch Map of Guernsey

Surveyed in 1898-99 and constructed on Cassini's Projection on the origin of Fort George. Contours are on the black plate. Without graticule.

1. *Advance Edition,* outline with coloured main roads and water tint, 1901 [▮BL].
   With a neat line border.

2. Outline edition, with coloured main roads and water tint, 1902.
   With a graduated border. The map was reprinted in 1905 with a decorative title panel, then ten or so times more to 1932.

3. IDWO 1885: *Map to accompany Guernsey Defence Scheme.*
   1. First issue, 1904. Also reissued updated to 1906 (?1907) and 1908.
      In *Guernsey Defence Scheme,* London, War Office A.900, A.1184, A.1265 [▮PRO (WO 33/313, 33/427, 33/474)].
   2. Reissued 1911. Further updated to 1911 [▮DGI].

M. Military issue overprinted with 1000 yard military grid in purple

1. Outline edition, with coloured main roads and water tint, issued 1928 [▮BL].

131. Three-inch Map of Guernsey (1)

Constructed on Cassini's Projection on the origin of Fort George. With a 1000 yard grid unique to the map (sheet co-ordinates 0 yards E to 17,000 yards E, 0 yards N to 14,000 yards N), the false co-ordinates of the Fort George origin being 13,000 yards E, 4000 yards N. Mapping was newly drawn and produced from 1933 revision.

1. Coloured edition, with layers, 1934. Reprinted 1946.

M. Military issue with Lambert Zone 1 Grid at 1 km intervals

The grid is in black, numbered in red.

1. GSGS 4205: First Edition, 1942 [▮DGI].
   The map is coloured, without the layers of the civilian map. First issues carry the legend *Regridded and Printed at the OS, 1942.*

   The following dependent issue is recorded:
   1. GSGS 4205: *Enemy Defences Information as at 8 Aug 44,* 1944 [▮Ob: photostat].

132. Three-inch Map of Guernsey (2)

Constructed on the Transverse Mercator Projection on the origin of 0°Lat,3°W. On Universal Transverse Mercator Grid sheet lines (sheet co-ordinates 521 km E to 538 km E, 5473 km N to 5486 km N). With Universal Transverse Mercator Grid at 1 km intervals. Mapping was transferred from the previous map on Cassini's Projection [✚**131**].

1. Coloured edition, with layers, 1958. Another edition, 1966.

2. Coloured edition, published 1966.
   Produced by BKS Survey Technical Services, Coleraine.

Military issues

3. M824 coloured edition, with layers.
   1. Edition 2-GSGS, 1958.
      With publication information overprinted in blue.
   2. Edition 3-GSGS, 1966.
      With publication and grid information overprinted in red.

   Superseded by Editions 4-GSGS (1975) and 5-GSGS (1986) at 1:25,000 (not listed here).

An earlier map of Guernsey to employ the Universal Transverse Mercator Grid was GSGS Misc.1768, a 1:50,000 map drawn in 1957 by the 135 Survey Engineer Regiment. The 1934 map [✚**131**] was its source. It is coloured without layers (sheet co-ordinates 522 km E to 537 km E, 5473 km N to 5486 km N). Edition 1-GSGS was published by Military Survey in 1957.

133. Two-inch Map of Jersey

On graticule sheet lines (sheet co-ordinates 49°8'N to 49°16'N, 2°16'W to 1°59'W).

A. Two-inch maps

Produced from "rapid survey" by No.3 Survey Section, Royal Engineers, 1901.

1. *Military Survey,* outline with water in blue, contours in brown, 1902.
   Without graticule. The *Military Survey* heading is cleared from reprints.

2. *Jersey Defence Scheme.*
   1. IDWO 1767, 1903. Also editions updated to 1906 and 1908.
      In *Jersey Defence Scheme,* London, War Office A.818, A.1088, A.1293 [▮PRO (WO 33/281, 33/297, 33/479)].
   2. GSGS 1767, 1911 [▮DGI]. Further updated to 1911.

With a graticule at 1' intervals

Surveyed by No.2 Survey Section, Royal Engineers, 1913, and constructed on the origin of South Hill Battery.

3. Coloured edition, with layers and hill shading.
   1. First issue, 1914.
   2. Revised and reprinted 1933 (published 1934). Reprinted 1947.

4. Coloured edition, 1958, published by States of Jersey, revised by BKS Air Survey Ltd.

M. Military issues overprinted with 1000 yard military grid

1. Coloured edition, with layers and hill shading.
   1. With the grid in red, [no military issue date], ?issued 1923 [▮PC].
   2. GSGS 3967: [First Edition], with the grid in purple, 1934 [▮DGI].

2. GSGS 3967A outline edition, with water in blue, contours in brown. Not found.

Military issues with Lambert Zone 1 Grid at 1 km intervals

The grid is black, numbered in red.

3. GSGS 3967 coloured edition, without the hill colouring of the civilian map.
   1. Second Edition, *regridded and printed OS,* 1942 [▮DGI].
   2. Third Edition, 1943 (issued 1944) [▮BL].
   3. AMS M824 (GSGS 3967): AMS 1, 1944 [▮Wn].

   The following issue dependent on ✣M.3.2 is recorded:
   4. *Enemy Defences Information as at 12 Aug '44,* 1944 [▮Ob: photostat].
      Issued by G-2 (Int.) Div. SHAEF.

B. Four-inch map

Enlarged from the two-inch map [✣A.3.2], and printed in separate west and east sections. With a graticule at 1' intervals. The southern neat line is relocated over 6½ miles north.

1. Outline edition, 1934. Reprinted 1945.

APPENDICES

Comparative one-inch sheet numbers

1. *Old Series* to *New Series*

Old	*New*	*Old*	*New*	*Old*	*New*	*Old*	*New*
91 NW	58	95 SE	55	101 SW	28	106 SW	18
91 NE	59	96 NW	42	101 SE	29	106 SE	19
91 SW	66	96 NE	43	102 NW	24	107 NE	11
91 SE	67	96 SW	52	102 NE	25	107 SW	16
92 NW	60	96 SE	53	102 SW	30	107 SE	17
92 NE	61	97 NW	40	102 SE	31	108 NE	5
92 SW	68	97 NE	41	103 NW	26	108 SW	7
92 SE	69	97 SW	50	103 NE	27	108 SE	8
93 NW	62	97 SE	51	103 SW	32	109 NW	6
93 NE	63	98 NW	38	103 SE	33	109 SW	9
93 SW	70	98 NE	39	104 SW	34	109 SE	10
93 SE	71	98 SW	48	104 SE	35	110 NW	1
94 NW	64	98 SE	49	105 NW	14	110 NE	2
94 NE	65	99 NE	37	105 NE	15	110 SW	3
94 SW	72	99 SE	47	105 SW	20	110 SE	4
94 SE	73	100	*see below*	105 SE	21		
95 NW	44	101 NW	22	106 NW	12		
95 SW	54	101 NE	23	106 NE	13		

Old Series Sheet 100 was renumbered *New Series* Sheet 36/45/46/56/57.

2. *New Series* to *Old Series*

New	*Old*	*New*	*Old*	*New*	*Old*	*New*	*Old*
1	110 NW	20	105 SW	39	98 NE	58	91 NW
2	110 NE	21	105 SE	40	97 NW	59	91 NE
3	110 SW	22	101 NW	41	97 NE	60	92 NW
4	110 SE	23	101 NE	42	96 NW	61	92 NE
5	108 NE	24	102 NW	43	96 NE	62	93 NW
6	109 NW	25	102 NE	44	95 NW	63	93 NE
7	108 SW	26	103 NW	45	*see above*	64	94 NW
8	108 SE	27	103 NE	46	*see above*	65	94 NE
9	109 SW	28	101 SW	47	99 SE	66	91 SW
10	109 SE	29	101 SE	48	98 SW	67	91 SE
11	107 NE	30	102 SW	49	98 SE	68	92 SW
12	106 NW	31	102 SE	50	97 SW	69	92 SE
13	106 NE	32	103 SW	51	97 SE	70	93 SW
14	105 NW	33	103 SE	52	96 SW	71	93 SE
15	105 NE	34	104 SW	53	96 SE	72	94 SW
16	107 SW	35	104 SE	54	95 SW	73	94 SE
17	107 SE	36	*see above*	55	95 SE		
18	106 SW	37	99 NE	56	*see above*		
19	106 SE	38	98 NW	57	*see above*		

3. *Isle of Lewis* to *Scotland First Edition*

Lewis	*Scotland*	*Lewis*	*Scotland*	*Lewis*	*Scotland*	*Lewis*	*Scotland*
1	111	3	104	5	106	7	99
2	112	4	105	6	98		

4. *Ireland quarter-sheet* to *small-sheet numbers*

The only quarter-sheet numbers listed here are those whose use is recorded or suspected.

Quarter	*Small*	*Quarter*	*Small*	*Quarter*	*Small*
1 SW	1	38 SE	143	49 SW	183
1 SE	2	40 NE	137	49 SE	184
2 NW	3	40 SW	146	50 NW	174
2 NE	4	40 SE	147	50 NE	175
2 SW	9	41 NW	138	50 SW	185
2 SE	10	41 NE	139	50 SE	186
3 NW	5	41 SW	148	51 NW	176
3 NE	6	41 SE	149	51 NE	177
3 SW	11	42 SE	160	51 SW	187
5 SE	22	43 NW	150	51 SE	188
6 NW	15	43 NE	151	52 NW	178
6 NE	16	?43 SW	161	52 NE	179
6 SW	23	?43 SE	162	52 SW	189
30 SE	110	?44 NW	152	53 NW	180
31 NW	101	44 SW	163	53 NE	181
31 NE	102	44 SE	164	54 NE	190
31 SW	111	45 NE	155	54 SE	197
31 SE	112	45 SW	165	55 NW	191
35 NE	119	45 SE	166	55 NE	192
?35 SW	127	46 NW	156	55 SW	198
35 SE	128	46 NE	157	55 SE	199
36 NW	120	46 SW	167	56 NW	193
36 NE	121	46 SE	168	56 NE	194
36 SW	129	47 NW	158	56 SW	200
36 SE	130	47 NE	159	56 SE	201
37 NE	131	47 SW	169	57 NW	195
37 SW	140	47 SE	170	57 NE	196
37 SE	141	48 NE	171	57 SW	202
38 NW	132	48 SE	182	58 NW	203
38 NE	133	?49 NW	172	58 NE	204
38 SW	142	49 NE	173	59 NW	205

A summary list of military map serial numbers

This is a summary list of the military map numbers and sections of the book where they may be found. Those marked * are noted, not listed. Subordinate numbers (eg GSGS 4620A) are ignored here. GSGS numbers are preceded by the earlier designations IBWO, IDWO, TSGS. Also listed are GSGS Misc., OR and Air series. United States Army Map Service (AMS) numbers appeared on some American printings of British military maps. National series are prefixed "M" in Europe, European series by "6", World series by "1". The system evolved into the NATO Standard Series Designation (SSD). Also listed are AWS (ID), AWS (CB), IDAM, MBAM (later ADI (Maps)), AF, LHQ and MDR numbers. The abbreviations are explained on page 240.

GSGS (IBWO/IDWO/TSGS)

Number	*Section*
IBWO 115	3
IDWO 1320	84*, 93
IDWO 1471	122*
IDWO 1767	133
IDWO 1885	130
TSGS 2028	94
TSGS 2360	94
GSGS 2631	52*
GSGS 2733	45
GSGS 2738	45
GSGS 2748	109*, 127*
GSGS 2758	102
GSGS 2838	109
GSGS 2861	53
GSGS 2935	109
GSGS 2957	121
GSGS 3024	102
GSGS 3036	109*
GSGS 3650	116*
GSGS 3710	109
GSGS 3721	109
GSGS 3786	127
GSGS 3787	105
GSGS 3788	109
GSGS 3803	120
GSGS 3900	109
GSGS 3901	109
GSGS 3906	109*, 116*
GSGS 3907	10-12, 19
GSGS 3908	18
GSGS 3912	109
GSGS 3917	27
GSGS 3933	54
GSGS 3942	73
GSGS 3943	25, 26
GSGS 3950	54
GSGS 3955	87
GSGS 3957	56
GSGS 3958	60
GSGS 3965	102
GSGS 3967	133
GSGS 3982	46, 70, 121*
GSGS 3984	121*
GSGS 3993	89
GSGS 3994	12
GSGS 4040	44*
GSGS 4042	47, 121*
GSGS 4072	80, 81
GSGS 4127	27*, 39
GSGS 4136	28
GSGS 4142	69
GSGS 4159	36
GSGS 4167	41
GSGS 4205	131
GSGS 4249	44
GSGS 4250	44*
GSGS 4338	71
GSGS 4369	83
GSGS 4370	104
GSGS 4395	89
GSGS 4464	119
GSGS 4620	10, 19, 20
GSGS 4622	108
GSGS 4626	119
GSGS 4628	56
GSGS 4639	18
GSGS 4646	103
GSGS 4648	108
GSGS 4649	81
GSGS 4650	60
GSGS 4653	105
GSGS 4676	89*
GSGS 4679	36
GSGS 4692	19
GSGS 4695	107
GSGS 4697	119*
GSGS 4715	78
GSGS 4735	56
GSGS 4736	61
GSGS 4782	81
GSGS 4813	89
GSGS 4830	79*
GSGS 4857	56
GSGS 4858	60
GSGS 4859	81
GSGS 4863	56
GSGS 4864	60
GSGS 4865	71
GSGS 4866	90*
GSGS 4941	63
GSGS 4954	20
GSGS 4956	90
GSGS 4959	20
GSGS 4965	20
GSGS 4968	20
GSGS 4970	105*
GSGS 4971	105*
GSGS 4974	20
GSGS 4976	20
GSGS 4982	60
GSGS 4987	20
GSGS 4988	20
GSGS 4989	20
GSGS 4990	114
GSGS 4993	105*
GSGS 5025	20
GSGS 5030	63
GSGS 5033	90
GSGS 5034	20
GSGS 5038	90
GSGS 5065	20
GSGS 5066	20
GSGS 5068	20
GSGS 5076	20
GSGS 5099	77
GSGS 5101	77
GSGS 5102	32
GSGS 5135	32
GSGS 5149	32
GSGS 5154	81*
GSGS 5162	63
GSGS 5169	20
GSGS 5172	20
GSGS 5201	105*
GSGS 5215	21
GSGS 5235	21
GSGS 5249	32
GSGS 5256	21
GSGS 5288	90
GSGS 5295	21
GSGS 5309	34
GSGS 5344	63
GSGS 5352	63
GSGS 5383	32
GSGS 5385	32
GSGS 5407	21*
GSGS 5670	21
GSGS 5822	21

US Army Map Service,* later *NATO Standard Series Designation,* to *GSGS series numbers

AMS	*GSGS*
1202	2957
1301	4646, 2758
1404	4830
6203	4464
6401	4782
6402	4830
M320	4370
M321	4370
M322	Section 90
M325	3993
M325	Section 90
M404	4072
M422	4369
M502	3982
M503	4042
M521	3957, 4628
M5213	4650
M5218	Section 77*
M522	4142, 4338
M523	Section 63
M524	3958, 4650
M524	Section 72
M561	2738
M621	Section 36
M661	4249
M721	3907
M722	4620, 4692
M723	Section 32
M724	3908, 4639
M725	4692
M726	Section 21
M728	Section 34
M824	3967
M824	Section 132
M924	4692

These AMS numbers were allocated, but not all were used. For series numbers for which there is no comparative GSGS number a reference is provided to the section of this book where details may be found.

GSGS (Air)

Number	*Section*
113	120
114	54
117	54
5010	46*
5015	70

GSGS Miscellaneous

Number	*Section*
Misc.299	56
Misc.302	10
Misc.363	10
Misc.364	10
Misc.365	56
Misc.406	18
Misc.412	105*
Misc.421	18
Misc.433	19
Misc.490	19, 56
Misc.491	19
Misc.501	89
Misc.502	89
Misc.505	89
Misc.506	89
Misc.507	89
Misc.509	104
Misc.516	10
Misc.517	89
Misc.1513	19
Misc.1519	36
Misc.1522	19, 20
Misc.1560	19
Misc.1561	56
Misc.1563	56
Misc.1575	81
Misc.1585	19
Misc.1598	105*
Misc.1605	19
Misc.1618	19
Misc.1622	19, 20
Misc.1636	89, 90
Misc.1663	19, 56
Misc.1698	114
Misc.1709	56
Misc.1764	20
Misc.1768	132*
Misc.1788	105*
Misc.1820	90
Misc.1863	20
Misc.1881	19
Misc.1974	20
Misc.1999	20
Misc.2000	20
Misc.2057	32
Misc.2132	20
Misc.2133	20
Misc.2134	20

GSGS Office Reference

Number	*Section*
OR 209	109
OR 1527	12
OR 1826	19
OR 5189	27*

Admiralty War Staff Intelligence Division

Number	*Section*
ID 1054	53
ID 1083	53
ID 1084	53
ID 1090	53
CB 1235	109

Intelligence Staff Air Ministry

Number	*Section*
IDAM 1	109

Map Branch Air Ministry

Number	*Section*
MBAM 3761	54, 59, 70*
MBAM 3798	54
ADI.AM 7528	105

Allied Forces

Number	*Section*
AF 5467	121
AF 7308	83

Land Forces Headquarters

Number	*Section*
Misc.6308	121

Middle East Drawing and Reproduction

Number	*Section*
MDR 533	121
MDR 653	83

Abbreviations

Most of the abbreviations that appear here are in general use, though over the years the precise form of their punctuation has evolved. For instance "GSGS" has seen various forms from the full G.S.,G.S. to the total absence of punctuation in use today. In most cases here abbreviations have been adopted which avoid punctuation. Some will be found on maps rather than within the text. For abbreviations used in bibliographic citations (such as BPP, IPP, OSPR, OSR) see the list of source material on page 248. Some of the library sigla have been constructed by the compiler. The ***symbols*** used may be found on a grey panel that irregularly appears throughout the book, for example on page 2.

ADI (Maps)	Assistant Directorate of Intelligence, Maps, Air Ministry
AF	Allied Forces
AM	Air Ministry
AMS	Army Map Service, United States Army
ARP	Air Raid Precautions
AWS (ID)	Admiralty War Staff (Intelligence Division)
BAOR	British Army of the Rhine
BGS	British Geological Survey
CAA	Civil Aviation Authority
CB	?Confidential Book
CCF	Combined Cadet Force
CR	Central Registry, Ordnance Survey
FC	Flying Corps
GS	Geological Survey of Great Britain / England and Wales / Scotland
GSGS	Geographical Section, General Staff
GSI	Geological Survey of Ireland, Dublin
GSNI	Geological Survey of Northern Ireland, Belfast
IBWO	Intelligence Branch, War Office
ICAO	International Civil Aviation Organization
IDAM	Intelligence Division, Air Ministry
IDWO	Intelligence Division, War Office
IGS	Institute of Geological Sciences
IMW	International Map of the World
LHQ	Land Forces Headquarters
M	NATO Standard Series Designation prefix for the European Regional Area
M	MCE(RE) suffix on military map print codes since c.1972
MBAM	Map Branch, Air Ministry
MCE(RE)	Mapping and Charting Establishment, Royal Engineers
MDR	Middle East Drawing and Reproduction
Misc.	Miscellaneous. Misc, (Misc), (Misc.) may also be found
OR	Office Reference
OS	Ordnance Survey (of Great Britain / England / England and Wales / Scotland / Ireland before 1922), London, Southampton, Chessington, Dublin
OSI	Ordnance Survey of Ireland (from 1922), Dublin
OSNI	Ordnance Survey of Northern Ireland, Belfast
OTC	Officers' Training Corps
PTA	Primary Training Area
R	42 Survey Engineer Regiment suffix on military map print codes since c.1972
RA	Royal Artillery
RAF	Royal Air Force
S	Ordnance Survey suffix on military map print codes since c.1972
SHAEF	Supreme Headquarters Allied Expeditionary Force
SPC(RE)	Survey Production Centre, Royal Engineers
TM	Transverse Mercator
TSGS	Topographical Section, General Staff
USAF	United States Air Force
USAREUR	United States Army Europe
UTM	Universal Transverse Mercator
WD	War Department

Library sigla

ALm	Military Museum, Aldershot
Bg	School of Geography, University of Birmingham
Bl	Department of Geology, University of Birmingham
BFq	Department of Geography, The Queen's University, Belfast
BL	Map Library, The British Library, London
BSg	Department of Geography, University of Bristol
Cu	Map Room, Cambridge University Library
CCS	Coll. The Charles Close Society, Map Room, Cambridge University Library
Dm	Military Archives, Dublin
Dn	National Library of Ireland, Dublin
Dna	National Archives, Dublin
Do	Oireachtas, Dublin
Dtc	Map Library, Trinity College, Dublin
Dtf	Freeman Library, Department of Geography, Trinity College, Dublin
Dtl	Department of Geology, Trinity College, Dublin
DGI	Directorate of Geographical Information
DRg	Department of Geography, University of Durham
Ebgs	British Geological Survey, Edinburgh
Eg	Department of Geography, University of Edinburgh
Eu	University Library, University of Edinburgh
EH	English Heritage, lately National Monuments Record Centre, the public archive of the Royal Commission on the Historical Monuments of England, Swindon
EXg	Department of Geography, University of Exeter
GSI	Geological Survey of Ireland, Dublin
GSNI	Geological Survey of Northern Ireland, Belfast
Lgh	Guildhall Library, London
Lk	Liddell Hart Collection, King's College, University of London
Lnm	National Maritime Museum, London
Lraf	Royal Air Force Museum, Hendon, London
LDg	Department of Geography, University of Leeds
LVg	Department of Geography, University of Liverpool
Mg	Department of Geography, University of Manchester
Nbgs	British Geological Survey, Keyworth, Nottingham
Ng	Department of Geography, University of Nottingham
NLS	Map Library, National Library of Scotland, Edinburgh
NLW	Map Department, National Library of Wales, Aberystwyth
NTg	Department of Geography, University of Newcastle-upon-Tyne
NYp	New York Public Library
Ob	Map Room, Bodleian Library, Oxford
Og	School of Geography, University of Oxford
OS	Ordnance Survey, Southampton
OSI	Ordnance Survey of Ireland, Dublin
OSNI	Ordnance Survey of Northern Ireland, Belfast
PC	Private collection
PRO	Public Record Office, London Maps currently (1998) in the process of transfer from DGI are marked PRO*
Rg	Department of Geography, University of Reading
RGS	Map Room, Royal Geographical Society, London
RML	Record Map Library, Ordnance Survey, Southampton
Sg	Department of Geography, University of Sheffield
Wc	Geography and Map Division, Library of Congress, Washington DC
Wn	National Archives and Records Administration, Washington DC

Grids and squaring systems

The enormously complex business of realising on a flat piece of paper an image of part of the Earth's surface requires a mass of formulae that will convert latitude and longitude values, or geographical co-ordinates, to *x,y* rectangular co-ordinates. To quote Brian Adams yet again "In modern times the projection co-ordinates have a dual purpose, serving also as the basis of a reference system; *x* and *y* become easting and northing, co-ordinate lines are drawn as a grid on the face of the map, and usually form its sheet lines." Thus most modern grids and squaring systems, which may be no more than unnumbered grids, lie parallel and perpendicular to the sheet lines of the maps to which they relate. Exceptional are those on Cassini's Projection which carry the War Office Cassini Grid. These are rarely square with each other because mostly different origins were adopted for projection and grid: that of the projection was usually at Delamere while that of the grid was at Dunnose on the Isle of Wight. But in general, the origin of the grid and projection share the innate connection that they lie at one and the same point. It could therefore seem sensible to calculate the values of a grid from the vertical and horizontal lines running through it - the central meridian and a perpendicular through the origin. However, since this would mean negative values for anywhere west or south of the origin, in practice grid values are calculated from false origins to the west and south of the land mass concerned. I append brief notes on the grids noted in this book.

War Office Cassini Grid

Grid values are calculated from a false origin 500,000 metres west and 100,000 metres south of the true origin of the grid at Dunnose. Its early form, the British System, was introduced in 1918 for use on the 1:20,000 map GSGS 2748 and extended to the one-inch in 1923. A 1000 metre (or 1 km) grid was organised into 50 by 50 km squares subdivided into 10 by 10 km sectors each given one of 25 letter designations. Any grid reference inevitably repeated at 50 km intervals. To accommodate the need for referencing smaller scale mapping, the Modified British System was adopted in 1931, wherein the single governing letter controlled an area 100 by 100 km. Thus a reference prefixed by a single letter did not repeat inside a distance of 500 km. This was adequate for one-inch maps, and only on quarter-inch and ten-mile maps was a superior second letter reference (ensuring no repetition inside 5000 km) relevant. This appeared in marginal calculations and on the face of ten-mile and some quarter-inch maps.

National Yard Grid

Introduced in 1931, this was calculated in yards from a false origin 1,000,000 yards west and 1,000,000 yards south of the origin of the Transverse Mercator Projection from which British maps using this projection were derived, at 49°N,2°W. Grid lines were printed across maps at convenient intervals, but because there were no numeric or literal controls as were used in the War Office Cassini Grid, all references had to be given in yards, in full.

National Grid

From a false origin south-west of the Isles of Scilly (400,000 metres west and 100,000 metres north of the origin of the Transverse Mercator Projection from which British maps using this projection were derived, at 49°N,2°W), the National Grid was from its first use in 1942 divided into one hundred primary squares each of 100 by 100 km, numbered from 00 in the south west to 99 in the north east. This 1000 by 1000 km square conveniently covered the British mainland, and the northern isles were accommodated by the addition of a prefatory "N" to an extension of this numbering system. In order to conform with the National Grid as adopted by the War Office, these numeric 100 by 100 km references were in 1950-51 replaced by pairs of letters, the first letter designating a 500 by 500 km square and the second a 100 by 100 km subdivision of that. These run in the traditional north-west to south-east sequence.

National Grid (Military System)

From the outset full National Grid references in the military system were prefixed by a pair of letters to define the 100 by 100 km squares and the greater 500 by 500 km squares beyond them, at odds with the civilian system which defined these squares by two-digit prefixes. The civilian system of numerical values was the one printed on Ordnance Survey maps, and in order to avoid confusion, these were blocked out by overprinting on copies designated for the military. Both letters always appeared overprinted on the map face of quarter-inch and smaller scale military maps, but on one-inch maps the single (second) letter prefix was deemed adequate control of the 100 by 100 km squares, since these could not repeat at less than 500 km (at which point the other letter would take effect) and therefore beyond the limits of any sheet. Such was the practice on War Office Editions and pre-1952 First Edition-GSGS issues of the standard topographical series. A degree of consistency was achieved from 1951 as the civilian system was converted from numerical to the military's two-letter references for 100 by 100 km squares; and as sheets were published by the Ordnance Survey carrying the new information, new GSGS editions were issued carrying new War Office publication dates. They were designated Second Edition-GSGS for the one-inch, and Fifth Edition-GSGS for the quarter-inch standard topographical series. Single letter references continued to be used on the map face of one-inch maps. Aspects of civilian marginalia had been blocked out on military issue sheets as long as it was inconsistent with the military system; after the change all except sheet prices was left visible. Uniformity of referencing was not achieved until 1981 with the adoption of the dual civil-military specification for the 1:50,000 series.

War Office Irish Grid and Irish National Grid

The grid used by the War Office over Ireland is superficially similar to the National Grid used there today, but being constructed on a different projection was different on the ground. The military grid was modified by 1931, in line with the British. Its false origin is 199,990 metres west and 249,975 metres south of the Irish true origin of Bonne's Projection at 53°30'N,8°W, and the false origin of the Irish National Grid is 200,000 metres west and 250,000 metres south of the same geographical origin. In each case the island is contained within a system of 100 by 100 km squares arranged in five rows of five, each defined by a single letter. Grid references on one-inch sheets do not require letter references, but they appear on half-inch and smaller scale maps, and British Military Survey uses them even at 1:50,000. Indeed a second letter "I" may appear as a prefix, presumably to avoid any possible confusion between Irish and British map references. Note that the Irish National Grid may be referred to in Great Britain, or even Northern Ireland, as the Irish Transverse Mercator (or TM) Grid.

Irish 5000 yard grid

In 1940 the Department of Defence in Dublin introduced its own military grid, for use on the half-inch map [**✢39**.M.3] and a specially produced one-inch map [**✢29**]. It was graduated at 5000 yard intervals, and was overprinted in red. No system of letter references controlling the numerical values seems to have been used. Brian Adams calculated the location of the false origin of the grid "as at or near the south-west corner of the one-inch sheet line system, south of Sheet 197 and west of 203........On Bonne's Projection of Ireland the western neat line of the original one-inch Sheet 197 is 597,280 feet west of the true (Lough Ree) origin and the southern neat line of Sheet 203 is 787,960 feet south. Whence, if the false origin of the yard grid were located precisely at the south-west corner of the one-inch system, the co-ordinates of the true origin would be 199,093·333....yards east, 262,653·333....yards north. We cannot guess whether they would have left them like that, or knocked off the thirds, or added two-thirds, or even rounded them up to the next ten...."

Military grids on Channel Island maps

The earliest military grids used on maps of Jersey and Guernsey were independent 1000 yard grids. The Jersey grid was calculated from a false origin 60,000 yards west and 60,000 yards south of the true origin at South Hill Battery, while for Guernsey a false origin was adopted 29,320 yards west and 49,710 yards south of the true origin at Fort George. There is currently no explanation available for these figures.

The Second World War started with no general military grid available in northern France, a situation which on Channel Islands mapping was rectified in 1942 when the Lambert Grid, a French metric grid, came into use. This was divided into three zones, numbered 1, 2, 3 north to south, each zone divided into lettered 100 by 100 km squares. The reference systems were coloured respectively red, purple and red. The Channel Islands were covered by the ***Lambert Zone 1 Grid***, Guernsey in sector "N", Jersey in sector "S". The origin of the grid was the intersection of the parallel 55 grades north with the longitude of the Paris Observatory (2°20'14") [NB a Grade is the one-hundredth part of a quadrant, and may be converted to degrees by multiplying by 0·9].

Similarly to the National Grid (see page viii) the ***Universal Transverse Mercator Grid*** provides co-ordinates for the construction of maps as well as a reference system. It was devised (in association with the Universal Polar Stereographic Grid) to form the basis for consistent world-wide topographical mapping, with minimal distortion, and was first used in the late 1940s. The world is divided into vertical zones, each six degrees of longitude wide. Mapping and gridding of each zone are constructed on the Transverse Mercator Projection on the zone's own central meridian. False co-ordinates of every zone origin are 500,000 metres east, 0 metres north for the northern hemisphere and 500,000 metres east, 10,000,000 metres north for the southern hemisphere. The Universal Transverse Mercator is rarely used for mapping of the British Isles, but regularly appears on British military maps elsewhere in the world, including the Channel Islands. The origin of mapping in this sector is 0°Lat,3°W, Channel Island references being located in 100 by 100 km square "WV" in the grid zone designated "30U". Maps carrying the Universal Transverse Mercator Grid listed in this book may be found in **✢20, 21, 44, 45, 47, 48, 79, 81, 90, 102, 103, 132**. For a fuller description see the War Office *Manual of Map Reading*, London, HMSO, 1956.

Sheet numbering of World and European Series

The sheet numbering system of the 1:1,000,000 *International Map of the World* [**✢101, 102**] is organised alpha-numerically in graticule sectors. Sheet numbers are prefixed "N" or "S" to locate the map north or south of the equator. A second letter increases in 4° bands north and south from the equator, thus "M" is between 48° and 52° of latitude. The number sequence is measured in 6° blocks of longitude away from the 180° meridian: that immediately west of Greenwich is "30". Thus the sheet containing London and south-west England is numbered *NM30*. While using a larger sheet size, GSGS 4646, the 1:1,000,000 Map of the World [**✢103**], employed combined sheet numbers based on the same system.

The sheets of the 1:500,000 *Aeronautical Map of Great Britain* [**✢82**] are organised as geographical quarters of sheets of the International Map of the World, and are suffixed "NW", "NE", "SW", "SE". In this case London is on Sheet *NM30NE*.

GSGS 3982, the 1:250,000 *Map of Europe (Air)* [**✢46**], consists of sheets each of which covers an area one-twelfth the size of a sheet in the International Map of the World. The sheet numbers are related; the "N" prefix is dropped, and the remainder of the International Map of the World alpha-numeric reference is subdivided into twelve parts as four rows of three. Thus Sheet *M31/4* covers part of south-east England.

The other military 1:1,000,000 world series that covers the British Isles employs a curious layout of sheets that was introduced into Great Britain via the United States Air Force Aeronautical Charts [**✢107**]. They are arranged in a boustrophedon system of graticule sectors that run in a continuous numerical sequence from north to south covering the globe in bands of 4° of latitude. They change direction at approximately 100°E. Sheet widths are variable. At the equator they usually cover 5° of longitude. Over the British Isles they are 8° or 9° of longitude south of 56°N, and 11° or 12° of longitude north thereof. Thus the west and east sheet lines of neighbouring sheets are rarely the same. Sheet *172* covers Ireland. Local series may vary the sheet lines further in order to maximise land coverage on each sheet. Some British-made series [**✢108**] prefix these sheet numbers with a "2" - in such cases Sheet *2172* covers Ireland. Associated 1:500,000 series [**✢78, 79**] divide these sheet numbers into quarters in the same zig-zag sequence, thus NW and NE are lettered "A" and "B", but SW and SE are lettered "D" and "C". In this system Sheet *230-A* covers London.

The standard sheet coverage in GSGS 4072 1:500,000 *Map of Europe (Air)* [**✢80**] during the war years is a graticule sector measuring 2° in latitude and 4° in longitude. Sheet numbers are prefixed "N" or "S" to locate the map north or south of the equator, followed by a second letter which identifies the disposition of the sheet as west or east of longitude 2°E. The subsequent sheet number measures the distances of the south-west corner in degrees first from the equator, then from 2°E, thus Sheet *NW50/2* would cover London. This sheet was, however, never made because the series did not cover Great Britain during the war, and special sheet lines prevailed for almost all the sheets which covered the British Isles after it. Thus the sheets are in most cases numbered irregularly, and London is in fact on Sheet *NW50/5½*.

Bibliography

Adams, B.W., 198 years and 153 meridians, 152 defunct, *Sheetlines* 25 (1989), 3-7; 26 (1989), 15-20; 27 (1990), 3-9.

Adams, B.W., An Irish miscellany : The projection of the original one-inch map of Ireland (and of Scotland); Combined sheets of the Irish one-inch coloured edition; County origins of Ireland, *Sheetlines* 30 (1991), 12-19.

Adams, B.W., "Parallel to the meridian of Butterton Hill" - do I laugh or cry?, *Sheetlines* 38 (1994), 15-19; with correction in *Sheetlines* 50 (1997), 58-59.

Andrews, J.H., *History in the Ordnance map : an introduction for Irish readers,* Dublin, Ordnance Survey, 1974; reprinted Kerry, David Archer, 1993.

Andrews, J.H., *A paper landscape : the Ordnance Survey in nineteenth century Ireland,* Oxford University Press, 1975.

Andrews, J.H., A record copy of the one-inch Irish hill map, *Sheetlines* 30 (1991), 4-5.

Bassett, D.A., *A source-book of geological, geomorphological and soil maps for Wales and the Welsh borders (1800-1966),* Cardiff, National Museum of Wales, 1967.

Batchelor, W.R., The Ordnance Survey half inch map - Second Series 1956-61, *Sheetlines* 16 (1986), 7-12.

Board, C., The 3rd edition of the quarter-inch map : a working note, *Sheetlines* 1 (1981), 2-4.

Board, C., The quarter-inch map, *Sheetlines* 9 (1984), 2-9.

Board, C., The secret map of the County of London, 1926, and its sequels, *London Topographical Record* 27 (1995), 257-280.

Board, C., The three-inch map of London, and its predecessors of 1926, *Sheetlines* 43 (1995), 48-50.

Clark, P.K. (summarised by Oliver, R.R.), Maps for the army : the Ordnance Survey's contribution, *Sheetlines* 7 (1983), 2-6.

Clarke, R.V., The use of watermarks in dating Old Series one-inch Ordnance Survey maps, *Cartographic Journal* 6 (1969), 114-129.

Clough, Brigadier A.B., *Maps and Survey,* London, War Office, 1952.

Cook, K.C. and McIntosh, R.P., *A preliminary list of Ordnance Survey one-inch district and tourist maps and selected precursors in the British Library,* London, The Charles Close Society, 1991.

Cruickshank, J.L., The four mile map before the first war, *Sheetlines* 14 (1985), 2-10.

Davidson, Viscount, *Final report of the departmental committee on the Ordnance Survey,* London, HMSO, 1938.

Dean, R.J., More about the Fifth Edition, *Sheetlines* 4 (1982), 10-12.

Dorington, Sir J., *Report of the departmental committee appointed by the Board of Agriculture to inquire into the present condition of the Ordnance Survey,* BPP(HC) 1893-94 [C.6895, C.6895-I], LXXII.

Forrest, D., GSGS Misc Series 1999 and 2000, *Sheetlines* 52 (1998), 17-20.

Garvan, B., The quarter-inch series, Third Edition, *Sheetlines* 5 (1982), 16-19.

Hall, S., *A history of series GSGS 4136 Ireland 1:63,360 1940-43* (an unpublished paper for the Ministry of Defence), 1979.

Harley, J.B. and Phillips, C.W., *The historian's guide to Ordnance Survey maps,* London, The Standing Conference for Local History, 1964.

Harley, J.B., *The Old Series of Ordnance Survey one-inch maps* (notes to facsimile 2 listed on page 249), Newton Abbot, David & Charles, 1969-71.

Harley, J.B., *Ordnance Survey maps : a descriptive manual,* Southampton, Ordnance Survey, 1975.

Hellyer, R., The archaeological and historical maps of the Ordnance Survey, *Sheetlines* 20 (1987), 2-8; 21 (1988), 6-15; 24 (1989), 14-16.

Hellyer, R., The archaeological and historical maps of the Ordnance Survey, *Cartographic Journal* 26 (1989), 111-133.

Hellyer, R., The physical maps of the Ordnance Survey, *Sheetlines* 32 (1992), 18-32.

Hellyer, R., *The "ten-mile" maps of the Ordnance Surveys,* London, The Charles Close Society, 1992; with additions and corrections in *Sheetlines* 41 (1994), 42-50.

Hellyer, R., The editions and printings of the Ordnance Survey of Great Britain Quarter Inch Fifth Series (1:250,000), 1957-1978, *Sheetlines* 37 (1993), 1-12 between 20 and 21.

Hellyer, R., Sheet lines : some notes on GSGS 3917 and other one-inch large sheet maps of Ireland, *Sheetlines* 43 (1995), 4-24.

Hellyer, R., One-inch engraved maps with hills : some notes on double printing, *Sheetlines* 44 (1995), 11-20.
Hellyer, R., Some previously unrecorded one-inch coloured maps of Ireland, *Sheetlines* 46 (1996), 27-28.
Hellyer, R., Some further notes on military mapping in Ireland, *Sheetlines* 46 (1996), 29-32.
Hellyer, R., Some unrecorded one-inch maps with hachures, *Sheetlines* 46 (1996), 35-37.
Hellyer, R., Some notes on the civilian use of Ordnance Survey small scale mapping during the Second World War, *Sheetlines* 48 (1997), 45-57.
Hellyer, R., A summary of printings of the half-inch map of Scotland and England and Wales since 1942, *Sheetlines* 48 (1997), 58-63.
[Herries] Davies, G.L., Notes on the various issues of Sir Richard Griffith's quarter-inch Geological Map of Ireland, 1839-1855, *Imago Mundi* 29 (1977), 35-44.
Herries Davies, G.L., *Sheets of many colours : the mapping of Ireland's rocks 1750-1890,* Dublin, Royal Dublin Society, 1983.
Herries Davies, G.L., *North from the hook : 150 years of the Geological Survey of Ireland,* Dublin, Gcological Survcy of Ircland, 1995.
Hodson, A.Y. (as editor), Shaded contours, *Sheetlines* 3 (1982), 10-11.
Hodson, A.Y., *Ordnance surveyors' drawings 1789-c.1840,* Reading, Research Publications, 1989.
Hodson, A.Y., *"An inch to the mile" : the Ordnance Survey one-inch map 1805-1974,* London, The Charles Close Society, 1991.
Hodson, A.Y., *Popular maps : the Ordnance Survey Popular Edition one-inch map of England and Wales 1919-1926,* London, The Charles Close Society, 1999.
James, Lieutenant-General Sir H. (ed), *Account of the methods and processes adopted for the production of the maps of the Ordnance Survey of the United Kingdom; drawn up by officers of Royal Engineers,* London, HMSO, 1875; revised in 1901 by Colonel D.A. Johnston, London, HMSO, 1902; also *Precis of the methods & processes of the Ordnance Survey,* 1895.
James, N.N., *A list of Ordnance Survey special and tourist maps 1861-1939,* Oxford, Bodleian Library Map Room, Maplist No.1, 1993.
James, N.N., *A list of Ordnance Survey catalogues, publication reports & other publications,* Oxford, Bodleian Library Map Room, Maplist No.2, 1993.
Jewitt, A.C., *Maps for empire : the first 2000 numbered War Office maps 1881-1915,* London, The British Library, 1992.
Maling, D.H., *Coordinate systems and map projections,* Second Edition, Oxford, Pergamon Press, 1991.
Margary, H. (ed.), *The Old Series Ordnance Survey maps of England and Wales* (Vols 1-8), Lympne Castle, Harry Margary, 1975, 1977, 1981, 1986, 1987, 1992, 1989, 1991. With cartobibliographies and introductory essays contributed by J.B. Harley, A.Y. O'Donoghue (now Hodson), J.B. and B.A.D. Manterfield, R.R. Oliver.
Messenger, K.G., The Fifth Edition one-inch map : an outsider's commentary, *Sheetlines* 3 (1982), 2-4.
Messenger, K.G., *The Ordnance Survey one-inch map of England and Wales Third Edition (Large Sheet Series),* London, The Charles Close Society, 1988.
Messenger, K.G., *The sheet histories of the Ordnance Survey one-inch Old Series maps of Essex and Kent,* London, The Charles Close Society, 1991.
Messenger, K.G., *The sheet histories of the Ordnance Survey one-inch Old Series maps of Devon and Cornwall,* London, The Charles Close Society, 1991.
Messenger, K.G., *A guide to the Ordnance Survey one-inch map of Scotland Third Edition in colour,* London, The Charles Close Society, 1991.
Mumford, I., Lithography, photography and photozincography in English map production before 1870, *Cartographic Journal* 11 (1974), 19-33.
Newman, Lieutenant-Colonel H.E.M., *The work of the Ordnance Survey outside Great Britain and Ireland* (unpublished paper in the Ordnance Survey Library), no date (c.1948).
Nicholson, T.R., An introduction to the Ordnance Survey aviation maps of Britain 1925-39, *Sheetlines* 23 (1988), 5-18.
Nicholson, T.R., The Ordnance Survey and smaller scale military maps of Britain 1854-1914, *Cartographic Journal* 25 (1988), 109-127.
Nicholson, T.R., Buried gold : the Ordnance Survey one inch/mile outline, coloured roads district map 1899-193?, *Cartographic Journal* 31 (1994), 123-131.

Nicholson, T.R., The first Ordnance Survey district maps of England, Wales and Scotland 1857-1898, *Cartographic Journal* 28 (1991), 176-180.
Nicholson, T.R., One-inch military "specials" 1923-1940, *Sheetlines* 33 (1992), 21-34.
Nicholson, T.R., A major military "special" : the 2-inch/mile map *War Department Land on Salisbury Plain,* 1899-1914, and its companions, *Sheetlines* 39 (1994), 20-27; additional information in: War Department Land on Salisbury Plain, *Sheetlines* 40 (1994), 46-47.
Oliver, R.R., What's what with the New Series, *Sheetlines* 5 (1982), 3-8.
Oliver, R.R. (as D141414), The "half-inch" at Tewin, *Sheetlines* 9 (1984), 14-16.
Oliver, R.R., The Ordnance Survey of Ireland - some recent experiences, *Sheetlines* 11 (1984), 2-9.
Oliver, R.R., New light on the New Series, *Sheetlines* 12 (1985), 7-11.
Oliver, R.R., British-produced 1:63,360 mapping in Ireland, 1922-1985, *Sheetlines* 13 (1985), 11-18.
Oliver, R.R., *The Ordnance Survey in Great Britain 1835-1870* (unpublished D.Phil. thesis at University of Sussex), 1986.
Oliver, R.R., The origins of Ordnance Survey quarter-inch mapping in Great Britain, 1837-72, *Sheetlines* 15 (1986), 9-14.
Oliver, R.R., The half-inch Second Series : further revelations and reflections, *Sheetlines* 17 (1986), 12-14.
Oliver, R.R., Lithography and the Ordnance Survey 1-inch Old Series, *Sheetlines* 19 (1987), 13-14.
Oliver, R.R., One-inch military maps of Great Britain, 1919-1950 : some notes on GSGS 3907 and 3908 (including "War Revision 1940" and "Second War Revision 1940"), *Sheetlines* 20 (1987), 9-12.
Oliver, R.R., *A guide to the Ordnance Survey one-inch New Popular Edition and Scottish Popular Edition,* Second Edition, London, The Charles Close Society, 1989.
Oliver, R.R., *A guide to the Ordnance Survey one-inch Fifth Edition,* Second Edition, London, The Charles Close Society, 1989.
Oliver, R.R., *A preliminary list of Ordnance Survey of Northern Ireland maps published at 1:50,000, 1:63,360, 1:126,720 and 1:253,440* (unpublished typescript), 1990.
Oliver, R.R., *The one-inch "Popular Edition" of Scotland : a preliminary list of printings* (unpublished typescript), 1990.
Oliver, R.R., *A guide to the Ordnance Survey one-inch Seventh Series,* London, The Charles Close Society, 1991.
Oliver, R.R., The one-inch maps of Ireland to 1922 : a summary, *Sheetlines* 30 (1991), 10-12.
Oliver, R.R., The "unpopular" one-inch Fourth Edition : an insight into early twentieth century Ordnance Survey small-scale revision policy, *Sheetlines* 32 (1992), 38-46.
Oliver, R.R., *Ordnance Survey maps : a concise guide for historians,* London, The Charles Close Society, 1993.
Oliver, R.R. (as editor), A preliminary list of Ordnance Survey mapping of the Channel Islands, *Sheetlines* 36 (1993), 53-56; with additions in *Sheetlines* 39 (1994), 41.
Oliver, R.R., Twenty years of the Ordnance Survey 1:50,000 map, *Sheetlines* 39 (1994), 6-9.
Oliver, R.R., A list of 1:50,000 editions, 1974-1994, *Sheetlines* 39 (1994), 10-19; with additions in *Sheetlines* 41 (1994), 50-52.
Oliver, R.R., The evolution of the Ordnance Survey National Grid, *Sheetlines* 43 (1995), 25-46; with amplification and correction in *Sheetlines* 46 (1996), 45-46.
Oliver, R.R., The sheet lines and overlaps of the one-inch Fifth and New Popular Editions, *Sheetlines* 44 (1995), 22-44.
Oliver, R.R., Cartographic discoveries, *Sheetlines* 49 (1997), 14-24.
Owen, T. and Pilbeam, E., *Ordnance Survey : map makers to Britain since 1791,* Southampton, Ordnance Survey, and London, HMSO, 1992.
Robinson, A.H., The 1837 maps of Henry Drury Harness, *Geographical Journal* 121 (1955), 440-450.
Seymour, W.A. (ed.), *A history of the Ordnance Survey,* Folkestone, Dawson, 1980.
Stamp, L.D., *The land of Britain : its use and misuse,* Third Edition, London, Longmans, Green and Co, 1962.
Willatts, E.C., The maps of the Land Utilisation Survey of Britain 1931-49, *Sheetlines* 23 (1988), 2-5.
Winterbotham, Brigadier H.StJ.L., The use of the new grid on Ordnance Survey maps, *Geographical Journal* 82 (1933), 42-54.

Source material

Great Britain

British parliamentary papers (House of Commons) (BPP(HC)), or (House of Lords) (BPP(HL)).
Report of committee on a military map of the United Kingdom, London, War Office, 1892.
Glossary of Technical Terms in Cartography, London, Royal Society, 1966.
Military publishers' designations (Map Curators' Group Publication No.2), London, The British Cartographic Society, no date [1985].

Register of GSGS Maps 1-2299, 2300-4795. A photocopy of the original (beginning 15.2.1881) is deposited in the Map Department, Public Record Office.
Catalogue of maps in the War Office, London, War Office, 1889. With supplements 1890-1914.
Catalogue of maps published by the Geographical Section, General Staff, London, War Office, 1920, 1923.
Catalogue of maps not on sale to the public, published by the Geographical Section of the General Staff, London, War Office, 1936.
Catalogue of maps published by the Directorate of Military Survey, London, War Office, 1943.
Numerical catalogue of maps published by the Directorate of Military Survey and Geographical Section General Staff, London, War Office, 1944, 1945.
Catalogue of maps published by the Geographical Section, General Staff, Provisional Edition, London, War Office, 1946, 1947.
Notes on GSGS maps of France, Belgium and Holland, London, War Office, 1943.
Manual of Map Reading and Field Sketching, (various titles and editions) London, War Office (later HMSO), 1906, 1912, 1921, 1929, 1940, 1955, 1961.
Notes on Map Reading, London, War Office, 1925, 1929, 1940.

Geological Survey catalogues: various titles. Biennial or more frequent issues to 1925, then 1931, 1934, 1937, then post-war. Summary information in OSC 1974-90.
Geological Survey Publication Reports: various titles.
Ordnance Survey Annual Reports (OSR): various titles.
The unpublished war-time annual reports are in the Public Record Office, OS 1/97 (1939-40); OS 1/139 (1940-41); OS 1/140 (1941-42); OS 1/141 (1942-43); OS 1/173 (1943-44); OS 1/201 (1944-45); OS 1/658 (1945-46).
Ordnance Survey Catalogues (OSC): various titles. Regular issues to 1924, then from 1967.
Ordnance Survey Publication Reports (OSPR): various titles.
Ordnance Survey of Great Britain, England and Wales, Indexes to the 1/2500 and 6-inch scale Maps, reprinted with an introduction by R.R. Oliver, Kerry, David Archer, 1991.
Ordnance Survey of Great Britain, Scotland, Indexes to the 1/2500 and 6-inch scale Maps, reprinted with an introduction by B.W. Adams, Kerry, David Archer, 1993.
Ordnance Survey of Ireland, Indexes to the 1/2500 and 6-inch scale Maps, c.1905.
A Description of the Ordnance Survey Small Scale Maps (various titles), [1919], 1920, 1921, 1923, 1925, 1927, [1930], [1935], [1937], 1947, reprinted with addendum 1951, 1957.
Public Record Office files, especially in classes OS 1, OS 5, WO 33, WO 279.
Ordnance Survey job files, held by The Charles Close Society, now deposited in the Map Room, Cambridge University Library.

Northern Ireland

Ordnance Survey of Northern Ireland descriptions and catalogues (various titles), 1935, 1952, 1959, 1962 (all with supplements), 1968, 1975, 1978, 1982 *et seq.*, 1994.
Ordnance Survey of Northern Ireland, *Map Publication Report*, ?1969 *et seq.*

Ireland

Irish parliamentary papers (IPP).
Ordnance Survey Office (Dublin) Quarterly Reports, 1864.
Ordnance Survey of Ireland (Suirbhéireacht Ordanáis) catalogues (various titles), 1927, 1933 (both with supplements), 1946, 1949 (with supplements), 1956, 1968, 1982, [1983].
List of memoirs, maps, sections, &c. published by the Geological Survey [of Ireland], Éire, [Dublin], Roinn tionscail agus tráchtála (Department of Industry and Commerce), 1962.
Map Reading : Training Regulation No.19 (Defence Force Regulations), Dublin, Stationery Office, 1942.

Facsimile reproductions

The following are the principal facsimile reproductions by publishers other than the Ordnance Surveys, with cross references to where the originals are listed. All are one-inch maps unless noted. Ordnance Survey facsimiles are listed in the main body of the book.

1. Harry Margary, Lympne Castle.

   +1.1 Map of the County of Kent. Published twice in atlas form, in *The Old Series Ordnance Survey Maps of England and Wales,* Volume 1, 1975, and in *The County of Kent : a reproduction of the first published Ordnance Survey map of Great Britain,* 1990.

   +2.1 The complete Old Series Map of England and Wales. Published in atlas format in *The Old Series Ordnance Survey Maps of England and Wales,* in eight volumes, 1975, 1977, 1981, 1986, 1987, 1992, 1989, 1991.

2. David & Charles, Newton Abbot, 1969-71.

   +2.1 The complete Old Series Map of England and Wales. Assembled into 97 full sheets with excess pieces relocated in empty areas of coastal sheets, the series renumbered north to south.

3. Alan Godfrey, Newcastle-upon-Tyne.

   +2.1 Old Series Map of England and Wales : Hachured: 1SW (on London 1:2500 Sheet 118), 62SW (on first issues of Staffordshire 1:2500 Sheets 63.14, 72.06), 87SW (on Yorkshire 1:2500 Sheet 283.07), 90NE (on Lancashire 1:2500 Sheet 75.09).

   +2.2 Old Series Map of England and Wales : Outline. Facsimiles published carrying Old Series numbers are listed here in the New Series sequence.

   +3.2 New Series Map of England and Wales : Outline: 4, 8-10, 19-21, 69, 128, 221 (on Hertfordshire 1:2500 Sheet 7.08), 238 (on Hertfordshire 1:2500 Sheet 33.12, also independently), 252 (on Wiltshire 1:2500 Sheet 15.07), 255, 257 (on London 1:2500 Sheet 68), 269, 285, 286.

   +4.1 Revised New Series Map of England and Wales : Outline: 18 (on Cumberland 1:2500 Sheet 23.04), 256 (on Middlesex 1:2500 Sheet 7.14).

   +6.1 Third Edition Map of England and Wales : Outline: 3, 5, 13, 14 (on Northumberland 1:2500 Sheet 64.13), 17 (on Cumberland 1:2500 Sheet 23.03), 89.

   +23.A.1 Map of Ireland : Second Edition : Outline, without contours: 25, 32, 33, 36 (on Co. Antrim 1:2500 Sheet 61.13), 37, 44-46, 57.

   +85.1 Ten-mile Map of Great Britain : small sheet series: 8 (on Co. Durham 1:2500 Sheet 2.14).

4. Caledonian Books, Collieston, Ellon, 1987.

   +14.1 Map of Scotland : Second Edition : Outline. Coverage of Scotland omitting the Outer Hebrides, Shetland and Orkney Islands, assembled into 94 sheets with excess pieces relocated in empty areas of coastal sheets. Sheets 26 and 33 are in fact *Third Edition* [**+15**.1].

5. Phoenix Maps, Dublin, 1989.

   +22.4 Map of Ireland : First Edition : Hachured. Complete coverage of Ireland in 205 sheets. Sheets 136, 145, 146 are in fact Second Edition, without contours [**+23**.A.3]. Printed by the Ordnance Survey of Ireland.

6. Crawford, O.G.S., *The Andover District,* Oxford Geographical Studies, 1922.

   +6.2 Third Edition Map of England and Wales : Hachured in brown: 283.

7. Scouts Mapping Service.

   +2.1 Old Series Map of England and Wales : Hachured: 1NW.

   +3.2 New Series Map of England and Wales : Outline: 317.

List of maps

Index

A

B